D1603716

VIBRATIONS AND WAVES

ELLIS HORWOOD BOOKS IN PHYSICS

Physics Series Editor: **C. Grey Morgan,** University College, Swansea

VIBRATIONS
AND WAVES

W. GOUGH, M.A., D.Phil.
J. P. G. RICHARDS, Ph.D.
R. P. WILLIAMS, Ph.D.
Department of Physics
University College
University College, Cardiff

ELLIS HORWOOD LIMITED
Publishers · Chichester

Halsted Press: a division of
JOHN WILEY & SONS
New York · Brisbane · Chichester · Toronto

First published in 1983 by

ELLIS HORWOOD LIMITED
Market Cross House, Cooper Street, Chichester, West Sussex, PO19 1EB, England

The publisher's colophon is reproduced from James Gillison's drawing of the ancient Market Cross, Chichester.

Distributors:

Australia, New Zealand, South-east Asia:
Jacaranda-Wiley Ltd., Jacaranda Press,
JOHN WILEY & SONS INC.,
G.P.O. Box 859, Brisbane, Queensland 40001, Australia

Canada:
JOHN WILEY & SONS CANADA LIMITED
22 Worcester Road, Rexdale, Ontario, Canada.

Europe, Africa:
JOHN WILEY & SONS LIMITED
Baffins Lane, Chichester, West Sussex, England.

North and South America and the rest of the world:
Halsted Press: a division of
JOHN WILEY & SONS
605 Third Avenue, New York, N.Y. 10016, U.S.A.

© 1983 W. Gough, J.P.G. Richards and R.P. Williams/Ellis Horwood Ltd.

British Library Cataloguing in Publication Data
Gough, W.
Vibrations and waves.
1. Vibration   2. Waves
I. Title   II. Richards, J. P. G.   III. Williams, R. P.
531'.32   QC136

Library of Congress Card No. 82-25836

ISBN 0-85132-581-3 (Ellis Horwood Limited — Library Edn.)
ISBN 0-85312-582-1 (Ellis Horwood Limited — Student Edn.)
ISBN 0-470-27446-8 (Halsted Press)

Typeset in Press Roman by Ellis Horwood Ltd.
Printed in Great Britain by Butler & Tanner, Frome, Somerset.

Table of Contents

8   **Table of Contents**

Preface

Most of the important branches of physics and engineering demand for their understanding a thorough knowledge of vibrating systems and wave behaviour. It is to provide a basic route to such an understanding that the authors have written this book.

The book is intended mainly for first- and second-year students of physics at universitities and polytechnics, but it is hoped that it will meet the needs of engineering students too. Its contents should be well within the grasp of anyone with high-school physics or mathematics to about British Advanced Level standard. The mathematical background required of the reader amounts to a knowledge of elementary calculus and trigonometry; virtually no previous knowledge either of vibrations or waves is demanded.

Because many different types of vibration and wave are susceptible to identical mathematical treatment, much of this book is concerned with those features common to them all. But this is not to say that the book is severely mathematical; indeed this is far from being the case. It is written by experimental physicists who, while recognizing the usefulness of employing the language of mathematics to describe physical phenomena, seek to treat their subject from a physical point of view. Accordingly, they endeavour to ensure that mathematical analysis is there to adorn and clarify physical reality and to draw parallels among physical phenomena which would otherwise appear unrelated.

Fashions change. Until about fifteen years ago, no introductory text on this subject would contain more than a passing reference to Fourier analysis. But now, the insight into our subject (as well as many other subjects) provided, in the early nineteenth century, by this remarkable man has percolated deeply into the outlook – and the curricula – of the modern physicist and engineer. This trend is reflected in the present book by two chapters devoted to the compelling dual viewpoint – time and frequency – from which Fourier's method enables us to look at vibratory phenomena.

Fashions indeed change. The technological revolution provided by the computer has affected outlooks profoundly, not the least in the realm of education.

Small computers are commonplace nowadays in educational institutions and increasingly in the home. In this book, the reader is encouraged to use a micro-computer as an aid to learning. Many examples and problems will be found which involve programming a computer to give visual output which will provide a 'feel' for many aspects of the subject.

The authors are indebted to Mr Malcolm Anderson for help in preparing the diagrams, to Mrs Pamela Tyrrell for typing part of the manuscript, and to the University of Wales and University College, Cardiff, for permission to reproduce examination questions.

The authors have, over the years, had stimulating — not to say formative — conversations on vibrations, waves, and many other subjects with their friend and colleague, Gwynne Howells, to whose memory this book is affectionately dedicated.

CHAPTER 1

Introduction

1.1 PREAMBLE

Although in our title, the terms *vibrations* and *waves* appear with equal prominence, they are given far from equal attention in the work itself; two chapters are devoted to vibrations, eight to waves. While the theory of vibrations has been developed primarily as essential background to waves, it is hoped that the treatment of vibrations is sufficiently full to be useful in its own right. But the book is essentially about waves. We begin by seeking to explain, in narrative terms, what waves are; and by describing, also in narrative terms, some of the kinds of wave that are to be treated fully later.

1.2 WHAT ARE WAVES?

A wave is a curiously difficult entity to define but the authors should attempt a definition — or at least discuss why a definition should be so difficult. Let us start by trying to imagine how the 'man-in-the street' would answer the question 'What is a wave?'. He would surely be unable to give a coherent answer, but at least two different significant ingredients might emerge. He might talk about waves on the surface of water and would describe them as 'moving along'. On the other hand, he might refer to the waves in a person's hair which, although they do not appear to move, indicate one property of waves which is to do with shape. So we arrive at the idea of a particular undulating shape moving along. If we now force him to concentrate on this aspect and ask him to give us some examples of waves, he might well produce the idea that if he shakes one end of a piece of string or cord (say a clothes line) then the movement (or disturbance) travels along the length of the cord; this he would describe as a wave. Further-more, he might assert that both sound and light are waves. When invited to expound upon any conceivable connection between sound and light, on the one hand, and waves on a clothes line, on the other, he might well become rather unsure, but, if he were the assertive kind, he would probably stick to his guns nevertheless.

And he would be right to do so, for he was correct all along. He had described most of the ingredients of waves without having had a scientific education. Let us try to translate his words into scientific terms.

Waves appear to be disturbances in some sort of medium. In the case of the clothes line the 'medium' was the cord itself and the 'disturbance' was a displacement of part of the cord. The disturbance was carried along by forces which different parts of the cord exerted upon their neighbours. In a similar way, the surface of a pool of water is capable of carrying a disturbance along. Here the 'medium' is the water and the 'disturbance' is an upward (or downward) movement of the surface. Sound waves in air fit into much the same mould. The 'medium' is the air itself and the 'disturbance' is a displacement of a region of the air which, owing to the elastic properties of the latter, travels along through the medium.

We have thus gone a long way towards establishing the essential nature of a wave. It is a disturbance of some sort (which may not necessarily be mechanical, as we shall see later) in a medium which, because of the properties of the latter, changes either in form or position, or both, as time goes on.

Let us consider the 'medium' a little further. Although it enables a disturbance to be propogated, it itself does not move bodily along. For example the disturbance at one end of the clothes line is propagated along its length, but none of the particles of which the cord is composed actually moves from one end of the line to the other. So a wave is a means of transmitting energy from one point to another without any net transfer of matter. Moreover, it is a means of transmitting *information* from one point to another. For example, not only does the energy in a sound wave reach our ears and activate our auditory systems, but the manner in which the energy fluctuates with time is capable of interpretation by our brains, enabling us to *perceive* the originally remote signal and (for suitable signals) to make sense of it.

It may have been noticed, during the discussion on the disturbance and the medium, that nothing at all was said about light waves and other forms of radiation such as γ-rays, X-rays, ultraviolet rays, infrared rays, and radio waves. The fact is that, while these waves fit generally into the picture we have drawn, they fail to do so in one important respect — they appear to require no medium whatsoever for their propagation. Indeed, although they can travel through some material media (light waves can travel through glass for example) they are not able to do so with as great a speed as they can through a vacuum. This was a source of such great mystery to the nineteenth-century physicist, since it was so apparent to him that all other waves required media for their propagation, that the existence of a medium, pervading the whole of space, was postulated. This was named the *luminiferous ether,* and much ingenuity was exercised in tracking down its properties. Eventually, following the classic experiment of Michelson and Morley in 1887 and the subsequent development of relativity theory, it was possible to dispense with the concept of the ether; the modern physicist now not only accepts the idea of electromagnetic waves travelling through a vacuum, but also describes them in the same mathematical way as other waves.

1.3 DESCRIPTION OF SOME OF THE WAVES WE SHALL STUDY

1.3.1 Waves in strings

In this section we shall deal briefly, and in a general way, with the different types of wave we shall meet later on in this book. We have already mentioned waves in strings, which are particularly suitable for study in that they exemplify many of the principles common to other types of wave in a way very easy to visualize. So, although these waves can hardly be said to be of central importance in physics, the principles involved certainly are.

Waves in strings may be either *transverse* or *longitudinal*. For a *transverse* wave, the direction of travel (or propagation direction) is at right angles to the disturbance. Let us imagine that a string is stretched horizontally, and that one end is agitated with an up-and-down movement; then we would have a transverse wave with disturbance in the up-and-down direction moving along the length of the string. At a given instant, the string might appear as in Fig. 1.1a. On the other hand, a *longitudinal* wave can be set up by taking one end of the string and successively stretching and releasing it along its own length. In this type of wave, the disturbance is in the direction of propagation, as illustrated in Fig. 1.1b.

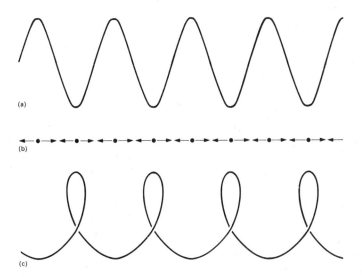

Fig. 1.1 – Sketches of profiles of three different waves on a string. (a) A transverse wave. Displacements are vertical. (b) A longitudinal wave. Arrows indicate the displacements at different parts of the string. (c) A perspective sketch of a circularly polarized wave. The wave is basically transverse since the displacements are everywhere at right angles to the direction of propagation.

Transverse and longitudinal waves have many properties in common with each other, as mathematical analyses later on in this book will show. But there is one great difference. When we specify a longitudinal wave, we know that the displacements of the particles in the cord (or whatever medium is sustaining the wave) are parallel to the direction of propagation. However, in the case of a transverse wave we have to specify not only the transverse nature of the wave motion but also the direction of the transverse displacement, since no particular perpendicular displacement is to be preferred to any other. For example, if the horizontally-stretched clothes line is displaced in either the vertical direction or the horizontal direction perpendicular to its length, a transverse wave will result. In fact, two transverse waves with different directions of displacement can be propagated at the same time along the cord; a particularly simple wave of this sort may be obtained by rotating one end of the clothes line in a circle whose plane is perpendicular to the length of the cord. In this case a wave is produced whose profile is illustrated in Fig. 1.1c. This is usually called a *circularly polarized wave*.

1.3.2 Waves in rods
Solid rods are capable of sustaining three different types of wave. The first and simplest is the longitudinal wave which is propagated because of the tensile elastic properties of the rod. It is quite easy to excite such waves. If a rod of length about one metre is held firmly at its centre and stroked along its length by a resined cloth, a longitudinal wave is propagated back and forth along the rod. It cannot be visually observed, but the effect of the wave can easily be audibly observed as a high-pitched sound of considerable purity. Because the rod is of comparatively small length, the *reflection* of the waves back along the rod when they reach either end becomes very important and determines the pitch of the note heard. We shall be dealing in detail with the phenomena of reflection in Chapter 6.

Transverse waves may exist in rods, but are more difficult to produce. They are mathematically much more complicated to analyse because, unlike either type of wave which exists on strings, different frequencies are propagated with different velocities. This is a phenomenon known as *dispersion* and will be studied in Chapter 9.

Finally, *torsional* waves may exist in rods. If a rod is twisted at one end, then the restoring torque causes a wave to be propagated. Here the 'disturbance' is not a linear displacement, but an angular twist. These waves are non-dispersive, that is, all frequencies are propagated at the same speed.

1.3.3 Waves on membranes
A membrane, for example the stretched skin on a drum, is the two-dimensional equivalent of a stretched sting. Here, as in the string, when any part of the skin is pushed in a direction perpendicular to its plane and then released, transverse

waves are set up. These waves, unlike those on the string, are two-dimensional — they spread out from the point of the initial disturbance in a way very similar to that in which surface waves on water spread out from a point of disturbance.

The simplest type of two-dimensional wave from the point of view of mathematical analysis is a 'straight-line' wave — one whose direction of propagation is constant over the whole surface and whose profile is the same along any line drawn in this direction. In general, the analysis of two-dimensional waves is not so simple, and indeed waves on a drum-head, which are reflected to the centre of the head when they reach the perimeter, require considerable sophistication for their analysis, which is outside the scope of this book.

1.3.4 Sound waves
We shall be discussing sound waves in considerable detail later on in the book. At this stage, we shall merely say that when a disturbance is created at some point, waves proceed from this point in all directions. Sound waves in gases are longitudinal because a gas is unable to sustain a torsional or shear force.

1.3.5 Waves in transmission lines
We turn back, now, to a one-dimensional example of wave motion, and one that is of great importance in certain electrical applications. An extreme convenience of electricity, as opposed to other forms of power, is that it can be conducted along metal wires to a point remote from the generator with the greatest ease. Normally, at least two parallel wires, or some similar arrangement such as coaxial wires, are required for this. There will thus be a small capacitance, and also inductance, between the wires which will cause, as we shall see in Chapter 5, a wave of voltage (and current) to travel along the line when the generator is delivering any voltage other than a perfectly steady d.c. The result of this is that the device at the end of the line remote from the generator does not 'see' the voltage variations at the generator, but a version of these as modified by the line. This can pose problems at high frequencies, but at lower frequencies, for example the 50 Hz mains, the effects of such modifications are utterly negligible.

1.3.6 Waveguides
Point sources of waves propagating into a three-dimensional medium produce spherical waves radiating outwards from the source at the centre. This means that a detector placed at successively greater distances from the source records successively weaker responses since the total flux of energy in the wave, which is constant, is being spread over the surface of a sphere of ever increasing surface area. This limits the effective range over which the detector can operate. In the case of sound waves, the point source would be reasonably well represented, several metres away, by a small loudspeaker, and the detector by a microphone or the ear. To increase the range it is possible to 'guide' the wave through a tube of constant internal size and shape so that the energy in the wave is not being

wasted in detectorless regions. An obvious example of this arrangement, which is technically known as a *waveguide*, is the speaking tube. Other types of wave guide exist, notably the electromagnetic waveguide whose use overcomes some of the difficulties of transmitting high-frequency electrical signals along transmission lines.

CHAPTER 2

The theory of vibrations

2.1 THE IMPORTANCE OF VIBRATION THEORY IN THE UNDERSTANDING OF WAVES

When a medium is disturbed by the passage of a wave through it, the particles comprising the medium are caused to vibrate. To take a simple example, corks floating on the surface of a pond will bob up and down owing to the influence of water waves. As will be seen later, the physical characteristics which describe a wave can be determined by observing the manner in which a particle in the path of the wave vibrates, so it is important at the outset to learn something of the nature and theory of vibrations.

2.2 VIBRATIONS OF A SINGLE PARTICLE

Vibrating particles are the frequent concern of writers on mechanics; the bob of a simple pendulum and the weight hanging freely from the end of a spring are obvious examples of particles which may be set in vibration, and most readers will have a good mental picture of how these vibrate. The motion is *periodic*; that is, after equal intervals of time (the *period T*) the system finds itself in exactly the same situation. The bob of the pendulum, for example, is found to be at the same position, moving with the same velocity and acceleration as it was T seconds earlier, and all these quantities will be the same T, $2T$, $3T$, etc. seconds later. Actually the swings of a pendulum die away in time, owing to frictional and viscous forces, but we are assuming an ideal pendulum which does not lose energy and goes on *ad infinitum*. During the interval of one period, a vibrating system is said to go through a *cycle* of situations, and the *frequency* (f) is defined as the number of cycles occurring in one second. Clearly, then, $f = 1/T$; the dimension of f is second^{-1}. This unit is termed the hertz (Hz).

2.2.1 Periodic motion of a point in one dimension
The simplest kind of periodic motion is that experienced by a point, moving along a straight line, whose acceleration is directed towards a fixed point on the

line and is proportional to its distance from the fixed point; this is called *simple harmonic motion* (s.h.m.). Suppose a point P (Fig. 2.1) moves along a straight line so that its position with respect to a fixed point O is completely specified by the single coordinate x. Let us examine the situation when the moving point is at P (position x) and moving away from O. The acceleration is d^2x/dt^2; this is directed towards O and proportional to the distance OP $= x$. Thus

$$\frac{d^2x}{dt^2} = -\omega^2 x \,,$$

where ω is a positive constant.

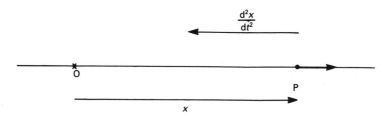

Fig. 2.1 — Simple harmonic motion in one dimension.

Note the minus sign; this is because the acceleration is directed in the opposite direction to that in which x is increasing.

On rearranging, this equation becomes

$$\boxed{\frac{d^2x}{dt^2} + \omega^2 x = 0}\,. \tag{2.1}$$

This is a linear, second-order differential equation; linear because x and its derivative appear to the power one only, and second order because the highest derivative is d^2x/dt^2. Equation (2.1) is referred to as the differential equation governing the motion. It is not the equation of motion. To find the equation of motion we have to solve (2.1) for x. It is shown in Appendix B (equation (B.3)) that the most general solution is

$$\boxed{x = a \sin(\omega t + \epsilon)}\,. \tag{2.2}$$

The two arbitrary constants, inevitable in the solution of any second-order differential equation, are, in this example, a and ϵ. That (2.2) is a solution of (2.1) can very easily be shown by differentiating (2.2) twice and substituting for x and d^2x/dt^2 in (2.1).

The constant a is the *amplitude* of the motion; it is the greatest possible value that x can have, since the maximum value of $\sin(\omega t + \epsilon)$ is unity. Thus the motion takes place entirely between the limits $x = \pm a$. The quantity $\omega t + \epsilon$ is known as the *phase* of the motion and ϵ is known as the *phase constant* or *epoch*. The form of (2.2) is shown in Fig. 2.2.

Also shown in Fig. 2.2 is the period T; if we add T to t in (2.2) the value of x must remain unaltered. Hence

$$x = a \sin(\omega t + \epsilon) = a \sin[\omega(t + T) + \epsilon].$$

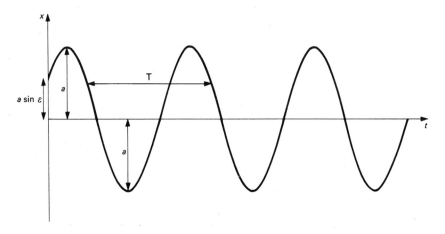

Fig. 2.2 – Plot of x against t for simple harmonic motion.

This requires that the argument of the sine (or the phase) has been increased by exactly 2π radians. Thus by inspection $\omega T = 2\pi$.

Therefore $\boxed{T = 2\pi/\omega}$ (2.3)

and $\boxed{\omega = 2\pi f}$,   (2.3a)

since we saw earlier that the frequency $f = 1/T$. Thus we have found a physical meaning for ω, and we can write the equation of motion in physically meaningful terms as

$$x = a \sin(2\pi f t + \epsilon) .$$ (2.4)

However, (2.2) is the more convenient form. ω is known as the *circular frequency* or *pulsatance* of the motion.

Example 2.1

A fairground Ferris wheel of radius 10 m has six equally spaced carriages and rotates one revolution every 20 s in a vertical plane. A man is walking along the ground, always keeping vertically below carriage A (Fig. 2.E1). Show that he moves with simple harmonic motion, and deduce the amplitude, frequency, circular frequency, maximum velocity, and maximum acceleration. His wife is walking similarly below carriage B. What is her equation of motion?

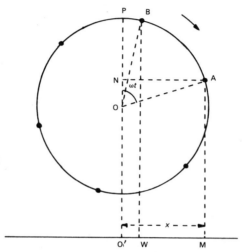

Fig. 2.E1 — Ferris wheel.

Let us suppose that the clock is started (i.e. $t = 0$) when A is at its highest point P. The man is then at O'. At a later time t, his displacement x from O' is $O'M$, which is clearly equal to NA. But $\angle POA = \omega t$, where ω is the angular velocity of the wheel. Also, since the wheel rotates through an angle 2π in 20 s, the angular velocity is $\omega = \pi/10$ rad s^{-1}. Therefore, the equation for the man's displacement is

$$x = 10 \sin\left(\pi t/10\right) \tag{2.E1}$$

By comparison with (2.4), we immediately see that the amplitude is 10 m, and the frequency is 1/20 Hz.

The circular frequency ω is $2\pi f$, which is $\pi/10$ rad s^{-1}. It should be noted that this is the same as the angular velocity of the wheel.

The velocity is obtained by differentiating (2.E1), giving $dx/dt = \pi \cos \pi t/10$. This has a maximum value π m s^{-1}, this maximum occurring when the man is at O'.

Differentiating again, we obtain the acceleration $d^2x/dt^2 = -(\pi^2/10)\sin \pi t/10$, which has a maximum value of $\pi^2/10$ m s^{-2}. It should be noted that the acceleration has maximum magnitude at the *extremities* of the motion, and is zero at O', when the velocity is maximum.

The equation of motion of the man's wife W is given by the displacement $x' = 10 \sin \angle POB$. Since $\angle BOA = \pi/3, x' = 10 \sin(\omega t - \pi/3) = 10 \sin(\pi t/10 - \pi/3)$.

The reader should appreciate that the graphs of x and x' against t (Fig. 2.E2) indicate that W 'lags behind' M. The phase difference between the two is $\pi/3$, or $60°$.

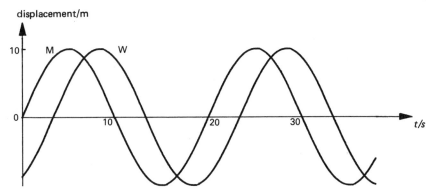

Fig. 2.E2 – Displacement-time graphs for M and W.

This problem illustrates an important feature concerning simple harmonic motion, namely that it can be regarded as *uniform circular motion projected on to a straight line*. Indeed, some elementary texts adopt this as a definition of s.h.m. As we have seen, the angular velocity of the circular motion is equal to the circular frequency of the corresponding s.h.m. Indeed, the same symbol ω is used for both.   ∎

In any given problem, the constants of integration a and ϵ are determined from the initial conditions. Suppose we are told that, at $t = t_0$, the point is x_0 from the origin and is moving with a velocity v_0. If we substitute these values into equation (2.4) and the first derivative of (2.4) we get

$$x_0 = a \sin(2\pi f t_0 + \epsilon) \tag{2.5}$$

$$\text{and} \quad v_0 = 2\pi f a \cos(2\pi f t_0 + \epsilon) \ . \tag{2.6}$$

We can now solve for a and ϵ; first we divide (2.5) by (2.6) and invert the resulting tangent to get

$$\epsilon = \tan^{-1}\left(\frac{2\pi f x_0}{v_0}\right) - 2\pi f t_0 \ .$$

Secondly we square and add the equations, using the identity $\cos^2 \theta + \sin^2 \theta = 1$,

$$\text{to get} \quad a^2 = x_0^2 + \frac{v_0^2}{4\pi^2 f^2} \ .$$

There are numerous situations in physics which can be treated to a very good approximation as involving simple harmonic motion; we shall develop just two, one mechanical and one electrical.

Our mechanical example is that of a mass suspended from one end of a light elastic string, the other end of which is rigidly clamped (Fig. 2.3). Suppose the string is light, has an unstretched length l_0 and an elastic constant λ; when a mass m is hung from the end and lowered slowly to the equilibrium position, the string will be stretched a distance l such that, by Hooke's law,

$$mg = \frac{\lambda l}{l_0} \, , \tag{2.7}$$

where g is the acceleration due to gravity. Since λ and l_0 are both constants for a given string, we can replace λ/l_0 by the single constant k, which is known as the 'stiffness' or force constant of the string; so (2.7) becomes

$$mg = kl \, . \tag{2.8}$$

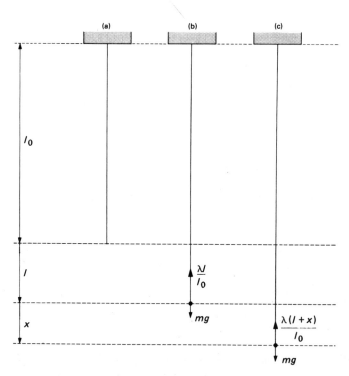

Fig. 2.3 – Motion of a mass suspended from a light, elastic string. (a) String hanging freely. (b) String with mass m suspended from end. (c) Mass in oscillation, at the instant when it is a distance x below equilibrium position.

If the mass is pulled down a small distance from the equilibrium position and released, vertical oscillations will ensue. Applying Newton's second law of motion (i.e. equating mass times acceleration to net force) to the situation shown in Fig. 2.3c, when the mass is instantaneously a distance x below the equilibrium position, we have

$$m \frac{d^2x}{dt^2} = mg - k(l + x) \ .$$

Note that x increases in the downward direction, and is therefore a positive quantity.

From (2.8)

$$m \frac{d^2x}{dt^2} = -kx$$

or $$m \frac{d^2x}{dt^2} + kx = 0 \ . \tag{2.9}$$

This has exactly the same form as equation (2.1), so we can write down the general solution of (2.9) as

$$x = a \sin \left(\sqrt{\left[\frac{k}{m}\right]} \, t + \epsilon \right), \tag{2.9a}$$

which is the equation of motion of the mass. Thus the mass performs simple harmonic oscillations with period

$$T = 2\pi \sqrt{\left(\frac{m}{k}\right)} :$$

the constants a and ϵ could be determined from initial conditions as explained earlier.

The electrical example is that of the circuit shown in Fig. 2.4 which comprises a capacitor C in series with a coil of pure inductance L. The capacitor is charged from a battery, which is then removed, and the key K closed. The capacitor will thereupon discharge through the coil. Suppose, at some instant subsequent to the closing of the key, the charges on the plates of the capacitor are $\pm q$ and the current i is flowing in the direction indicated. The potential differences across C and L will have the values shown, the arrows indicating the direction of increasing potential. The algebraic sum of the potential differences round a closed circuit must be zero at any instant, so

$$L \frac{di}{dt} + \frac{q}{C} = 0 \ .$$

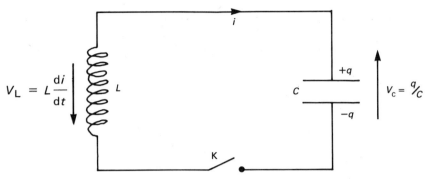

Fig. 2.4 – Circuit containing inductance and capacitance.

But $i = \dfrac{dq}{dt}$,

so we have $L \dfrac{d^2q}{dt^2} + \dfrac{q}{C} = 0$.   (2.10)

This charge on the capacitor thus fluctuates with time according to the solution of (2.10), which is

$$q = q_0 \sin\left(\frac{1}{\sqrt{(LC)}}\, t + \epsilon\right).$$ (2.11)

As before, q_0 and ϵ could be determined from the initial conditions.

In both the above examples, the oscillations continue indefinitely with constant amplitude. In real systems the oscillations eventually die away, and this will be investigated fully in Chapter 3. The reason the oscillations continue indefinitely here is that no energy leaves the system, and we can make use of this fact in deducing (2.9) by the following alternative method. If we define the potential energy of the system of Fig. 2.3 to be zero when the mass is at the equilibrium level, then when the displacement is x the P.E. is $\frac{1}{2}kx^2$ and the kinetic energy is $\frac{1}{2}m\,(dx/dt)^2$. The total energy $U = $ P.E. $+$ K.E. does not change with time, so its derivative is zero. Thus

$$\frac{dU}{dt} = \frac{d}{dt}\left\{ \tfrac{1}{2}\, kx^2 + \tfrac{1}{2}\, m \left(\frac{dx}{dt}\right)^2 \right\}$$

so $kx\left(\dfrac{dx}{dt}\right) + m\left(\dfrac{dx}{dt}\right)\left(\dfrac{d^2x}{dt^2}\right) = 0$

giving $m(d^2x/dt^2) + kx = 0$ as before.

Similarly, for the circuit of Fig. 2.4, the magnetic P.E. stored by the inductor is $\frac{1}{2} Li^2$, and the electrostatic P.E. stored by the capacitor is $\frac{1}{2} (q^2/C)$. The sum of these, which is the total electromagnetic energy of the circuit U, is constant. Equating dU/dt to zero and substituting $i = dq/dt$ quickly leads to (2.10).

2.2.2 Periodic motion of a point in two dimensions

Suppose a point is subjected simultaneously to two simple harmonic motions at right angles to one another. A physical example of this is the motion of the spot on a cathode-ray oscilloscope screen when alternating voltages are applied simultaneously to the X- and Y-plates.

Suppose that the voltage across the X-plates causes the spot to move according to the equation

$$x = a \sin 2\pi ft ,\tag{2.12}$$

and that across the Y-plates causes the spot to move according to the equation

$$y = b \sin(2\pi ft + \epsilon) .\tag{2.13}$$

This means that the alternating voltages have the same frequency f, different amplitudes, and differ in phase by ϵ radians. When the voltages are simultaneously applied, we can find the path described by the spot by eliminating the time t from equations (2.12) and (2.13) as follows. Expanding (2.13) we get

$$y = b \sin 2\pi ft \cos \epsilon + b \cos 2\pi ft \sin \epsilon .\tag{2.14}$$

From equation (2.12) we see that

$$\sin 2\pi ft = \frac{x}{a} ,$$

so that $\cos 2\pi ft = \sqrt{\left(1 - \frac{x^2}{a^2}\right)}.$

Inserting these values into (2.14) and simplifying, we obtain

$$a^2 y^2 + b^2 x^2 - 2abxy \cos \epsilon - a^2 b^2 \sin^2 \epsilon = 0 .\tag{2.15}$$

Readers may recognize this as the general equation for an ellipse. The form can readily be determined, and the curve sketched, by putting specific values of x and y into (2.15).

When $y = 0$ $x = \pm a \sin \epsilon,$
$\quad\quad\ x = 0$ $y = \pm b \sin \epsilon,$
$\quad\quad\ x = \pm a$ $y = \pm b \cos \epsilon,$
$\quad\quad\ y = \pm b$ $x = \pm a \cos \epsilon.$

These points are plotted to give the curve shown in Fig. 2.5.

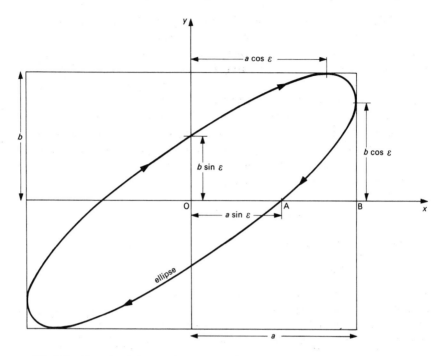

Fig. 2.5 – Two simple harmonic motions, of equal frequency, at right angles.

Thus the picture we see on the screen will, in general, be an ellipse, and it is worth noting that the phase angle ϵ can be determined from it since

$$\frac{OA}{OB} = \sin \epsilon \ .$$

For special values of ϵ ($\epsilon = 0$ and π) the ellipse degenerates into a straight line, whilst for $\epsilon = \frac{1}{2}\pi$ and $\frac{3}{2}\pi$ the major and minor axes of the ellipse coincide with the x- and y-axes. These particular instances are shown in Fig. 2.6. The situation shown in Fig. 2.6a could have easily been predicted; since the x- and y-motions are in phase with one another, the maximum of x will occur at the same instant as the maximum of y. The situation shown in Fig. 2.6b for $\epsilon = \frac{1}{2}\pi$ [and Fig. 2.6d for $\frac{3}{2}\pi$] is also of interest. If $a = b$ we have a circular path; this point will be pursued further during the discussion of polarization in Chapter 11.

The curves in Fig. 2.6 are examples of Lissajous' figures. If the frequencies of the two signals are not the same, the figures become more complicated and are not, in general, stationary except when the frequencies are in the ratio of two whole numbers.

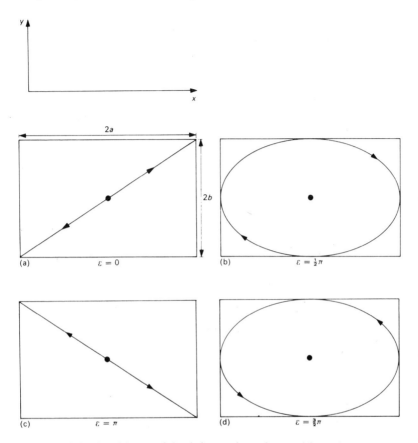

Fig. 2.6 – Special cases of simple harmonic motions at right angles.

2.3 VIBRATIONS OF TWO COUPLED PARTICLES: NORMAL MODES

We now need to investigate systems consisting of two particles coupled together. Examples of the types of system we have in mind are shown in Fig. 2.7.

Eventually we shall obtain equations of motion of the masses shown in Fig. 2.7c, but before we embark on the mathematics it is very important that the reader should obtain a clear picture of the ways in which the particles in such systems can vibrate, so we strongly recommend that anyone meeting this subject for the first time should try — or at least imagine — the following simple experiment. The apparatus required is a 'Slinky' spring (obtainable from a toy shop) and about a metre of the type of chain used to secure wash-basin stoppers. The spring is cut into halves; the upper ends are clamped at the same level, as shown in Fig. 2.8, and the ends of the chain are connected to the lower ends of the springs.

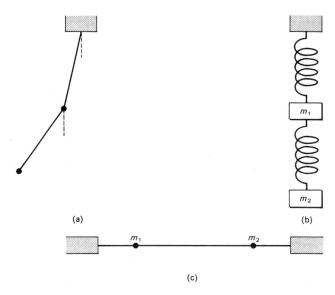

Fig. 2.7 — Systems with coupled particles. (a) Double pendulum.
(b) Two suspended masses and springs.
(c) Stretched elastic string, loaded with two masses.

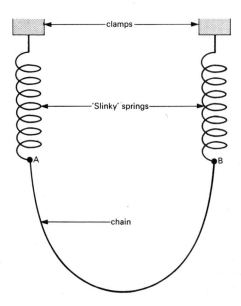

Fig. 2.8 — Spring-and-chain experiment to illustrate motion of a two-particle system.

The system so obtained is rather different from those shown in Fig. 2.7, since it has a distributed mass rather than point masses. This makes the analysis much harder, but this does not matter since we do not intend to treat this system mathematically. We want to note how the positions of the points A and B, where the chain joins the springs, vary with time when the system is set into vertical motion.

First, raise A and B by equal amounts and release them from rest. A and B should be seen to oscillate up and down with simple harmonic motion. Clearly A and B are exactly in phase — they are both at the top of the motion (or both at the bottom) at the same instant. Find an approximate value for the period. We will refer to this particular motion as mode 1.

Next lower A and raise B by equal amounts to the configuration shown in Fig. 2.9b and release them from rest.

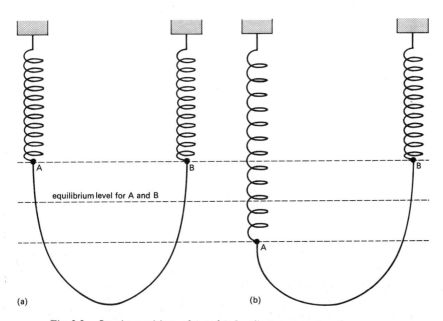

equilibrium level for A and B

(a)   (b)

Fig. 2.9 — Starting positions of A and B for the two normal modes.
(a) Mode 1. (b) Mode 2.

Once more the points A and B should be seen to perform simple harmonic motion, but now in exact antiphase (A is at the top of its motion whilst B is at the bottom, and vice versa). We will refer to this motion as mode 2. Note that the period is not the same as for mode 1.

Bring the system to rest once more, and start motion by drawing A, alone, down and releasing it. The motion which follows (mode 3) should be seen to be of a much more complicated character than previously; neither A nor B oscillates with simple harmonic motion, but the variation of the position of each with time should be somewhat as shown in Fig. 2.10. Note that the oscillations of both points successively build up and die away, and that A is oscillating with its greatest amplitude when B has minimum amplitude, and vice versa. The kinetic energy of the system is, in fact, being periodically transferred from one side to the other.

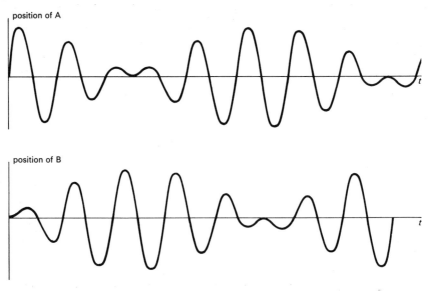

Fig. 2.10 – Graphs of position against time for A and B when the system of Fig. 2.9 is in a general state of motion.

Mode 1 and mode 2 are known as *normal modes*; a system of two particles is said to be in a normal mode when both particles are executing simple harmonic motion with the same frequency. Mode 3 is a general state of motion. Note that there are two distinct normal modes for this system, and that they have different frequencies associated with them. A system whose configuration is completely described by two coordinates, such as the positions of the points A and B in our example, is said to have two *degrees of freedom*. Such a system has two distinct normal modes of vibration. Note that it is incorrect in general to equate the number of degrees of freedom to the number of particles, since any particle may have up to three degrees of freedom. In our example the points A and B move up and down only, so the position of each is completely specified by a single coordinate.

Now that the reader has a qualitative idea of the way in which a system with two particles vibrates, the time has come to provide a proper quantitative analysis of the problem. We will take the system of Fig 2.7c, a stretched light elastic string fixed at both ends and loaded with two equal masses at the points of trisection; it will be seen later why this choice is an appropriate one for a book on waves. Let us assume that such a system has been set in motion, and that at a given instant the two masses are displaced transversely, as shown in Fig. 2.11.

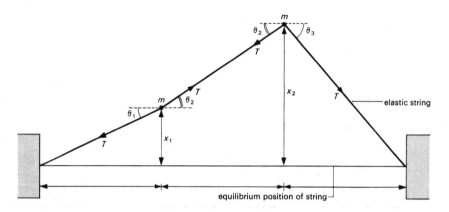

Fig. 2.11 – Loaded elastic string at some instant during motion.

The following assumptions are made:

(a) The displacements x_1 and x_2 of the masses from their equilibrium positions are always small in comparison with the length of the string.
(b) The changes in the original tension T due to these small displacements can be ignored in comparison with T itself.
(c) The effects of gravity are ignored.

To obtain the differential equations governing the motions of the particles, we apply Newton's second law of motion. For the first mass,

$$m \frac{d^2 x_1}{dt^2} = T \sin \theta_2 - T \sin \theta_1 ,$$

which, when we replace $d^2 x_1/dt^2$ by $\ddot{x}_1$ for brevity, becomes

$$m\ddot{x}_1 = T \sin \theta_2 - T \sin \theta_1 , \qquad (2.16)$$

and for the second mass

$$m\ddot{x}_2 = -T \sin \theta_2 - T \sin \theta_3 ; \qquad (2.17)$$

where the angles $\theta_1, \theta_2, \theta_3$ are those shown in Fig. 2.11.

Since x_1 is small,

$$\sin \theta_1 \cong \tan \theta_1 = \frac{x_1}{a} \quad ;$$

similarly $\sin \theta_2 \cong \dfrac{x_2 - x_1}{a}$

and $\sin \theta_3 \cong \dfrac{x_2}{a}$.

Inserting these values into (2.16) and (2.17), and rearranging, we obtain

$$m\ddot{x}_1 + \frac{2Tx_1}{a} - \frac{Tx_2}{a} = 0 \ , \tag{2.18}$$

$$m\ddot{x}_2 + \frac{2Tx_2}{a} - \frac{Tx_1}{a} = 0 \ . \tag{2.19}$$

Equations (2.18) and (2.19) are simultaneous differential equations. Rather than solve them directly, we will investigate the conditions under which the system will oscillate in a normal mode. We have already seen, from the experiment, that in a normal mode the particles execute simple harmonic motion with the same frequency; we can therefore write down the equations of motion for the two masses as

$$x_1 = A \sin \omega t \ , \tag{2.20}$$

$$x_2 = B \sin \omega t \ . \tag{2.21}$$

In the slinky spring experiment, the reference points A and B moved either in phase or in antiphase during normal mode vibrations. This is generally true. There is no need therefore to include an epoch (for example the epoch ϵ in 2.2) since the particles will either be exactly in phase or exactly in antiphase; in the latter case, A and B will have opposite signs because

$$\sin(\omega t + \pi) = - \sin \omega t \ .$$

Substituting from (2.20) and (2.21) into (2.18) and (2.19) we obtain, after cancelling out the trigonometric terms,

$$- m\omega^2 A + \frac{2TA}{a} - \frac{TB}{a} = 0 \tag{2.22}$$

and $- m\omega^2 B + \dfrac{2TB}{a} - \dfrac{TA}{a} = 0 \ . \tag{2.23}$

We can eliminate the ratio A/B between these equations to get

$$\left[-m\omega^2 + \frac{2T}{a} \right]^2 = \frac{T^2}{a^2} \quad ;$$

so $$-m\omega^2 + \frac{2T}{a} = \pm \left(\frac{T}{a} \right) \quad .$$

Thus, solving for ω^2 we have

$$\omega^2 = \frac{T}{ma} \quad \text{or} \quad \frac{3T}{ma} \quad .$$

Thus there are two different circular frequencies with which this system oscillates in a normal mode; these are

$$\omega_1 = \sqrt{\left(\frac{T}{ma} \right)} \tag{2.24}$$

and $$\omega_2 = \sqrt{\left(\frac{3T}{ma} \right)} \quad . \tag{2.25}$$

If we now substitute the value of ω_1 into (2.22) we get

$$A = B \quad .$$

Thus, in this (the first) normal mode, the amplitudes of motion of the masses are the same, and the latter move in phase at all times; the vibration will there- fore be as shown in Fig. 2.12a.

If we substitute ω_2 into (2.22) we get

$$A = -B \quad ;$$

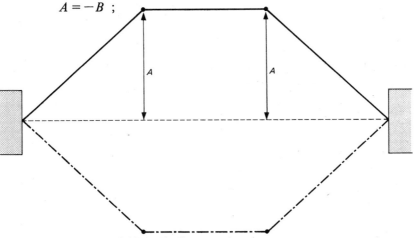

Fig. 2.12a – The first normal mode.

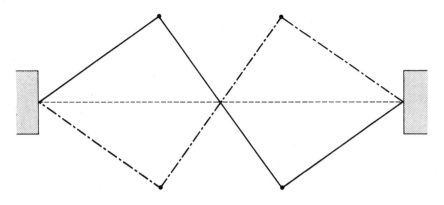

Fig. 2.12b – The second normal mode.

in the second normal mode, therefore, the amplitudes are the same but the motions are in antiphase, as indicated in Fig. 2.12b. The frequencies f_1 and f_2 corresponding to the normal modes are referred to as the *natural frequencies* of the system. (Remember $f = \omega/2\pi$.)

We must now find the equations of motion of the masses when the system is in a general state of motion. Knowledge that in the normal modes $x_1 = x_2$ or $x_1 = -x_2$ at all times suggests how we should proceed. If we add together equations (2.18) and (2.19) we obtain

$$m(\ddot{x}_1 + \ddot{x}_2) + \frac{2T}{a}(x_1 + x_2) - \frac{T}{a}(x_1 + x_2) = 0 , \qquad (2.26)$$

and if we subtract them we get

$$m(\ddot{x}_1 - \ddot{x}_2) + \frac{2T}{a}(x_1 - x_2) + \frac{T}{a}(x_1 - x_2) = 0 . \qquad (2.27)$$

Writing $x_1 + x_2 = u$ in (2.26),
and $x_1 - x_2 = v$ in (2.27),
so that $\ddot{x}_1 + \ddot{x}_2 = \ddot{u}$
and $\ddot{x}_1 - \ddot{x}_2 = \ddot{v}$,
we find that these equations simplify to

$$m\ddot{u} + \frac{T}{a}u = 0 ,$$

$$m\ddot{v} + \frac{3T}{a}v = 0 .$$

These we recognise as the differential equations for simple harmonic motion (see (2.1)), so we can immediately write down their solutions (see (2.2)) as follows:

$$u = x_1 + x_2 = C \sin\left\{\sqrt{\left(\frac{T}{ma}\right)}\, t + \alpha\right\}$$

and

$$v = x_1 - x_2 = D \sin\left\{\sqrt{\left(\frac{3T}{ma}\right)}\, t + \beta\right\},$$

where C, D, α, and β are the arbitrary constants of integration. We can solve for x_1 and x_2 as follows:

$$x_1 = \frac{u + v}{2}$$

$$= \tfrac{1}{2} C \sin\left\{\sqrt{\left(\frac{T}{ma}\right)}\, t + \alpha\right\} + \tfrac{1}{2} D \sin\left\{\sqrt{\left(\frac{3T}{ma}\right)}\, t + \beta\right\} \qquad (2.28)$$

and

$$x_2 = \frac{u - v}{2}$$

$$= \tfrac{1}{2} C \sin\left\{\sqrt{\left(\frac{T}{ma}\right)}\, t + \alpha\right\} - \tfrac{1}{2} D \sin\left\{\sqrt{\left(\frac{3T}{ma}\right)}\, t + \beta\right\}. \qquad (2.29)$$

Equations (2.28) and (2.29) are the equations of motion of the masses when the system is in a general state of motion. It will be seen that the motion in each case is the sum of two simple harmonic terms, and that the frequencies of these simple harmonic terms are, respectively, the frequencies associated with the two normal modes in which the system is capable of oscillating. This last point can be checked by comparing the circular frequency terms in (2.28) and (2.29) with ω_1 and ω_2 in equations (2.24) and (2.25). Mathematically, equations (2.28) and (2.29) are said to be *linear combinations* of the normal-mode solutions.

The type of motion obtained when a particle executes two simple harmonic motions of different frequencies simultaneously is known as *beats*. This is the effect shown in Fig. 2.10. At certain times the two motions will be in step with one another, resulting in a large displacement; but since the frequencies are different they will gradually get out of step and will eventually tend to cancel each other out, then later they will get back into step and so on.

The phenomenon of beats is more usually associated with the combination of two collinear simple harmonic motions of nearly the same frequency. Suppose we have two such motions of the same amplitude a, but whose circular frequencies differ by a small amount $\Delta\omega$. On combining, we get

$$y = a \sin \omega t + a \sin (\omega + \Delta\omega)t .$$

Applying the trigonometrical formula

$$\sin A + \sin B = 2 \sin \tfrac{1}{2}(A + B) \cos \tfrac{1}{2}(A - B) \ ,$$

we have

$$y = 2a \cos \left[\frac{\Delta \omega}{2} t\right] \sin \left[\left(\omega + \frac{\Delta \omega}{2}\right)t\right] \ .$$

This can be written as

$$y = A \sin \bar{\omega}t \ ,$$

where $\quad A = 2a \cos \left(\frac{\Delta \omega}{2} t\right)$

and $\bar{\omega}$ is the mean of the two original circular frequencies. The result is therefore similar to simple harmonic motion, except that the amplitude A changes slowly with time.

Probably the best example of this is the note produced when two tuning forks of the same nominal frequency are struck simultaneously. This note is heard to build up and die away alternately with low frequency. Since the ear recognizes intensity but not phase, it is unable to distinguish between the maxima and minima of A, so the apparent frequency of the beats (the so-called beat frequency) is $\Delta f = \Delta \omega / 2\pi$ (the difference between the individual frequencies of the forks).

Fig. 2.13 shows how the resultant disturbance y varies with time. It can be seen that the beat period $T_B = 2\pi / \Delta \omega$ is exactly one half of the period T_A.

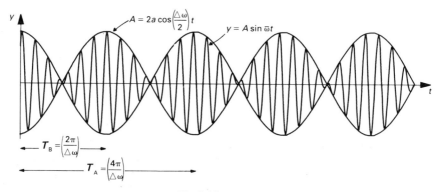

Fig. 2.13 – Beats.

2.4 SYSTEMS WITH MORE THAN TWO PARTICLES
Systems of more than two particles can be analysed along the lines of section 2.3, but the mathematics becomes rather cumbersome. A system comprising a

stretched elastic string loaded with three evenly spaced equal masses can be shown to have three normal modes of vibration and three natural frequencies. The normal modes are shown in Fig. 2.14. For this system, the general equation of motion for any of the particles can also be shown to be a linear combination of the three normal-mode solutions.

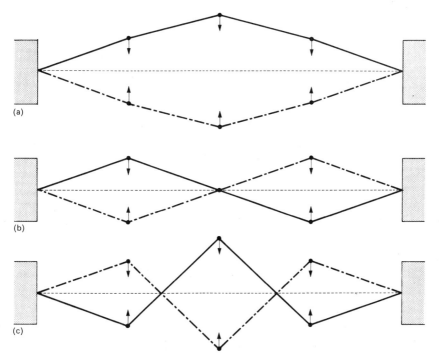

Fig. 2.14 – Normal modes for a three-particle system. (a) Mode 1 (lowest frequency). (b) Mode 2 (note that the central mass is permanently at rest). (c) Mode 3 (highest frequency).

We can extend the pattern further. A system of N particles (each particle having one degree of freedom only) can be shown to have N normal modes of vibration and N natural frequencies, and the general state of motion is a linear combination of the N normal mode solutions.

An important extension of these ideas is encountered in the vibrations of a stretched heavy string. Such a string can be regarded as a system comprising an infinite number of particles, and will have an infinite number of normal modes and natural frequencies. It is possible to analyse the behaviour of a vibrating string in this way, but it is much more convenient to regard the string as a continuous medium, and to treat the problem by means of waves, as is done in Chapter 5.

PROBLEMS

(2.1) Show that an alternative solution of the defining equation (2.1) of simple harmonic motion is $x = \alpha \sin \omega t + \beta \cos \omega t$, where α and β are constants. (Note that since there are two arbitrary constants, this is also a general solution.) Comparing this solution with (2.2), express (i) α and β in terms of a and ϵ, (ii) a and ϵ in terms of α and β.

Hence, deduce the amplitude of the motion described by $x = 4 \sin \omega t + 3 \cos \omega t$. How could the answer have been obtained by a simple geometric construction? (Note that this is a particular case of the more general problem of adding two s.h.m.'s with arbitrary phase difference, which is also accomplished by a simple geometric construction (Chapter 11)).

(2.2) It can be shown that for a simple pendulum (i.e. a heavy mass at the end of a light string fixed at its upper end) of length l, the horizontal displacement x from its equilibrium position is given by $d^2x/dt^2 + (g/l)x = 0$ (so long as $x \ll 1$), where g is the acceleration due to gravity.

Show that the period is $2\pi(l/g)^{\frac{1}{2}}$, and deduce the period of a pendulum of length 2 m, taking g to be 10 m s^{-2}. If the bob has mass 0.1 kg, and the amplitude is 0.02 m, deduce (i) the energy of the bob, (ii) the maximum tension in the string.

(2.3) A U-tube having a uniform bore and vertical limbs contains a total length l of liquid. If the liquid in one limb is momentarily depressed, determine the period of subsequent oscillations.

(2.4) A mass is hung from the end of a spring fixed at its upper end, and set into vertical oscillations. It is also allowed to oscillate laterally as a simple pendulum (for which the period is $2\pi(l/g)^{\frac{1}{2}}$). Show that it is impossible for the mass to describe an elliptical path, since this would necessitate that the unstretched length of the spring be zero.

If the frequency of vertical oscillations is double that of horizontal oscillations, show that the equilibrium extension of the spring is one third of its natural length.

(2.5) Use a calculator to plot the Lissajous figure traced by a particle moving in two dimensions, where $x = 2 \sin \omega t$, $y = \sin 3\omega t/2$. t should start at zero and increase until the path starts to repeat itself. After how many cycles of (i) the x motion (ii) the y motion does this occur?

If the frequencies of the x and y motions were respectively 5.0 Hz and 5.2 Hz, after how many cycles of each would a repetition of the path now occur? (Do not plot a graph for this part of the question.)

(2.6) Set up an oscilloscope and two sinusoidal oscillators, one connected to the external X input, and the other to the Y input. Keep the frequency of the first fixed at about 100 Hz, and vary that of the second from about 40 Hz to 1 kHz. Observing the screen will give valuable insight concerning the appearance of Lissajous' figures.

(2.7) Use the computer program (Appendix A) to display the position of the mass with coordinate x_1 (equation (2.28)) for the system shown in Fig. 2.11, as a function of time. The ratio of the two normal-mode frequencies is $\sqrt{3}$.

In response to the question 'Number of waves to be added?', type in 2. Then input

Amplitude	Phase constant	Circular wavenumber	Wave speed
1	0	20	0
1	0	34.6	0

Experiment with different amplitudes (C, D) and phase constants (α, β).

(2.8) Two stationary railway coaches of masses M and m are coupled together on a level frictionless track by a light coupling of stiffness k. The first is given an impulse at the end remote from the coupling. Find the period of subsequent oscillations.

(2.9) A light spring of stiffness $2k$ is suspended vertically from a rigid support and carries a mass $2m$ at its free end. A second light spring of stiffness k is attached to this mass and carries a mass m at its lower end. Deduce the natural frequencies and the normal modes of oscillation of the system.

The system is at rest, and the mass $2m$ is suddenly given a vertical velocity u. Derive the equation of motion of this mass.

(2.10) A light elastic string under tension T is stretched between two fixed supports a distance l apart. It carries three particles, each of mass $m/3$, at distances $l/6$, $l/2$ and $5l/6$ from one support. Neglecting the effects of gravity, calculate the frequencies of the normal modes of transverse vibration, indicating their forms.

CHAPTER 3

Damped and forced vibrations

3.1 REAL VIBRATING SYSTEMS

The vibrating systems we considered in Chapter 2 vibrated for ever with un-diminished amplitude. Real physical systems do not, of course, vibrate indefinitely. For example the suspended mass on an elastic string of Fig. 2.3 eventually comes to rest; the charge oscillations of Fig. 2.4 eventually die away. The equations of motion derived in Chapter 2 (2.9a and 2.11) and the theory leading up to them will now have to be revised to take account of the decay of real vibrations.

The reason for the decay is that the energy originally stored in the system (mechanical potential energy in displacing the suspended mass from its rest position; electrical potential energy in charging the capacitor) is gradually transformed into heat energy by a number of processes. The suspended mass, as it moves, experiences a viscous force due to the air through which it passes. Work has to be done to overcome this force, and hence energy is lost. Even if the mass were in vacuum, there would be hysteresis losses in stretching the elastic string, and also frictional losses where the upper (fixed) end of the string is clamped. In the LC circuit of Fig. 2.4, there will inevitably be some electrical resistance (ignored in Chapter 2) which will convert electrical energy to heat energy by Joule (I^2R) heating.

Before we refine our theory to take account of these effects, we give a physical example of the way the amplitude decreases with time for real systems. Fig. 3.1 is from a C.R.O. display of charge oscillations for the circuit of Fig. 2.4 when resistance is included. (The plates of C are connected to the Y plates of a C.R.O., with the timebase chosen to display a convenient number of oscillations.) Our theory must now be extended fully to account for the features shown.

3.2 DAMPED OSCILLATIONS IN ONE DIMENSION

We return to the mass suspended from an elastic string. Consider the situation shown in Fig. 3.2 when the mass is in motion downward, and its instantaneous position is x (measured from the equilibrium level). In addition to the gravitational

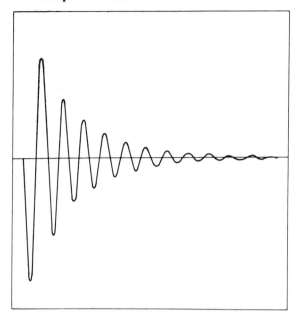

Fig. 3.1 – Oscilloscope display of charge oscillations in a real circuit.

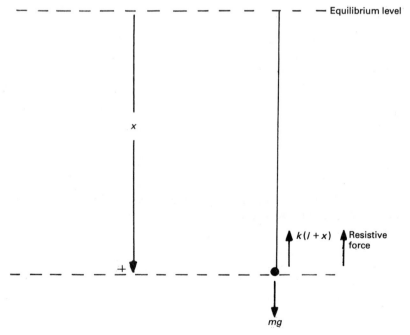

Fig. 3.2 – Forces on oscillating suspended mass.

force mg and the tension $k(l + x)$, we now have a resistive force to take into account. We can at once tell the direction of this force at any instant; since it opposes motion it must be upward in the figure, for the mass is moving downward at the instant shown. What is the magnitude of this resistive force? Here we must appeal to experiment. It is an experimental fact that when a particle moves through a viscous fluid, such as a gas, the resistive force is proportional to the velocity of the particle relative to the fluid, provided the velocity is not too great. Frictional forces can also be shown experimentally to be proportional to relative velocity. The resultant of all the forces which resist the motion may be regarded as a single *damping* force. Further, we will assume that this force at any instant is proportional to the particle velocity v

i.e. Damping force $= D\ v = D\ dx/dt$ \hfill (3.1)

where D is the coefficient of damping and has the physical dimension $[D] = [MT^{-1}]$. Applying Newton's second law of motion to the particle of Fig. 3.2 gives

$$m\ d^2x/dt^2 = mg - k(l + x) - D\ dx/dt \ . \tag{3.2}$$

Note carefully the signs given to the three forces on the right of this equation; mg is positive because it is downward, that is in the direction of x increasing. The other two are negative because they are upward. Since $mg = kl$ (2.8), (3.2) becomes, on collecting terms,

$$m\ d^2x/dt^2 + D\ dx/dt + kx = 0 \ . \tag{3.3}$$

This is the differential equation governing damped vibrations in one dimension (single coordinate x). Before we solve it in order to find the actual equation of motion, it is worthwhile to derive it from energy considerations by an extension of the argument given in section 2.2.1. At the instant shown in Fig. 3.2, the total energy of the system is

$$U = \text{potential energy (P.E.)} + \text{kinetic energy (K.E.)}$$

$$\text{so } U = \tfrac{1}{2}\, m \left(\frac{dx}{dt}\right)^2 + \tfrac{1}{2}\, kx^2 \ . \tag{3.4}$$

In an infinitesimal time dt during which the mass descends a distance dx, the work dW done against damping forces is given by force × distance $= D(dx/dt)\,dx$.

$$\text{therefore } \quad dW = D \left(\frac{dx}{dt}\right)\left(\frac{dx}{dt}\right)\ dt$$

$$= D \left(\frac{dx}{dt}\right)^2\ dt \ . \tag{3.5}$$

This must be equal to the *loss* in energy of the mass and string.

Thus $\quad dW = -\dfrac{dU}{dt}\,dt$

$$= -\frac{d}{dt}\left\{\tfrac{1}{2}m\left(\frac{dx}{dt}\right)^2 + \tfrac{1}{2}\,kx^2\right\}dt \ , \tag{3.6}$$

therefore $\quad D\left(\dfrac{dx}{dt}\right)^2 dt = -\left\{m\left(\dfrac{d^2x}{dt^2}\right)\left(\dfrac{dx}{dt}\right) + kx\left(\dfrac{dx}{dt}\right)\right\}dt \ .$

So, cancelling (dx/dt) throughout and collecting terms we find, as before

$$m\,\frac{d^2x}{dt^2} + D\,\frac{dx}{dt} + kx = 0 \ . \tag{3.3}$$

The equation for the electrical circuit of Fig. 3.3 which corresponds to (3.2) is obtained by applying Kirchhoff's second network law to the circuit. The

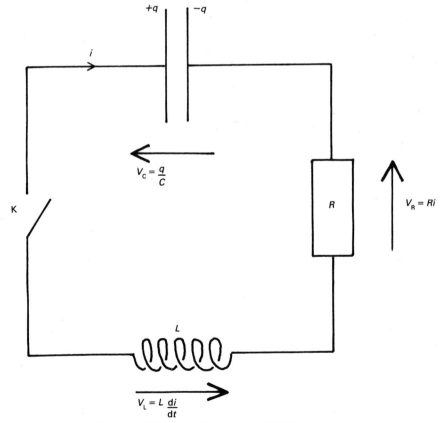

Fig. 3.3 – LCR circuit showing potential differences.

capacitor is initially charged and the key K open. At some instant after closing the key K, suppose the charge in the capacitor is q and the current flowing is i. The potential differences across each element at this instant are as shown. The algebraic sum of potential differences round the circuit going anticlockwise from A to A is zero, so

$$L \frac{di}{dt} + Ri + \frac{q}{C} = 0 \ .$$

Now $i = \dfrac{dq}{dt}$ and $\dfrac{di}{dt} = \dfrac{d^2q}{dt^2}$, so

$$L \frac{d^2q}{dt^2} + R \frac{dq}{dt} + \frac{q}{C} = 0 \ . \tag{3.7}$$

This is the same as (2.10) but with the additional term $Ri = R(dq/dt)$.

Equation (3.7) has exactly the same form as (3.3), so we can point out analogies between the various pairs of corresponding quantities. Displacement x is analogous to instantaneous charge q; velocity $v = (dx/dt)$ to current $i = (dq/dt)$; mass m to inductance L; mechanical damping D to electrical damping, or resistance, R; and mechanical stiffness k to the reciprocal of electrical capacitance $1/C$.

To find exactly how the position x of our mass (or the instantaneous charge q) varies with time, we must find the general solution of (3.3) (or (3.7)). Since both equations have the same form, we can write them both as

$$\boxed{\ddot{x} + 2b\dot{x} + \omega_0^2 x = 0} \tag{3.8}$$

where $2b$ $= D/m$ (mechanical case)   (3.9)

             $= R/L$ (electrical case)   (3.10)

ω_0^2 $= k/m$ (mechanical case)   (3.11)

             $= 1/LC$ (electrical case)   (3.12)

and x in (3.8) represents the displacement or the charge. Note we have used $\dot{x} = dx/dt$ etc. as in Chapter 2. The constants $2b$ and ω_0^2 have been chosen in this way to simplify the subsequent algebra. Although (3.8) has been derived for two specific physical examples, it is of much wider importance in physics. It is a second-order linear differential equation. Its general solution, derived fully in Appendix B, is

$$x = A \exp \left\{ -b + \sqrt{b^2 - \omega_0^2} \right\} t + B \exp \left\{ -b - \sqrt{b^2 - \omega_0^2} \right\} t \tag{3.13}$$

where A and B are the arbitrary constants of integration which have to be determined from initial conditions, such as knowledge of the position and velocity of the particle at some instant.

There are three cases to be considered.

Case I. $b > \omega_0$ (Heavy damping)
When $b > \omega_0$, we see from (3.9) to (3.12) that, for the vibrating mass $D > 2\sqrt{(mk)}$, or for the LCR circuit $R > 2\sqrt{(L/C)}$. In physical terms this means a large amount of damping; for example a pendulum suspended in a jar of treacle or a circuit of high resistance. Mathematically, the condition $b > \omega_0$ means that the quantity $b^2 - \omega_0^2$ is positive and the square root is real. Since $-b \pm \sqrt{(b^2 - \omega_0^2)}$ is clearly negative, x is the sum of two exponentially decaying terms. The plot of x against t is typically as shown in Fig. 3.4. There are no oscillations. In the case of the mass on the spring the displaced mass creeps back, or relaxes, to its equilibrium position.

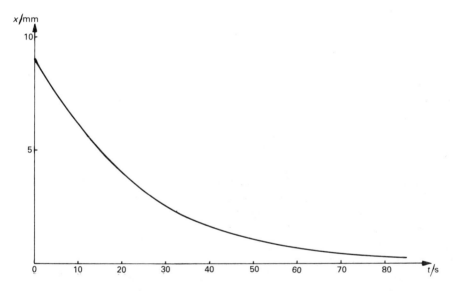

Fig. 3.4 – Heavy damping. Mass displaced 9 mm and released from rest: $\omega_0 = 0.2$ s^{-1}, $b = 0.5$ s^{-1}, $A = 9.4$ mm and $B = -0.4$ mm in (3.13).

Case II $b = \omega_0$ (Critical damping)
The solution (3.13) breaks down in this case and, as Appendix B shows, the solution is

$$x = (At + B) \exp(-\omega_0 t) . \tag{3.14}$$

Again, A and B are the arbitrary constants, determined from initial conditions. There are no oscillations. A typical motion of this kind is shown in Fig. 3.5.

It is very similar to that of case I; but, depending on the values of the constants, an overshoot is possible. Motion of this kind is known as 'critically damped'.

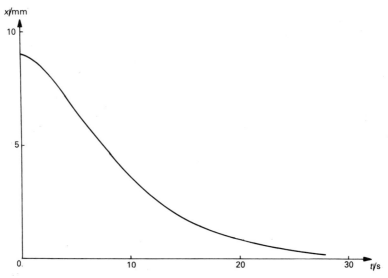

Fig. 3.5 – Critical damping. Mass displaced 9 mm and released from rest: $\omega_0 = b = 0.2$ s^{-1}, $A = 1.8$ mm s^{-1}, $B = 9.0$ mm in (3.14).

Example 3.1 *Damping in a moving-coil galvanometer*

Damping is of great importance in electrical meters for the following reason. Suppose that such a meter initially carrying no current is suddenly connected to a source. The meter will ultimately register a certain value, but it is clearly desirable that it should reach this final reading as quickly as possible. Now this will not happen if the movement is heavily damped so that it responds in a sluggish manner. It is also undesirable that the movement be lightly damped, since the needle will 'overshoot', and perform several oscillations about the final reading before attaining it. The optimum condition is that the damping should be approximately critical.

The main contribution to the damping in a moving-coil galvanometer is 'electromagnetic damping', and we will assume that other causes of damping (air resistance etc.) are negligible.

The theory of the moving-coil galvanometer is well known. The coil has N turns, each of area A, and carries a current i. It moves in a radial magnetic field of induction B, and experiences a torque $BANi$. If it has rotated through an angle θ, the suspension exerts a restoring torque $c\theta$, where c is a constant. The equation of motion of the coil is

$$I \frac{d^2\theta}{dt^2} + c\,\theta = BANi \tag{3.E1}$$

where I is the moment of inertia about the suspension axis.

To calculate the effective damping term, we note that the flux threading the coil can be expressed $BAN\theta$. (The reader may be troubled by this step, but a full justification will not concern us here.) There will be a back e.m.f. equal to the rate of change of this flux, namely $BAN\, d\theta/dt$.

If the galvanometer is connected to a source of e.m.f. V, and the total resistance of the circuit is R, then

$$R\,i = V - BAN\,\frac{d\theta}{dt}$$

Substitution in (3.E1) gives

$$I\,\frac{d^2\theta}{dt^2} + \frac{(BAN)^2}{R}\,\frac{d\theta}{dt} + c\,\theta = \frac{BAN}{R}\,V\,. \qquad (3.\text{E2})$$

This is the equation (3.8) for damped oscillations. (There should be no cause for concern that the R.H.S. is not zero. A simple shift in the origin of θ via the substitution $\theta' = \theta - (BAN/cR)\,V$ would clearly yield an equation in θ' which is identical to (3.E2) but with the R.H.S. equal to zero.)

By comparison with (3.7), we immediately see that the condition for critical damping $(b = \omega_0)$ is

$$\frac{(BAN)^2}{2RI} = \sqrt{\frac{c}{I}}$$

whence the resistance R required for critical damping is

$$R_c = \tfrac{1}{2}(BAN)^2/(Ic)^{\frac{1}{2}}$$

Case III $b < \omega_0$ (Light damping)
This is physically the most interesting and important case. The solution is obtained in Appendix B (equation (B.15)) and may be written as

$$\boxed{\begin{aligned} &x = a e^{-bt}\,\sin(\omega t + \epsilon) \\ &\text{where } \omega = \sqrt{(\omega_0^2 - b^2)} \end{aligned}} \qquad (3.15)$$

Now (3.15) has the same form as (2.2), but the amplitude term a in (2.2) has been replaced by $a\,e^{-bt}$, and the circular frequency term has become $\sqrt{(\omega_0^2 - b^2)}$.

Let us look at these in turn. We see that the amplitude of the motion decreases exponentially with time on account of the e^{-bt} term. Further, we see that there are now oscillations on account of the $\sin(\omega t + \epsilon)$ term. A plot of (3.15) is shown in Fig. 3.6. This has the same shape as Fig. 3.1, so our theory seems to be producing sensible answers. What we have is something very similar to s.h.m., but with the amplitude getting less and less, and after an infinite time disappearing altogether. Mathematically, we have the product of two terms

ae^{-bt} and sin $(\omega t + \epsilon)$ at each value of t; the curve is said to lie between the asymptotes $\pm\, ae^{-bt}$.

What is the period of this motion? Here we have a difficulty, for the motion never exactly repeats itself. The point A (Fig. 3.6) is never again reached. However, by comparison with undamped s.h.m. we can define the period as the elapsed time between a zero of x and the next-but-one zero of x, such as the points U and W in Fig. 3.6. Clearly

$$\omega T = 2\pi, \text{ or } T = 2\pi/\omega \ .$$

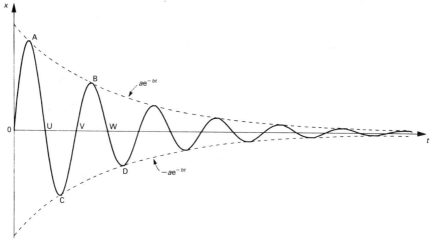

Fig. 3.6 – Damped s.h.m.: plot of (3.15).

Thus the period $T = \dfrac{2\pi}{\omega} = \dfrac{2\pi}{\sqrt{(\omega_0^2 - b^2)}}$.   (3.16)

If the damping is very light, so that $\omega_0^2 \gg b^2$,

we see that $T = \dfrac{2\pi}{\omega} \doteq \dfrac{2\pi}{\omega_0}$.   (3.17)

We can find the values of x at the various maxima and minima by the usual process of equating $\dot{x} = \mathrm{d}x/\mathrm{d}t$ to zero.
Thus from (3.15) we see

$$\frac{\mathrm{d}x}{\mathrm{d}t} = -b\, ae^{-bt} \sin(\omega t + \epsilon) + \omega ae^{-bt} \cos(\omega t + \epsilon)$$

$$= ae^{-bt}[-b \sin(\omega t + \epsilon) + \omega \cos(\omega t + \epsilon)]$$

$$= 0 \text{ at maxima and minima,}$$

so $\tan(\omega t + \epsilon) = \omega/b$.   (3.18)

Suppose (3.18) is satisfied at a particular time when x is maximum. Then since ω and b are constants, the succeeding times at which it is again satisfied are those for which $\tan(\omega t + \epsilon)$ takes the same value. This will clearly be when ωt has increased by $\pi, 2\pi, 3\pi$, etc., i.e. when t has increased by $\pi/\omega, 2\pi/\omega, 3\pi/\omega$, etc. Since maxima and minima alternate (see Fig. 3.6), it is clear that π/ω, $3\pi/\omega, 5\pi/\omega$, etc. correspond to minima, and $2\pi/\omega, 4\pi/\omega, 6\pi/\omega$, etc. correspond to maxima. The period T is, of course, $2\pi/\omega$. Consider two successive maxima. Since $(\omega t + \epsilon)$ has increased by 2π, $\sin(\omega t + \epsilon)$ must be the same for both.

Thus
$$\frac{x_n}{x_{n+2}} = \frac{ae^{-bt}}{ae^{-b(t+T)}} = e^{bT} . \tag{3.19}$$

The right-hand side of (3.19) is independent of n, which tells us this is the ratio of any pair of successive maxima, or successive minima. (It should now be obvious that the ratio of a maximum to the following minimum is $-\exp(\pi b/\omega)$.) The successive maxima thus form a geometrical progression of constant ratio e^{bT},

i.e.
$$\frac{x_1}{x_3} = \frac{x_3}{x_5} = \ldots = \frac{x_n}{x_{n+2}} = e^{bT} . \tag{3.20}$$

There are several parameters which may be chosen to describe the manner in which a damped vibrating system decays. Prominent among them are the logarithmic decrement λ, the time-constant τ, and the quality factor Q.

Logarithmic decrement is defined as

$$\boxed{\lambda = \ln\left(\frac{x_n}{x_{n+2}}\right) ,} \tag{3.21}$$

that is, as the natural logarithm of the ratio of successive maxima. Thus, from (3.19)

$$\lambda = bT . \tag{3.22}$$

The time-constant τ is the time taken for the amplitude to fall to $1/e$ of its initial value. It follows from (3.20) that

$$\tau = 1/b . \tag{3.23}$$

The quality factor Q is defined as $2\pi \div$ (the fraction of the energy of the system lost to damping forces in 1 cycle).

Thus
$$Q = 2\pi \times \frac{\text{Energy in system at start of cycle}}{\text{Energy lost during cycle}} \tag{3.24}$$

If our system is the suspended vibrating mass, then at the instant the mass is at the nth (maximum) displacement x_n, its velocity is zero and the energy of the system is entirely potential and of value $\frac{1}{2}kx_n^2$ where k is the stiffness of the string.

The energy lost in one cycle is thus $\frac{1}{2}k(x_n^2 - x_{n+2}^2)$,

$$\text{and } Q = 2\pi \times \frac{\frac{1}{2}kx_n^2}{\frac{1}{2}k(x_n^2 - x_{n+2}^2)}$$

$$= 2\pi / \left\{ 1 - \frac{x_{n+2}^2}{x_n^2} \right\}$$

$$= \frac{2\pi}{(1 - e^{-2bT})} \text{ by (3.19)} . \tag{3.25}$$

If the damping is light, so that b is small,

$$e^{-2bT} \doteq 1 - 2bT ,$$

so $\quad Q = \dfrac{2\pi}{2bT} = \dfrac{\pi}{bT} .$ (3.26)

Also, from (3.23), $Q = \pi\tau/T = \pi \times$ (number of oscillations in one time-constant). (3.26a)

Q is thus independent of the actual energy possessed by the vibrating system at any given instant. The quality factor Q has greater importance in forced damped vibrations, but it is worth introducing the idea at this stage.

3.3 FORCED VIBRATIONS

The preceding sections of this chapter treat vibrating systems which, once set into vibration (for example by displacing a mass or charging a capacitor), the system is left to itself. There is no further interference by the outside world; in particular no further energy is introduced. Such vibrations are sometimes referred to as free vibrations, and the frequency of such vibrations is entirely determined by the system itself (see, for example, equation (3.16) above).

When a vibrating system is subjected to a continuous periodic disturbance of some kind, the resulting vibrations are quite different. For example, when a tuning fork is arranged as shown in Fig. 3.7 with a prong between the poles of an electromagnet fed with a.c., the fork sounds not with its own natural frequency but with the frequency f of the alternating current. Forced vibrations of this kind are of immense importance throughout physics and engineering, and we shall treat them in some detail.

We will expand our simple mechanical and electrical systems of Figs. 3.2 and 3.3 to incorporate driving forces as shown in Fig. 3.8. In the mechanical system, a sinusoidally varying vertical force is applied to the now-familar mass m suspended from an elastic string of stiffness k. The force has maximum value F_0 and varies sinusoidally with time with circular frequency p. A possible practical method of applying a force of this kind is an a.c.-fed electromagnet (as in Fig. 3.7). The

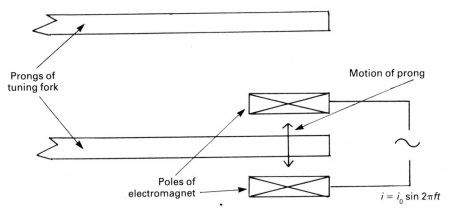

Fig. 3.7 – Forced vibration of a tuning fork.

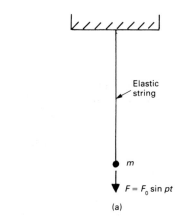

(a)

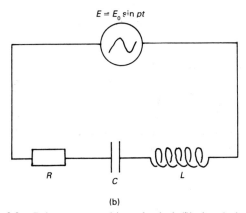

(b)

Fig. 3.8 – Driven systems: (a) mechanical, (b) electrical.

electrical case is more straightforward. The original circuit of Fig. 3.3 is simply driven by an a.c. source, having zero impedance, of peak e.m.f. E_0 and circular frequency p as shown in Fig. 3.8b. When we include the driving force in (3.3) we obtain, by a straightforward application of Newton's second law of motion,

$$m\ddot{x} + D\dot{x} + kx = F_0 \sin pt \ . \tag{3.27}$$

When we apply Kirchhoff's second network law (the e.m.f. in a circuit is equal to the algebraic sum of the potential differences round the circuit at any instant) we obtain

$$L\ddot{q} + R\dot{q} + (1/C)q = E_0 \sin pt \ . \tag{3.28}$$

The equations (3.27) and (3.28) have exactly the same mathematical form, and we write for both of them

$$\boxed{\ddot{x} + 2b\dot{x} + \omega_0^2 x = P \sin pt} \tag{3.29}$$

where $2b$ and ω_0^2 are still given by (3.9) to (3.12) above, and now

$$P = F_0/m \text{ (mechanical case)} \tag{3.30}$$

$$P = E_0/L \text{ (electrical case)} \ . \tag{3.31}$$

The second-order, linear differential equation of (3.29) is solved toward the end of Appendix B where it is shown that the general solution, is

$$\boxed{x = ae^{-bt}\sin(\omega t + \epsilon) + \frac{P \sin(pt - \delta)}{\{(\omega_0^2 - p^2)^2 + 4p^2b^2\}^{1/2}}} \tag{3.32}$$

where $\delta = \tan^{-1}\left\{\dfrac{2bp}{\omega_0^2 - p^2}\right\} \ . \tag{3.33}$

Here a and ϵ are arbitrary constants, and we define $\omega^2 = \omega_0^2 - b^2$ as we did in (3.15). Now (3.32) consists of two terms. The first term

$$ae^{-bt}\sin(\omega t + \epsilon) \tag{3.33a}$$

is the solution we have already obtained (3.15) when there is no driving force. This is known as the complementary function (C.F.). Note that the circular frequency ω of this term is that of the free vibrations of the system, and note also the presence of the damping term e^{-bt}. The form of the C.F. is shown in Fig. 3.6. Note too that the arbitrary constants a and ϵ appear entirely in this term; it is therefore this *damped* term which depends on the initial conditions. The second term

$$\frac{P \sin(pt - \delta)}{\{(\omega_0^2 - p^2)^2 + 4p^2b^2\}^{1/2}} \tag{3.33b}$$

is known as the particular integral (P.I.) of (3.29). It has the circular frequency p of the driving force, and a constant (undamped) amplitude

$$\frac{P}{\{(\omega_0^2 - p^2)^2 + 4p^2b^2\}^{\frac{1}{2}}} \ .$$

The P.I. is completely independent of the arbitrary constants a and ϵ, and therefore of the initial conditions. Note that the P.I. is of the same frequency as the driving force but differs in phase from the driving force by the (constant) phase angle δ (3.33).

The C.F., P.I., and their sum (the full general solution, and hence the actual equation of motion) are shown in Fig. 3.9. The net displacement (Fig. 3.9c) at any instant is given by simply adding the ordinates in 3.9a and 3.9b. In the early stages of the motion the resultant is a form of 'beats' (see the end of section 2.3), the usual consequence of compounding two vibrations of unequal frequency. The contribution of the C.F. (Fig. 3.9a) diminishes with time until, after a time of t_A from the start of the motion, this term has effectively disappeared altogether as a result of damping. After t_A, we are left with the steady P.I. term only. The motion thus comprises two distinct stages: (a) the transient

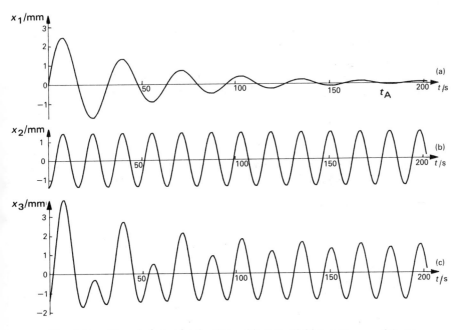

Fig. 3.9 – Forced damped vibrations. (a) C.F. (3.33a) with $a = 3.0$ mm, $\omega_0 = 0.2$ s^{-1}, $b = 0.02$ s^{-1} and $\epsilon = 0$. (b) P.I. (3.33b) with $p = 0.4$ s^{-1}, $\delta = -\pi/2$ rad, and amplitude $P/\{(\omega_0^2 - p^2)^2 + 4p^2b^2\}^{\frac{1}{2}} = 1.5$ mm. (c) General solution (i.e. sum of C.F. and P.I. with $x_3 = x_1 + x_2$ at each value of t).

stage when the motion is the beat resultant of C.F. and P.I., and (b) the *steady-state* stage where the motion is a steady s.h.m. of amplitude A given by

$$A = \frac{P}{\{(\omega_0^2 - p^2)^2 + 4 p^2 b^2\}^{\frac{1}{2}}} \qquad (3.34)$$

and of circular frequency p equal to that of the driving force. Note that both A and p are independent of initial conditions. This is known as forced s.h.m.

The time for which the transients persist is determined by b, and hence by the damping factor. The greater the value of b, the more quickly do the transients die away. (The transient amplitude falls to e^{-1} of its initial value in a time $1/b$). As emphasized earlier, the transients depend upon the initial conditions, because they involve the constants a and ϵ which require knowledge of the initial conditions for their determination. The relative importance of transients depends on the nature of the vibrating system. In a pipe organ (driven vibrations of a column of air in a pipe) the starting transients are of crucial importance and determine the character of the perceived sound. For a.c. circuits, on the other hand, the starting transients can usually be ignored, and traditional treatments of alternating current are concerned only with the steady forced vibrations of charge in the circuit.

3.4 RESONANCE
3.4.1 Displacement and charge resonance
We now examine how the amplitude of steady-state forced vibrations varies with the circular frequency p of the applied force. As we saw (3.32) in the steady-state

$$x = A \sin(pt - \delta) \qquad (3.35)$$

where $A = P/\{(\omega_0^2 - p^2)^2 + 4 p^2 b^2\}^{\frac{1}{2}}$. $\qquad (3.36)$

How does the amplitude A vary with p? And, in particular, for what value of p is A maximum, and what is this maximum value? Now A is maximum when

$$y = (\omega_0^2 - p^2)^2 + 4 p^2 b^2 \qquad (3.37)$$

is minimum.

The condition for a stationary value, maximum or minimum, is

$$dy/dp = 0 \ .$$

Thus $dy/dp = -4p (\omega_0^2 - p^2) + 8pb^2 = 0$

$$\text{or } p^2 = \omega_0^2 - 2b^2 \qquad (3.38)$$

which will be satisfied so long as $\omega_0^2 \geqslant 2b^2$. If this were not the case, there would be no maximum or minimum, but this is a situation of no physical interest which will not be considered further. We could, if we wish, check that condition

(3.38) is for maximum A (minimum y) by differentiating again and testing the sign of d^2y/dp^2.

Thus the maximum amplitude is obtained when the frequency of the applied force is

$$f = \frac{p}{2\pi} = \frac{\sqrt{\omega_0^2 - 2b^2}}{2\pi} \qquad . \qquad (3.39)$$

This value lies between the frequency for free undamped vibrations, $\omega_0/2\pi$, and that for free damped vibrations $\sqrt{\omega_0^2 - b^2}/2\pi$ (3.16).

We obtain the value for maximum amplitude A_0 by substituting

$$p = \sqrt{(\omega_0^2 - 2b^2)} \quad \text{from (3.38) into (3.36)}.$$

Thus $\quad A_0 = \dfrac{P}{2b(\omega_0^2 - b^2)^{\frac{1}{2}}}$. $\qquad (3.40)$

This phenomenon of the amplitude taking a maximum value is known as resonance. We say that the response of the vibrating system to the applied force (as demonstrated by the maximum amplitude of vibration produced) is greatest at the resonant circular frequencey given by (3.38). A typical variation of amplitude A of forced s.h.m. with applied circular frequency is shown in Fig. 3.10.

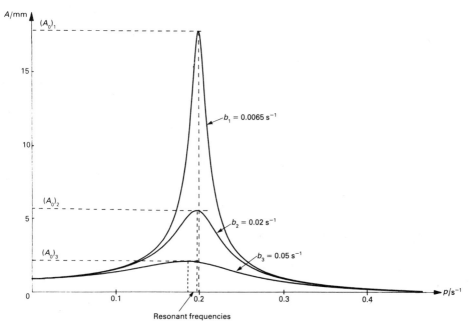

Fig. 3.10 – Amplitude resonance curves. Variation of A with p (3.36) for different values of b; $\omega_0 = 0.2$ s^{-1}, $P = 0.047$ mm s^{-2}. Note that the resonant frequency decreases as b increases.

In physical terms this represents the variation in maximum displacement from equilibrium of the driven suspended mass (Fig. 3.8a) or the maximum instantaneous value of charge on the capacitor in the circuit of Fig. 3.8b. Note (a) the resonant frequency is not the same as either the free or the damped natural frequency of the vibrating system, (b) the resonant frequency decreases as the damping increases, (c) for light damping (small b) the resonance curve is sharp and high, while for heavy damping (large b), the curve is broad and low.

The type of resonance encountered here is referred to as displacement resonance (in the mechanical case) or charge resonance (in the electrical case) to distinguish them from resonance of another character which we treat in the following section. The variation of the phase angle δ (3.35) between the driving force and the forced motion is of interest. As p is increased steadily from zero, the variation of δ with p, given by (3.33), is shown in Fig. 3.11.

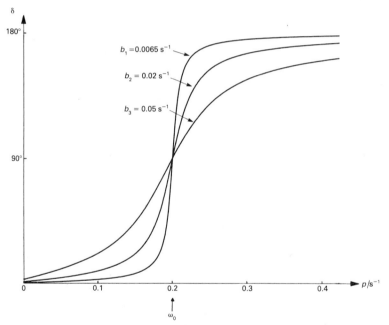

Fig. 3.11 — Variation of phase angle δ with applied circular frequency (3.33) for different values of b: $\omega_0 = 0.2$ s^{-1}.

When $p \ll \omega_0$ the driving force and the motion are in phase ($\delta = 0$). As p increases, the motion increasingly lags in phase. At $p = \omega_0$ the phase lag is 90° and we say that the driving force and the motion are in quadrature. Finally, when $p \gg \omega_0$, the motion lags in phase by 180° and is in antiphase with the driving force. The variation of δ with p is gradual for heavy damping (large b), but becomes increasingly abrupt as the damping decreases.

3.4.2 Velocity and current resonance

As the frequency of the applied force in the mechanical system of Fig. 3.8a is varied, then as well as the amplitude of the resulting forced vibrations changing in the manner we have just seen, the maximum *velocity* of the particle will change also. This too has a maximum, and we speak of *velocity resonance*. Similarly the current in the circuit of Fig. 3.8b will have a maximum as we vary p, and this is known as current resonance. It might be thought that velocity (current) will resonate at the same frequency as the amplitude (charge), but, as we shall show, this turns out not to be the case. We can treat velocity and current together, for they are analogous, i.e.

$$\text{velocity} = dx/dt \tag{3.41}$$

and current $i = dq/dt$. $\tag{3.42}$

We obtain an expression for dx/dt directly from (3.32). Let us assume the steady state has been reached so we can ignore the first term in (3.32). Thus

$$v = \frac{dx}{dt} = \frac{Pp \cos{(pt - \delta)}}{\{(\omega_0^2 - p^2)^2 + 4p^2b^2\}^{\frac{1}{2}}} \tag{3.43}$$

or $v = v_0 \cos(pt - \delta)$ $\tag{3.44}$

where $v_0 = P / \left\{ \left(\frac{\omega_0^2 - p^2}{p} \right)^2 + 4b^2 \right\}^{\frac{1}{2}}$. $\tag{3.44a}$

Note that we have divided top and bottom by p.

The condition for maximum value of v_0 can be seen very easily; it is $p = \omega_0$, the undamped circular frequency of the system. The maximum value of the velocity $(v_0)_{max}$ is given by

$$(v_0)_{max} = \frac{P}{2b} \quad . \tag{3.45}$$

We note that the resonant frequency is independent of damping. The resonance curves are shown in Fig. 3.12. As with amplitude resonance, light damping produces a sharp, high resonance, while heavy damping produces a low, broad resonance.

3.5 POWER TO MAINTAIN FORCED VIBRATIONS

We can most conveniently find the energy expended in maintaining steady-state forced vibrations by considering the suspended mass of Fig. 3.8a to which is applied a sinusoidally-varying force $F = F_0 \sin pt$.

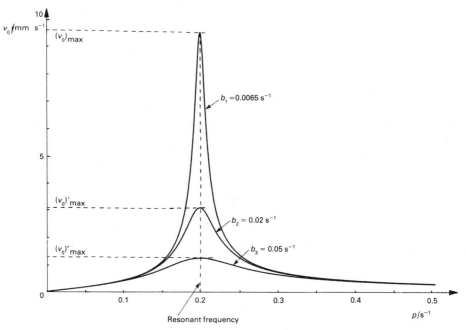

Fig. 3.12 – Velocity resonance curves. Variation of v_0 with p (3.44a) for different values of b: $\omega_0 = 0.2$ s^{-1} and $P = 0.125$ mm s^{-2}. Note the same resonant frequency for each value of b.

In a displacement dx, the driving source expends an amount of work

$$dW = F_0 \sin(pt)\, dx \ .$$

In one complete cycle, the amount of work done is

$$W = \int_{1 \text{ cycle}} F_0 \sin(pt)\, dx = \int_0^{2\pi/p} F_0 \sin(pt)\, \frac{dx}{dt}\, dt$$

since the period T is equal to $2\pi/p$.

Substituting dx/dt from (3.43) and using (3.30) we have

$$W = \frac{p\, F_0^2}{m\, \{(\omega_0^2 - p^2)^2 + 4\, p^2 b^2\}^{\frac{1}{2}}} \int_0^{2\pi/p} \sin(pt) \cos(pt - \delta)\, dt$$

If we expand $\cos(pt - \delta)$, note that $\displaystyle\int_0^{2\pi/p} \sin^2(pt)\, dt = \pi/p$,

$$\int_0^{2\pi/p} \sin(pt) \cos(pt)\, dt = 0, \text{ and } \sin \delta = \frac{2\, bp}{\{(\omega_0^2 - p^2)^2 + 4\, p^2 b^2\}^{\frac{1}{2}}}$$

(from 3.33), we arrive eventually at

$$W = \frac{2\pi F_0^2 \, pb}{m\{(\omega_0^2 - p^2)^2 + 4 \, p^2 b^2\}} \tag{3.46}$$

The equation (3.46) represents the net expenditure of energy by the driving source in one cycle. This must therefore be the work done in overcoming damping forces in one cycle. We can find the mean power consumption as follows: (3.46) gives the total energy consumed in one complete cycle of duration $T = 2\pi/p$. The mean power $\mathscr{P}$ is therefore given by

$$\mathscr{P} = \frac{W}{T} = \frac{p}{2\pi} \frac{2\pi F_0^2 pb}{m\{(\omega_0^2 - p^2)^2 + 4 \, p^2 b^2\}} \, ,$$

or
$$\mathscr{P} = \frac{F_0^2 p^2 b}{m\{(\omega_0^2 - p^2)^2 + 4 \, p^2 b^2\}} \, . \tag{3.47}$$

If (3.47) is written in the form

$$\mathscr{P} = \frac{F_0^2 b/m}{\dfrac{(\omega_0^2 - p^2)^2 + 4 \, b^2}{p^2}} \tag{3.48}$$

we see that the power $\mathscr{P}$ has its maximum value (as p varies) when the first term in the denominator of (3.48) is zero; that is, when $p = \omega_0$. This is exactly the same condition as for velocity resonance, as was shown above in the discussion immediately preceding (3.45). Thus power resonance (maximum energy transfer) and velocity resonance occur at the same (driver) frequency. The maximum value for the power, $\mathscr{P}_0$, is obtained by putting $\omega_0 = p$ in (3.48).

Thus
$$\mathscr{P}_0 = \frac{F_0^2}{4mb} \, . \tag{3.49}$$

A typical power resonance curve is shown in Fig. 3.13 in which p_0 ($=\omega_0$) is the resonant circular frequency, and p_1 and p_2 are the circular frequencies at which the power $\mathscr{P}$ is one half of the resonant value. A convenient measure for the sharpness of the resonance is the ratio

$$p_0/(p_2 - p_1) \, . \tag{3.50}$$

Now $\mathscr{P}$ falls to half its maximum value when the two terms in the denominator of (3.48) are equal.

Thus
$$(\omega_0^2 - p^2)^2 = 4 \, p^2 b^2 \, , \tag{3.51}$$

or
$$\omega_0^2 - p^2 = \pm 2pb$$

and
$$(\omega_0 + p)(\omega_0 - p) = \pm 2pb \, . \tag{3.52}$$

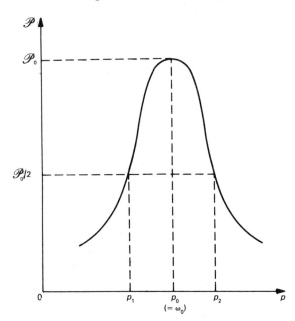

Fig. 3.13 – Power resonance curve.

If the resonance is fairly sharp we may make the approximations

$$p \approx p_0, \quad \omega_0 + p \approx 2p_0, \quad \omega_0 - p \approx (p_2 - p_1)/2 \ .$$

Thus $\dfrac{p_0}{p_2 - p_1} = \dfrac{p_0}{2b} = \dfrac{\omega_0}{2b}$.   (3.53)

But the quality factor Q (section 3.2 above) was found to be

$$Q = \pi/bT \ .$$ (3.26)

So, since $T = 2\pi/\omega_0$, we see $Q = p_0/(p_2 - p_1)$ or, in terms of actual frequencies ($p_0 = 2\pi f_0$ etc), we have

$$\boxed{Q = \frac{f_0}{f_2 - f_1}} \ .$$ (3.54)

The quantity $(f_2 - f_1)$ is known as the *bandwidth* of the system. The Q factor has a useful interpretation in terms of amplification. In the case of displacement resonance, we found that the amplitude A_0 at resonance is given by

$$A_0 = \frac{P}{2b(\omega_0^2 - 2b^2)^{\frac{1}{2}}} \ .$$ (3.40)

If we write $P = F_0/m$, and assume light damping ($\omega_0^2 \gg 2b^2$), this becomes

$$A_0 = \frac{F_0}{2bm\omega_0} \ . \tag{3.55}$$

If we substitute for b from (3.26) we obtain

$$A_0 = \frac{QF_0}{m\omega_0^2} \ , \tag{3.56}$$

or $\qquad A_0 = \frac{QF_0}{k} \tag{3.57}$

where k, the stiffness, is substituted from (3.11). Now k is the restoring force for unit displacement. A slowly-applied force F_0 would produce an equilibrium displacement F_0/k; (3.57) shows us that at resonance we have a maximum displacement of Q times this value. Hence Q can be regarded as a displacement amplification factor.

Q has perhaps its greatest importance in relation to electrical circuits. If we rewrite the above relationships in electrical quantities (and we leave this as an exercise for the reader) it is easy to show that, for the circuit of Fig. 3.8b:

$$Q = \frac{\omega_0 L}{R} \tag{3.58}$$

and $\qquad \omega_0 = \frac{1}{\sqrt{(LC)}} \ . \tag{3.59}$

The Q of a circuit determines its ability to select a narrow band of frequencies from a wide range of input frequencies. This is obviously important for radio receivers. The 'selectivity' of the tuner stage in a receiver is its ability to select the required signal only; and this ability is, in turn, determined by the Q for the circuit.

Radio receivers operating in the MHz region have Q values of several hundreds. Microwave cavities have Q values of the order of 10^5.

Example 3.2 *How much power is expended by a child on a swing?*
We can perform an order of magnitude calculation of this power using some of the ideas which have been developed. The swing is a damped oscillator which is maintained at constant amplitude by a periodic force exerted by the child. (The mechanism whereby energy is transferred from the child to the swing is of some interest, but need not concern us.)

Now the distance l from the centre of mass of the child to the point of support is approximately 2.5 m, and the periodic time is about 3 s. If the child were to stop applying the force, the oscillations would die away with a time-constant of (typically) about 80 s. Hence, Q for this oscillator, which is π times the number of oscillations in this time, is about 80.

But $Q = \dfrac{2\pi \times \text{stored energy}}{\text{energy dissipated per cycle}}$ from (3.24)

Here, the stored energy is $mgl(1 - \cos\theta)$, where m is the mass of the child, and θ the amplitude of swing. Taking $m \approx 40$ kg, $g \approx 10$ m s^{-2}, and $\theta \approx 45°$, we find that the stored energy is about 300 J.

Hence the energy dissipated per cycle $\approx \dfrac{2\pi \times 300}{Q} \approx 25$ J.

Finally, since the period ≈ 3 s, the mean power expended in maintaining the oscillations is ~ 8 W.

Example 3.3 *Emission and absorption of light by atoms*
The study of light emitted by a source is very important in physics since it gives valuable insight into the nature of the source, and the physical processes concerned with the emission. A hot solid (for example, a tungsten filament in a lamp) emits radiation predominantly in visible and infrared regions. Because of the strong forces between the atoms in a solid, the radiation cannot be regarded as arising from free atoms, but rather from an assembly of strongly coupled atoms.

If, however, the light source is a suitably excited atomic vapour of low density, the emission is from an assembly of free atoms, and the observed radiation is directly related to the nature of a single atom. A familiar example of such a source is a sodium lamp used for street lighting. Such a source emits radiation at several sharply defined wavelengths.

The emission of light by an atom is a process which is intimately bound up with the quantum theory, and usually developed from this standpoint. Nevertheless, it is possible to understand some aspects of the subject by making the very simple postulate that *a free atom behaves like a classical system of particles capable of oscillating in several normal modes*. If the atom is excited so as to vibrate in one of these normal modes, it emits radiation of the same frequency.

In the case of sodium, the predominant wavelengths are 589.0 nm and 589.6 nm, and the corresponding frequencies c/λ are 5.093×10^{14} Hz and 5.088×10^{14} Hz. (There are several other wavelengths emitted, but we ignore these for simplicity.)

Now since the atom is emitting radiation, it loses energy, and the motion of the oscillator is exponentially damped. In the case of sodium, the amplitude decays with a time-constant $\tau \sim 3 \times 10^{-8}$ s.

The Q value is therefore (from (3.26a)) $\pi \times 5 \times 10^{14} \times 3 \times 10^{-8} \approx 5 \times 10^{7}$.

If an atom can be thought of as a damped oscillator, can it exhibit forced vibrations? The answer is that it can, but since Q is so high, the amplitude of forced vibrations is very small unless the driving frequency is very close to the natural frequency. This is illustrated by considering sodium vapour of low density, illuminated by light from a tunable laser (Fig. 3.E1).

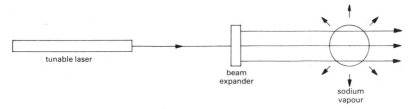

tunable laser

beam
expander

sodium
vapour

Fig. 3.E1 – Resonance fluorescence.

Unless the laser frequency is very close to one of the resonant frequencies of the sodium atom, the light passes through the vapour with very little attenuation. But if the laser is carefully tuned to a resonant frequency, the sodium atoms absorb the light, and subsequently re-emit it in all directions. This process is known as *resonance fluorescence.*

From (3.54) the accuracy of tuning must be better than 1 part in 10^7.

It should be stated that our analysis is rather over-simplified, since it does not consider the Doppler shift in resonant frequency of the atom due to its motion.

We emphasize too that this treatment of resonance fluorescence, while appropriate to the scope of this book, is no substitute for the fuller and more satisfactory analysis to be found in texts on spectroscopy.

PROBLEMS

(3.1) A simple pendulum of length l has a spherical bob of radius r and density ρ, which is immersed in a bath of liquid of density ρ_0 and viscosity η. Show that for the oscillations to be critically damped, $r = \frac{3}{2}\left(\dfrac{\eta^2 l}{\rho(\rho - \rho_0)g}\right)^{\frac{1}{4}}$ (The damping force is given by Stokes' formula $6\pi\eta r v$, where v is the velocity).

If r is greater than this value, will the motion be more than, or less than, critically damped?

Calculate the value of r for critical damping in water, if $l = 0.5$ m and $\rho = 5 \times 10^3$ kg m^{-3}. Take $\eta = 10^{-3}$ kg m^{-1} s^{-1}, and $g = 10$ m s^{-2}.

(3.2) Show that the time-constant for the decay of energy of an exponentially damped oscillator is one half of the time-constant for the decay of amplitude.

(3.3) A critically damped oscillator is released from rest at time $t = 0$ at a distance a from its equilibrium position. Show that its equation of motion is $x = a(1 + bt)e^{-bt}$, where b is the constant used in this chapter.

Prove that the oscillator does not 'overshoot' the equilibrium position.

(3.4) A critically damped oscillator is released at time $t = 0$ at a distance a (> 0) from its equilibrium position, with velocity v_0 towards this position. Show that 'overshoot' will occur if $v_0 > ab$.

Taking $a = 1$, $b = 2$ and $v_0 = 4$, plot a graph of the displacement against time.

(3.5) A simple pendulum of length 1 m is set into oscillation with amplitude 0.05 m. After 5 minutes, the amplitude has fallen to 0.025 m. Deduce (a) the constant b in the nomenclature of this chapter, (b) the time-constant, (c) the logarithmic decrement, (d) the Q value, (e) the energy dissipated per cycle when the amplitude was 0.05 m, if the mass of the bob is 0.1 kg.

If an external device were used to sustain the oscillations, to approximately what accuracy should the frequency of this device be matched to the natural frequency of the pendulum?

(3.6) Perform the following experiment. Take a length of string about 50 cm, and tie a mass of about 20 g to one end. Hold the other end steady, and observe the oscillations. Now move the upper end of the string to and fro at a significantly higher frequency. After a little time, the mass will be moving at this latter frequency, approximately in antiphase with the movement of the hand.

Now reduce the driving frequency, and observe the resonance which occurs when it is near the natural frequency. The phase difference is then about $90°$, the driving force leading the mass.

It is possible, but less easy, to show that when the driving frequency is significantly below the natural frequency, the motions of the mass and the hand are approximately in phase.

(3.7) The damper of a particular piano string may be held off by depressing the corresponding key, or by operating the sustaining pedal. When this is done, if a clarinet near the string emits a quick burst of the same note, the string will produce a faint sound. Explain this.

Estimate the Q value of the string by a quick experiment. Hence estimate the closeness in frequency to which the clarinet and piano must be tuned to achieve the above behaviour.

(3.8) An inductance 0.1H, a capacitor 10^{-7} F, and a resistor R are all connected in series. For what range of values of R will no oscillations occur?

If $R = 100\,\Omega$, deduce (a) the frequency of the damped oscillations, (b) the time-constant, (c) the Q value, (d) the energy dissipated in the first cycle, if initially the capacitor is charged to a p.d. of 10 V, and no current flows.

(3.9) An inductance 10^{-4} H, a capacitance 10^{-10} F, a resistance $200\,\Omega$, and a sinusoidal oscillator of e.m.f. 1 V (peak value) are all connected in series. Deduce (a) the frequency of the natural damped oscillations of the circuit, (b) the frequencies of charge resonance and current resonance, (c) the Q value.

Draw a rough sketch of the current in the circuit against oscillator frequency, indicating the maximum value of current, and the range of frequencies of particular interest. Draw a rough sketch of the phase difference between the e.m.f. of the oscillator and (i) the current, (ii) the p.d. across the capacitor, against frequency in both cases.

CHAPTER 4

Mathematical description of wave motion

4.1 WAVES IN ONE DIMENSION: THE FUNCTION $y = f(x - ct)$

Suppose we have a very long horizontal elastic string, originally at rest. Let us choose coordinate axes such that the x-axis is along the string, the y-axis vertically upwards, and the origin at some convenient point. The situation is shown in Fig. 4.1.

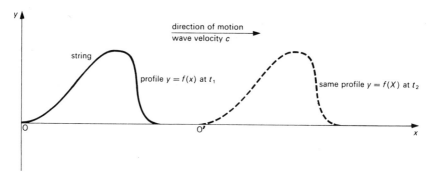

Fig. 4.1 — Waves on a long string.

Suppose now that the string is set in motion by its being given a sudden flick at a point to the left of the origin. Experience tells us that this would result in a disturbance travelling down the string, the particles comprising the string being momentarily displaced from their original positions. Let us assume that this disturbance takes place parallel with the y-axis (i.e. that is a true transverse wave) so that we may take the y-value of any point on the string as a measure of the disturbance of that point at a given instant of time. If a high-speed photograph is taken during the passage of the disturbance, the string will be seen to be distorted into a curve. This curve is referred to as the *wave profile*. We shall assume that this profile moves down the string with constant velocity c, and *without change of shape* i.e. with no *dispersion*. Thus if we take two photographs at times t_1 and t_2, both would show the same profile, but in the second photograph the profile would be displaced along the string in the direction of propagation. Let us describe the shape of the profile at time t_1 by the function

$$y = f(x) \ .$$

On the second photograph, taken at time t_2, let us mark the point O' on the x-axis which is at the same position relative to the profile as the origin O was in the photograph taken at time t_1. Let distance along the x-axis referred to O' be measured by the quantity X. Thus the shape of the profile referred to O' at time t_2 is

$$y = f(X) \ .$$

It is obviously not convenient to have our origin of coordinates moving along with the profile; we want to refer the profile to the fixed point O. Now since the profile is moving with constant velocity c, the distance OO' is $c(t_2 - t_1)$. Thus

$$X = x - c(t_2 - t_1) \ .$$

The profile at time t_2 is then described by

$$y = f[x - c(t_2 - t_1)] \ .$$

Finally, if our clock was started as the profile passed the point O, that is, $t_1 = 0$, then the profile at any subsequent time t is obtained by replacing the quantity $t_2 - t_1$ in this equation with the single quantity t, to give

$$\boxed{y = f(x - ct)} \ . \tag{4.1}$$

This is an extremely important equation in the theory of wave motion. It completely defines a one-dimensional transverse wave of constant profile moving with constant velocity c along the positive direction of the x-axis. It is easy to show on the same lines, and it is left to the reader to do so, that a wave which is the same in all respects but moving in the opposite direction (i.e. along the direction of x decreasing) is given by

$$y = f(x + ct) \ . \tag{4.2}$$

Equations (4.1) and (4.2) are examples of functions of two variables; to find y, we must know the values of the variables x and t (we must also know the form of the function f and the velocity c, but these do not change). Physically, this means that in order to find the disturbance suffered by a point on the string, we must specify not only its position along the string (x), but also the time (t) at which we wish to know the disturbance.

Neither (4.1) nor (4.2) is a completely general description of wave motion in one dimension, for each depends on a specific direction of propagation. We now look for a single expression which has the same generality for one-dimensional waves as

$$\frac{d^2x}{dt^2} + \omega^2 x = 0 \tag{2.1}$$

has for one-dimensional vibrations.

We start by differentiating (4.1) (or (4.2) for the result is the same for both) to eliminate from it all reference to the function f and the direction of propagation, as follows. In equation (4.1), let us write

$$z = x - ct \ . \tag{4.3}$$

Then, differentiating $y = f(x - ct) = f(z)$ with respect to t, we obtain

$$\frac{\partial y}{\partial t} = \frac{df}{dz} \frac{\partial z}{\partial t} \ .$$

(The symbol ∂ indicates partial differentiation; for a full treatment of this subject see Mathematical Methods for Science Students by G. Stephenson, second edition, Longman 1973. Note, however, the d's in df/dz since the function is one of z only.) But

$$\frac{\partial z}{\partial t} = -c \quad \text{(from 4.3)}$$

and so

$$\frac{\partial y}{\partial t} = -c \frac{df}{dz} \ . \tag{4.4}$$

Similarly,

$$\frac{\partial y}{\partial x} = \frac{df}{dz} \frac{\partial z}{\partial x} \ ,$$

but, as

$$\frac{\partial z}{\partial x} = 1, \quad \text{(from 4.3)}$$

we have

$$\frac{\partial y}{\partial x} = \frac{df}{dz} \ . \tag{4.5}$$

Eliminating df/dz between (4.4) and (4.5) we obtain

$$\frac{\partial y}{\partial t} = -c \frac{\partial y}{\partial x} \ . \tag{4.6}$$

Now we repeat the same process, but starting with $y = f(x + ct)$. Let $x + ct = w$; this leads to

$$\frac{\partial y}{\partial t} = + c \frac{df}{dw} \tag{4.7}$$

and

$$\frac{\partial y}{\partial x} = \frac{df}{dw} . \tag{4.8}$$

Eliminating df/dw between (4.7) and (4.8) gives

$$\frac{\partial y}{\partial t} = + c \frac{\partial y}{\partial x} . \tag{4.9}$$

We see that equations (4.6) and (4.9), though very similar, are not identical; different results have been obtained for different directions of propagation. Let us see if we can eliminate all reference to direction of propagation by further differentiation. Differentiating (4.4) a second time with respect to t we have

$$\frac{\partial^2 y}{\partial t^2} = - c \frac{\partial}{\partial t} \left(\frac{df}{dz} \right)$$

$$= - c \frac{d}{dz} \left(\frac{df}{dz} \right) \frac{\partial z}{\partial t} .$$

But

$$\frac{d}{dz} \left(\frac{df}{dz} \right) = \frac{d^2 f}{dz^2}$$

and

$$\frac{\partial z}{\partial t} = - c \quad \text{(from 4.3)}$$

Therefore

$$\frac{\partial^2 y}{\partial t^2} = c^2 \frac{d^2 f}{dz^2} . \tag{4.10}$$

Similarly, differentiating (4.5) with respect to x leads to

$$\frac{\partial^2 y}{\partial x^2} = \frac{d^2 f}{dz^2} . \tag{4.11}$$

Finally, eliminating $d^2 f/dz^2$ between (4.10) and (4.11) gives

$$\boxed{\frac{\partial^2 y}{\partial x^2} = \frac{1}{c^2} \frac{\partial^2 y}{\partial t^2}} . \tag{4.12}$$

If we repeat the same process, starting with

$$y = f(x + ct) \ ,$$

we obtain precisely the same final result as (4.12). This means that we have now obtained an equation which is completely independent of the direction of propagation. Equation (4.12) is an example of a *second-order partial differential equation*. It is known as the non-dispersive wave equation. The importance of this equation lies in its complete generality with regard to the form and direction of travel of waves which can be propagated in accordance with it. Examples of the occurrence of this equation in physics will be treated in the next chapter, and its solutions will be discussed in detail in Chapter 6.

4.2 HARMONIC WAVES

So far we have left the form of the function f in the equation

$$y = f(x - ct) \tag{4.1}$$

completely arbitrary. In other words, our wave profile may have the shape of any continuous curve. It turns out that the simplest wave to treat analytically is one whose profile is a pure sine curve. We can express such a wave as

$$y = f(x - ct) = a \sin k(x - ct) \ , \tag{4.13}$$

where a and k are constants whose significances will appear shortly. Such a wave is known as a *sine wave*.

Suppose a wave described by equation (4.13) is propagated along a stretched elastic string of the kind described earlier in this chapter. How would a point on the string be disturbed due to the passage of the wave? We can answer this question by inserting the position of the point in question into (4.13). Let its position be x_1.

Hence $$y = a \sin k(x_1 - ct) \tag{4.14}$$

or $$y = -a \sin k(ct - x_1) \ . \tag{4.15}$$

This equation tells us how the disturbance or transverse position y of the point varies with time t. Note that y is now a function of the single variable t, since x has been given the constant value x_1. Equation (4.14) or (4.15), is therefore the equation of motion of the point at $x = x_1$.

We saw, in Chapter 2, that a point executing simple harmonic motion has the equation of motion

$$y = a \sin(2\pi ft - \epsilon) \ . \tag{2.4}$$

Comparing (2.4) with (4.15) we see that these equations are really the same, except that the constants are differently arranged, so the point on the string will oscillate with simple harmonic motion. Furthermore, since we get the same form of equation (4.14) no matter what value of x is inserted, it follows that any point on the string along which a sine wave is propagated is caused to oscillate with simple harmonic motion. (For this reason, sine waves are also referred to as *harmonic* waves). Thus all points along the string execute s.h.m. of the same amplitude and frequency but differing in phase. Points just ahead of x_1 will lag in phase while points just before x_1 will lead in phase.

A wave whose profile is that of a cosine function is very similar; sine and cosine functions have exactly the same form, the only difference between them being the point at which the origin is chosen. Since the choice of origin is always completely arbitrary, the first minus sign in (4.15) can be removed by a new choice of origin.

In order to get a complete picture of the motion of the point at $x = x_1$, we must compare corresponding terms in (4.15) and (2.4). We can now identify the quantity a in (4.15) with the amplitude of the motion caused by the wave. The wave itself is said to have amplitude a.

Comparing (2.4) and (4.15) we see that

$$2\pi f = kc$$

or $$k = \frac{2\pi f}{c} .$$ (4.16)

We thus have a physical meaning for k in terms of the frequency f of the oscillations caused by the wave, and of the wave velocity c. Further, since the period T of a simple harmonic motion is $1/f$, we can identify the period of the wave as $2\pi/kc$.

If, for equation (4.13), y is plotted against x for a given value of $t(t_1$ say), the curve shown in Fig. 4.2, which represents (essentially) a high-speed photograph of the string during the passage of a harmonic wave, is obtained. Since the sine function is periodic, the wave profile repeats itself after fixed intervals of x. The repeat distance is known as the *wavelength* and is designated by λ.

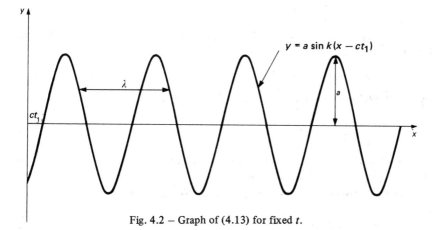

$$y = a \sin k(x - ct_1)$$

Fig. 4.2 – Graph of (4.13) for fixed t.

If we increase x by λ in equation (4.13) the value of y will, by definition, be unaltered,

i.e. $y = a \sin k(x - ct) = a \sin k(\overline{x + \lambda} - ct)$.

It follows that

$$k\lambda = 2\pi$$

or $$\boxed{k = \frac{2\pi}{\lambda}}$$ (4.17)

From (4.16) and (4.17) we see that

$$k = \frac{2\pi}{\lambda} = \frac{2\pi f}{c} \ .$$

which gives the extremely important result

$$\boxed{c = f\lambda \ .}$$ (4.18)

Thus the product of the frequency and the wavelength is equal to the speed of the wave. We are now in a position to rewrite (4.13) in a number of equivalent forms,

$$y = a \sin \frac{2\pi}{\lambda} (x - ct) \ ,$$

$$y = a \sin 2\pi \left(\frac{x}{\lambda} - ft \right) \ ,$$

$$y = a \sin 2\pi \left(\frac{x}{\lambda} - \frac{t}{T} \right) .$$

If we now define the *wavenumber* σ as the number of wavelengths per metre, then $\sigma = 1/\lambda$, and

$$y = a \sin 2\pi(\sigma x - ft) \ .$$

By a different initial choice of origin, we could equally well have arrived at the expression

$$y = a \sin 2\pi(ft - \sigma x) \ .$$ (4.19)

Both representations of sine waves are commonly used, and they differ only in the choice of origin along the x-axis.

A mathematically more compact way of writing (4.19) is

$$\boxed{y = a \sin (\omega t - kx)}$$ (4.20)

where the *circular frequency* $\omega = 2\pi f$ as in section (2.2.1), and the *circular wavenumber* $k = 2\pi/\lambda$ as shown in (4.17) above.

4.3 EXPONENTIAL REPRESENTATION OF A HARMONIC WAVE

It can be shown from the elementary theory of complex numbers that

$$\exp i\theta = \cos \theta + i \sin \theta \ , \tag{4.21}$$

from which it follows that

$$\exp(-i\theta) = \cos \theta - i \sin \theta \ , \tag{4.21a}$$

where i is the imaginary quantity $\sqrt{(-1)}$. Here $\exp i\theta$ is a complex quantity, which is expressed as the sum of a real part, $\cos \theta$, and an imaginary part, $\sin \theta$. In this notation $\cos \theta$ may be referred to as the *real part* of $\exp i\theta$ — abbreviated to Re $(\exp i\theta)$, and $\sin \theta$ as the *imaginary part* of $\exp i\theta$ — abbreviated to Im $(\exp i\theta)$.

In this notation, equation (4.20) may be written as

$$y = a \sin(\omega t - kx) = \text{Im}[a \exp i(\omega t - kx)] \ .$$

Finally, we drop the Im from the written expression since it will be understood, when a sine wave is expressed in this form, that it is the imaginary part of the expression that has physical meaning. Thus,

$$\boxed{y = a \exp i(\omega t - kx)} \ . \tag{4.22}$$

Similarly, when we wish to treat a cosine wave in this way, the real part of (4.22) is implied.

The advantage of this procedure is that exponentials are much easier to handle mathematically than sines and cosines; they are easier to integrate, differentiate and sum as series. The procedure is as follows. We express our sine (or cosine) waves in exponential form; then we carry out our manipulation and take the imaginary (or real) part of the result as the quantity which is physically meaningful.

That the exponential and trigonometrical treatments yield identical results is demonstrated in the following simple example of wave addition. Suppose we have two harmonic waves with identical amplitudes, frequencies and wave numbers moving in opposite directions;

$$y_1 = a \sin(\omega t - kx)$$

and $y_2 = a \sin(\omega t + kx) \ .$

The sum of these is clearly

$$y = y_1 + y_2 = 2a \sin \omega t \cos kx \ . \tag{4.23}$$

If we now express the two waves as exponentials (the imaginary part being tacitly understood), the sum is

$$y = a \exp i(\omega t - kx) + a \exp i(\omega t + kx) \ ,$$

which, on factorizing, becomes

$$y = a \exp i\omega t [\exp ikx + \exp(-ikx)] \ . \tag{4.24}$$

By eliminating $\sin \theta$ between (4.21) and (4.21a) we see that

$$\cos \theta = \tfrac{1}{2} [\exp i\theta + \exp(-i\theta)] \ .$$

Hence (4.24) becomes

$$y = 2a \exp i\omega t \cos kx \ .$$

Finally, writing

$$\exp i\omega t = \cos \omega t + i \sin \omega t$$

(by 4.21) and taking the imaginary part, we have

$$y = 2a \sin \omega t \cos kx \ ,$$

which is the same as (4.23). The reader will hardly gain the impression from this example that the exponential representation saves labour, but it does demonstrate that the correct result is obtained. Several further examples in this book will, however, bring home the usefulness of this approach. Finally, in adding two waves together we have anticipated some of the content of Chapter 6, where the physical significance of wave addition is discussed fully.

4.4 WAVES IN TWO AND THREE DIMENSIONS: WAVEFRONTS

4.4.1 Two-dimensional waves: Straight-line wavefronts
So far, we have confined our attention to waves in one-dimensional media, of which the stretched elastic string is an example. We must now extend our theory first to two, and finally three, dimensions. A convenient example of waves in a two-dimensional medium is that of water waves in, say, a ripple tank. Let us imagine that the surface of the water in the ripple tank has been disturbed, for example by dropping a long stick so that it enters the water horizontally. A disturbance will proceed along the surface in the form of a straight-line crest which, for the purpose of the present argument, we shall assume moves with constant velocity, and without change of shape, in directions perpendicular to the stick.

We shall need two Cartesian coordinates x and y to specify the position of a point on the surface of the water, and we shall designate the disturbance, which in this case is the vertical displacement of a point on the surface from its undisturbed position, by ϕ.

Fig. 4.3 shows schematically what we would see on a high-speed photograph of such a system taken from above, whilst Fig. 4.4 shows a vertical section in the direction in which the disturbance is travelling, which corresponds exactly to the one-dimensional wave we examined at the beginning of this chapter.

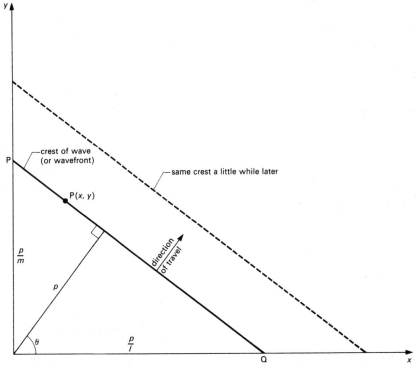

Fig. 4.3 – Straight-line water wave viewed from above.

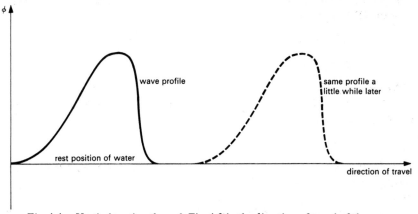

Fig. 4.4 – Vertical section through Fig. 4.3 in the direction of travel of the wave.

We meet now for the first time the concept of the wavefront, in the present case this is any continuous line joining points undergoing identical disturbance. Thus a crest is a wavefront, but so also is any other line joining points of equal disturbance. The importance of this concept resides in the fact that if we fix the state of disturbance as defining the wavefront, then the wavefront moves forward with the wave. In the present example the wavefront is a straight line, but we shall see later this is not always the case.

We must now look for a way of describing waves propagated with constant velocity and shape in two dimensions, corresponding to $f(x - ct)$ for one-dimensional waves. What we do is to replace x in the one-dimensional equation by a quantity, containing both x and y, which is constant along a given wavefront. Suppose that a given wavefront has the instantaneous position given by the line PQ in Fig. 4.3. Now any point along this line will satisfy the equation

$$lx + my = p \ , \tag{4.25}$$

where, l, m and p are constants. [This is not the usual form of equation for a straight line used in coordinate geometry, but if we divide through by m and rearrange we get

$$y = -\left(\frac{l}{m}\right) x + \left(\frac{p}{m}\right) \ ,$$

which is now in the more usual form

$$y = Ax + B \ .$$

The reason why we have used this apparently more complicated form will be seen when we discuss waves in three dimensions.]

The meanings of the constants l, m and p will be seen from Fig. 4.3. Let p be the length of the perpendicular (or normal) from the origin to the line PQ. If this normal, which is in the direction of travel of the wave, makes an angle θ with the Ox axis, then

$$\cos \theta = l$$

and $\sin \theta = m \ .$

Thus l is the cosine of the angle the normal makes with the Ox axis and m is the cosine of the angle the normal makes with the Oy axis; l and m are known as the *direction cosines* of the normal. Clearly

$$l^2 + m^2 = 1 \ .$$

Thus (4.25) expresses the equation of a straight line in terms of the direction cosines of the line normal and the perpendicular distance from the origin to the line.

Since the wave is travelling in the direction of p, and since the value of p is constant for a wavefront at a given time, the function $\phi = f(p - ct)$ is that which describes the wave. As

$$p = lx + my ,$$

(4.25)

we can write the wave function finally as

$$\phi = f(lx + my - ct) .$$

(4.26)

Thus (4.26) specifies a wave in two dimensions, of constant profile and constant velocity, with wavefronts which are straight lines, moving in the direction having direction cosines (l,m). Similarly it can be shown that

$$\phi = f(lx + my + ct)$$

represents a wave of identical profile moving in the opposite direction. If we eliminate the functional form f, and reference to the direction of propagation, from (4.26) by differentiation, along similar lines to the one-dimensional case, we obtain the partial differential equation

$$\boxed{\frac{\partial^2 \phi}{\partial x^2} + \frac{\partial^2 \phi}{\partial y^2} = \frac{1}{c^2}\frac{\partial^2 \phi}{\partial t^2} .}$$

(4.27)

This is the partial differential equation governing straight-line wave propagation in two dimensions; but in fact it covers wavefronts of any shape.

Example 4.1

Deduce the two-dimensional wave equation in polar coordinates (r,θ).

The two-dimensional wave equation (4.27) involving Cartesian coordinates (x,y) can be solved in a wide variety of problems. It will be appreciated, however, that this form of the wave equation is not always the most appropriate one to use. For example, if one were to investigate the vibrations of a circular membrane fixed around its circumference, it would be foolish to attempt this using Cartesian coordinates. The problem calls for two-dimensional polar coordinates (r,θ) (Fig. 4.E1). r and θ are related to x and y via the equations

$$x = r \cos \theta, \ y = r \sin \theta .$$

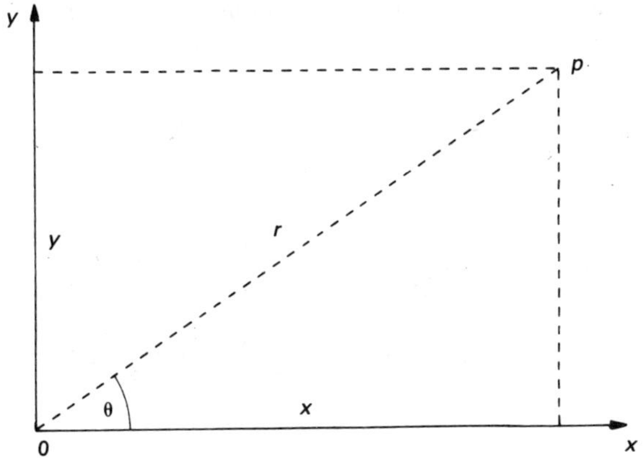

Fig. 4.E1 –

We take u to be the wave disturbance (not ϕ, since this symbol is sometimes used to mean the polar angle). Then

$$\frac{\partial u}{\partial r} = \frac{\partial u}{\partial x}\frac{\partial x}{\partial r} + \frac{\partial u}{\partial y}\frac{\partial y}{\partial r} = \cos\theta\,\frac{\partial u}{\partial x} + \sin\theta\,\frac{\partial u}{\partial y}.$$

Likewise,

$$\frac{\partial u}{\partial \theta} = \frac{\partial u}{\partial x}\frac{\partial x}{\partial \theta} + \frac{\partial u}{\partial y}\frac{\partial y}{\partial \theta} = -r\sin\theta\,\frac{\partial u}{\partial x} + r\cos\theta\,\frac{\partial u}{\partial y}.$$

Multiplying the first of these equations by $\cos\theta$, the second by $\sin\theta/r$ and subtracting gives

$$\frac{\partial u}{\partial x} = \cos\theta\,\frac{\partial u}{\partial r} - \frac{1}{r}\sin\theta\,\frac{\partial u}{\partial \theta}$$

and similarly,

$$\frac{\partial u}{\partial y} = \sin\theta\,\frac{\partial u}{\partial r} + \frac{1}{r}\cos\theta\,\frac{\partial u}{\partial \theta}.$$

It follows then that

$$\frac{\partial^2 u}{\partial x^2} = \left(\cos\theta\,\frac{\partial}{\partial r} - \frac{1}{r}\sin\theta\,\frac{\partial}{\partial \theta}\right)\left(\cos\theta\,\frac{\partial u}{\partial r} - \frac{1}{r}\sin\theta\,\frac{\partial u}{\partial \theta}\right)$$

$$= \cos\theta\left(\cos\theta\,\frac{\partial^2 u}{\partial r^2} + \frac{1}{r^2}\sin\theta\,\frac{\partial u}{\partial \theta} - \frac{1}{r}\sin\theta\,\frac{\partial^2 u}{\partial r\partial\theta}\right)$$

$$- \frac{1}{r}\sin\theta\left(-\sin\theta\,\frac{\partial u}{\partial r} + \cos\theta\,\frac{\partial^2 u}{\partial r\partial\theta} - \frac{1}{r}\cos\theta\,\frac{\partial u}{\partial \theta} - \frac{1}{r}\sin\theta\,\frac{\partial^2 u}{\partial \theta^2}\right).$$

Similarly,

$$\frac{\partial^2 u}{\partial y^2} = \left(\sin\theta\,\frac{\partial}{\partial r} + \frac{1}{r}\cos\theta\,\frac{\partial}{\partial \theta}\right)\left(\sin\theta\,\frac{\partial u}{\partial r} + \frac{1}{r}\cos\theta\,\frac{\partial u}{\partial \theta}\right)$$

$$= \sin\theta\left(\sin\theta\,\frac{\partial^2 u}{\partial r^2} - \frac{1}{r^2}\cos\theta\,\frac{\partial u}{\partial \theta} + \frac{1}{r}\cos\theta\,\frac{\partial^2 u}{\partial r\partial\theta}\right)$$

$$+ \frac{1}{r}\cos\theta\left(\cos\theta\,\frac{\partial u}{\partial r} + \sin\theta\,\frac{\partial^2 u}{\partial r\partial\theta} - \frac{1}{r}\sin\theta\,\frac{\partial u}{\partial \theta} + \frac{1}{r}\cos\theta\,\frac{\partial^2 u}{\partial \theta^2}\right)$$

Adding these,

$$\frac{\partial^2 u}{\partial x^2} + \frac{\partial^2 u}{\partial y^2} = \frac{\partial^2 u}{\partial r^2} + \frac{1}{r}\frac{\partial u}{\partial r} + \frac{1}{r^2}\frac{\partial^2 u}{\partial \theta^2} \ .$$

The appropriate wave equation is therefore

$$\frac{\partial^2 u}{\partial r^2} + \frac{1}{r}\frac{\partial u}{\partial r} + \frac{1}{r^2}\frac{\partial^2 u}{\partial \theta^2} = \frac{1}{c^2}\frac{\partial^2 u}{\partial t^2} \ .$$

4.4.2 Two-dimensional harmonic waves: vector representation
A harmonic wave in two dimensions is typified by a water wave whose vertical section in the direction of travel is a sine curve. We may therefore mathematically describe such a wave, whose wavefronts are straight lines, by the equation

$$\phi = a \sin \omega(lx + my - ct)/c \ . \tag{4.28}$$

The quantity ω/c is obtained by the same process as that which led to equation (4.16) earlier in this chapter, whilst a represents the amplitude of the wave,

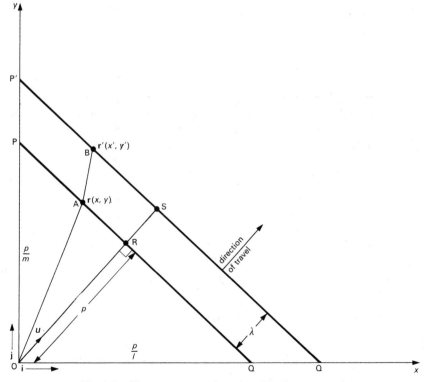

Fig. 4.5 – Vector representation of straight-line wave.

as before. A high-speed photograph of water waves of this kind taken from above would be characterized by a family of equispaced parallel crests, the perpendicular distance between adjacent crests being the wavelength λ.

Two adjacent crests, PQ and P'Q', are shown in Fig. 4.5. (Actually PQ and P'Q' need not be crests, but any pair of adjacent identical wavefronts.) Let us define unit vectors **i** and **j** parallel to Ox and Oy respectively, and let the unit vector along the direction of wave travel (i.e. the perpendicular to the wavefront) be **u** as shown. Take any point $A(x,y)$ with vector position **r** on the wavefront PQ; we can express the vector **r** in terms of its components as follows:

$$\mathbf{r} = x\mathbf{i} + y\mathbf{j} \ .$$

Similarly we can express the unit vector **u** as

$$\mathbf{u} = l\mathbf{i} + m\mathbf{j} \ ,$$

where l and m are the direction cosines of **u**. The scalar product of **r** and **u** is

$$\mathbf{r}.\mathbf{u} = (x\mathbf{i} + y\mathbf{j}).(l\mathbf{i} + m\mathbf{j})$$
$$= lx + my = p \ . \tag{4.29}$$

The equation $\mathbf{r}.\mathbf{u} = p$ is the vector equation for a straight line, and it enables us to write (4.28) in the vector form,

$$\phi = a \sin \frac{\omega}{c} (\mathbf{r}.\mathbf{u} - ct) \ . \tag{4.30}$$

Now PQ and P'Q' are identical wavefronts, so that if we replace **r** in (4.30) by the vector position of *any* point on P'Q' it follows from the definition of a wavefront that the value of ϕ must remain unaltered. Let B [vector position **r**', coordinates (x',y')] be such a point. Thus

$$\phi = a \sin \frac{\omega}{c} (\mathbf{r}.\mathbf{u} - ct) = a \sin \frac{\omega}{c} (\mathbf{r}'.\mathbf{u} - ct) \ . \tag{4.31}$$

But $\mathbf{r}.\mathbf{u}$ is the distance OR (Fig. 4.5) and $\mathbf{r}'.\mathbf{u}$ is the distance OS. Thus

$$\mathbf{r}'.\mathbf{u} - \mathbf{r}.\mathbf{u} = RS = \lambda \ . \tag{4.32}$$

since λ is the perpendicular distance between PQ and P'Q'.

Substituting from (4.32) into (4.31) we have

$$\phi = a \sin \frac{\omega}{c} (\mathbf{r}.\mathbf{u} - ct) = a \sin \frac{\omega}{c} [(\mathbf{r}.\mathbf{u} + \lambda) - ct] \ .$$

Clearly

$$\frac{\omega}{c} \lambda = 2\pi$$

and
$$\frac{\omega}{c} = \frac{2\pi}{\lambda} \; ,$$

so, we can rewrite (4.30) in the form

$$\phi = a \sin \left(\frac{2\pi \, \mathbf{r}.\mathbf{u}}{\lambda} - \omega t \right) .$$

We now extend the earlier definition of the wavenumber σ $(= 1/\lambda)$ so that it becomes the *wavevector* σ. The direction of σ is perpendicular to the wavefront (that is, parallel to the unit vector $\mathbf{u}$) whilst the magnitude $|\sigma|$ is $1/\lambda$, as before. Hence

$$\frac{\mathbf{u}}{\lambda} = \sigma$$

and the above equation becomes

$$\phi = a \sin \left(2\pi \; \sigma.\mathbf{r} - \omega t \right) \tag{4.33}$$

or, writing $\omega = 2\pi f$,

$$\phi = a \sin 2\pi \; \sigma.\mathbf{r} - ft) \tag{4.34}$$

A mathematically more compact form is obtained by introducing the *circular wavevector* $\mathbf{k} = 2\pi\sigma$, so that (4.33) becomes

$$\phi = a \sin \left(\mathbf{k}.\mathbf{r} - \omega t \right) \tag{4.35}$$

This is the vector representation of a harmonic wave we shall most commonly use, particularly in its exponential form

$$\boxed{\phi = a \exp i(\mathbf{k}.\mathbf{r} - \omega t)} \cdot \tag{4.36}$$

4.4.3 Plane waves in three dimensions

Equations (4.34) to (4.36) can be taken over, without change of form, into three dimensions. The three-dimensional equivalent of the straight line in two dimensions is the plane, so that the straight-line wavefronts of the previous section become plane wavefronts in three dimensions, and now $\mathbf{r}$ specifies a point in three-dimensional space.

If we wish to specify a three-dimensional plane wave in Cartesian form, we can extend the two-dimensional equation (4.26) to

$$\phi = f(lx + my + nz - ct) \; , \tag{4.37}$$

where (l,m,n) are the direction cosines of the normal to the plane wavefront (Fig. 4.6). The partial differential equation, which is the three-dimensional equivalent of (4.27), is

$$\frac{\partial^2 \phi}{\partial x^2} + \frac{\partial^2 \phi}{\partial y^2} + \frac{\partial^2 \phi}{\partial z^2} = \frac{1}{c^2} \frac{\partial^2 \phi}{\partial t^2} \; , \tag{4.38}$$

which is easily verified by differentiating (4.37).

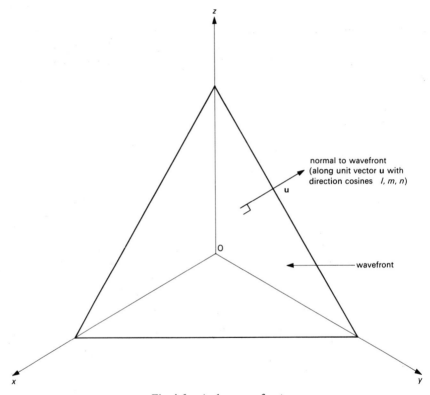

Fig. 4.6 – A plane wavefront.

It is convenient to write (4.38) in the form

$$\boxed{\nabla^2 \phi = \frac{1}{c^2} \frac{\partial^2 \phi}{\partial t^2}} \; ,$$

where ∇^2 (referred to in speech as 'del squared') is an abbreviation of

$$\frac{\partial^2}{\partial x^2} + \frac{\partial^2}{\partial y^2} + \frac{\partial^2}{\partial z^2} \; ,$$

and is often referred to as the Laplacian.

4.5 CIRCULAR AND SPHERICAL WAVEFRONTS

Straight-line wavefronts (in two dimensions) and plane ones (in three) are by
no means the only wavefronts encountered in physics, though they are the
simplest to treat mathematically. If we have a point source of disturbance in
two dimensions, such as a pebble dropping on to a previously still surface of
water, the resulting wavefronts are of circular form since the disturbance proceeds
outwards from the point of entry with equal speed in all directions. In three
dimensions, the wavefronts arising from a point source of disturbance are
spherical in form.

PROBLEMS

(4.1) Which of the following disturbances represent a travelling wave in one
dimension? In each case, what is the speed of the wave, and in which direction is
it travelling? (Ignore the fact that some of these are unrealistic, since the disturbance may tend to infinity.)

(i) $y = (3x - 4t)^2$ (ii) $y = x^2 t^2$

(iii) $y = e^{-\alpha x} e^{i\omega t}$ (iv) $y = e^{ikx} e^{i\omega t}$

(v) $y = \exp\{-\alpha(2x - t)^2\}$ (vi) $y = \sin 3t \sin 4x$

(vii) $y = \sin(x + 2t) + \sin(2x + 3t)$ (viii) $y = \sin(x + 2t) + \sin(2x + 4t)$.

(4.2) Use a calculator to plot one cycle of the disturbance $y = \sin 2\pi(0.2 x - 5t)$
at (i) $t = 0$, (ii) $t = 1/10$ of the period, (iii) $t = 1/4$ of the period. The progressive
nature of the wave should be obvious from the graphs. What are the wave speed,
wavelength, frequency, and circular wavenumber?

(4.3) Use the computer program (appendix A) to demonstrate travelling sinusoidal
waves (A.7(d)). Experiment with various circular wavenumbers k and wave
speeds c, but note that c should be a positive quantity.
    Note that (i) an instantaneous 'photograph' of the wave shows that y varies
sinusoidally with x, (ii) observation at a particular x shows that y varies sinusoidally with time (this is very clear if, for instance, the left-hand edge of the
screen is observed).

(4.4) A travelling sinusoidal wave of frequency f moves in the positive direction
of x with speed c. P and Q are points on the x-axis having coordinates x and
$x + dx$ respectively. What is the phase difference between the disturbances at
P and Q? Does that at Q 'lead' or 'lag behind' that at P?

(4.5) The human ear can perceive sounds over a frequency range 30 Hz to 15 kHz.
The speed of sound in air is 340 m s^{-1}. What are the wavelengths at these
extremities?

(4.6) The speed of electromagnetic waves in free space is 3×10^8 m s^{-1}. Calculate (i) the wavelength of a VHF radio signal at 100 MHz, (ii) the wavelength of waves emitted by a wire connected to the domestic mains supply (50 Hz), (iii) the frequency of visible light of wavelength 500 nm, (iv) the frequency of X-rays of wavelength 0.1 nm.

(4.7) Analyse the problem of 'beats' (section 2.3) using complex wave notation, letting the disturbances be $a \exp i\omega_1 t$ and $a \exp i\omega_2 t$. Show that the resulting wave has circular frequency $\frac{1}{2}(\omega_1 + \omega_2)$, and that the square of the amplitude oscillates with circular frequency $|\omega_1 - \omega_2|$.

(4.8)

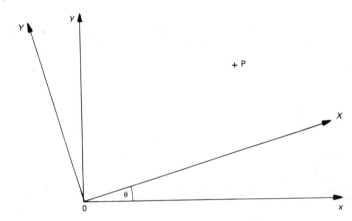

The coordinates of a point P are (x,y) when measured in relation to the axes (x,y) and (X,Y) in relation to the axes (X,Y) rotated through θ as shown. Show that $X = x \cos \theta + y \sin \theta$, and $Y = -x \sin \theta + y \cos \theta$. Hence show that equation (4.28) describes a plane wave moving, as expected, along the X-axis.

(4.9) Show that a possible solution of the two-dimensional wave equation is $\phi = A \sin k_1 x \sin k_2 y \sin \omega t$. What are the significances of k_1 and k_2? What is the wave speed?

CHAPTER 5

Waves in physical media

5.1 INTRODUCTION

In Chapter 4 we derived the partial differential equation governing wave propagation in one dimension,

$$\frac{\partial^2 y}{\partial x^2} = \frac{1}{c^2} \frac{\partial^2 y}{\partial t^2} , \qquad (4.12)$$

from purely geometrical considerations. We assumed a wave profile was being transmitted without change of shape and with constant velocity, but gave no physical justification for these assumptions. We will now look at some instances of wave propagation which will lead to equations of the type (4.12).

5.2 TRANSVERSE WAVES IN AN INFINITELY LONG, STRETCHED ELASTIC STRING

Suppose our infinitely long elastic string is initially at rest (in equilibrium) and lies along the Ox axis of coordinates. We will measure the transverse disturbance due to the passage of the wave by y. Let the mass per unit length of string be μ and let the tension in the string be T.

We will make the following assumptions:

(a) The value of y is very small compared with any wavelength with which we are concerned, and the disturbed string makes small angles with the x axis, i.e.

$$\frac{\partial y}{\partial x} \ll 1 .$$

(b) There is no motion other than in the y-direction.
(c) The tension in the string is unaltered by the passage of the wave.
(d) The effects of gravity can be ignored; i.e. the weight of the string is left out of our considerations.

We now obtain the partial differential equation governing the propagation of transverse waves along the string, by applying Newton's second law of motion to a short element of the string at an instant during the passage of the wave. We consider the motion of the element of length δx whose equilibrium position is PQ (Fig. 5.1). At an instant during the passage of the wave, the element is displaced to the instantaneous position P'Q'.

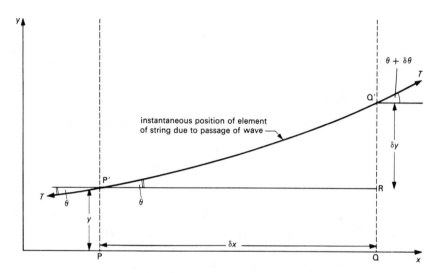

Fig. 5.1 – Element of string displaced by passage of wave.

The angles made by the string with the Ox axis at the points P' and Q' are θ and $\theta + \delta\theta$ as shown in Fig. 5.1 ; the only forces acting on the element are the tensions exerted by the adjoining sections of strings at P' and Q'. The net force acting in the Oy direction is therefore

$$T\sin(\theta + \delta\theta) - T\sin\theta = T\,\delta\theta = T\frac{\partial\theta}{\partial x}\,\delta x \qquad (5.1)$$

by assumption (a).

Also, since θ is small,

$$\tan\theta \cong \theta = \frac{\delta y}{\delta x} \ (\Delta\ \text{P'Q'R of Fig. 5.1}) \ . \qquad (5.2)$$

Therefore, in the limit as $\delta x \to 0$

$$\theta = \frac{\partial y}{\partial x}, \ \frac{\partial\theta}{\partial x} = \frac{\partial^2 y}{\partial x^2} \ ,$$

and the net force on the element, by (5.1), is

$$T \frac{\partial^2 y}{\partial x^2} \, \delta x \ .$$

$$(5.3)$$

The mass × accleration for the element is

$$(\mu \delta x) \, \frac{\partial^2 y}{\partial t^2} \, ,$$

so equating net force to mass × acceleration (Newton's second law of motion) we have

$$\frac{\partial^2 y}{\partial x^2} = \frac{1}{T/\mu} \frac{\partial^2 y}{\partial t^2} \ .$$

$$(5.4)$$

This equation is in the same form as equation (4.12), so we see at once, subject to all the assumptions we have made, that transverse waves of any profile can be propagated along a stretched elastic string, and that they will travel with the unique speed $\sqrt{(T/\mu)}$. We can alter this speed only by changing the tension or the density of the string (or both).

5.3 LONGITUDINAL WAVES IN A FLUID (LIQUID OR GAS)

Suppose we have an infinitely long hollow tube (Fig. 5.2), of circular cross-section of area A, containing a fluid (liquid or gas). Suppose that originally the fluid is at rest, its density is ρ and the pressure is P_0. Consider the small cylinder of fluid of length δx between R and S, shown in Fig. 5.2a, originally at rest with an equal pressure P_0 exerted at both ends by the surrounding fluid. Suppose the fluid is set into longitudinal agitation, for example by inserting a piston in the tube somewhere to the left of R and causing it to oscillate axially. Clearly this will set the adjacent fluid into longitudinal oscillation, and this disturbance will

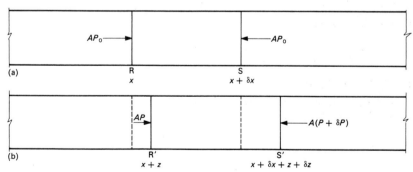

Fig. 5.2 – Waves in a fluid. In (a) the fluid is at rest in equilibrium, whilst in (b) the passing wave has displaced the cylinder RS to R'S'.

pass along the fluid in the form of a longitudinal wave. Suppose that at a given instant the cylinder RS has become displaced to a new position such that R moves a distance z to R' and S moves a distance $z + \delta z$ to S'. The variable z measures the longitudinal displacement of a point due to the passage of the wave. Let the pressure on the left-hand face now be P and that on the right-hand face $P + \delta P$.

We derive the differential equation governing the propagation of longitudinal waves in two steps. First we relate the change in dimensions of the cylinder to the change in pressure; then we equate the rate of change of momentum of the cylinder to the force acting upon it, by Newton's second law of motion.

The bulk modulus K of a material is a measure of the pressure increase required to change its volume by a given amount. It is defined formally as

$$K = \frac{\text{stress}}{\text{strain}} = \frac{\text{extra pressure applied}}{\text{fractional change in volume}} . \tag{5.5}$$

Proceeding to the limit of vanishingly small change in volume, we obtain the differential expression

$$K = - V \frac{dP}{dV} . \tag{5.6}$$

The minus sign appears because an increase in pressure produces a decrease in volume.

Applying the definition (5.5) to changes that have occurred to the cylinder RS between Fig. 5.2a and 5.2b, gives

$$K = \frac{(P - P_0)}{A\delta z / A\delta x} , \tag{5.7}$$

and defining the *acoustic pressure $p = P - P_0$* (5.8)
gives

$$p = - K \frac{\delta z}{\delta x}$$

or, in the limit as $\delta x \rightarrow 0$

$$p = - K \frac{\partial z}{\partial x} . \tag{5.9}$$

Here δP has been ignored in comparision with p.

Equating the net force on the displaced cylinder $R'S'$ to the product of mass and acceleration (Newton's second law) gives

$$PA - (P + \delta P)A = (A\rho\delta x) \frac{\partial^2 z}{\partial t^2}$$

$$\text{or} \quad - \delta P = \rho\delta x \frac{\partial^2 z}{\partial t^2} . \tag{5.10}$$

Here we cannot ignore δP, for it is this (small) excess pressure that produces the motion of the cylinder of fluid.

From (5.8) $\delta p = \delta P$, since P_0 is constant, so 5.10 becomes

$$-\delta p = \rho \delta x \, \frac{\partial^2 z}{\partial t^2}$$

or
$$-\frac{\partial p}{\partial x} \, \delta x = \rho \delta x \, \frac{\partial^2 z}{\partial t^2} \; . \tag{5.11}$$

But, from (5.9),

$$\frac{\partial p}{\partial x} = -K \, \frac{\partial^2 z}{\partial x^2} \; ;$$

substituting this into (5.11) and tidying up gives

$$\frac{\partial^2 z}{\partial x^2} = \frac{1}{K/\rho} \, \frac{\partial^2 z}{\partial t^2} \; . \tag{5.12}$$

Thus longitudinal waves may be propagated in a fluid, and have a speed c given by

$$\boxed{c = \sqrt{\left(\frac{K}{\rho} \right)}} \tag{5.13}$$

5.4 PRESSURE WAVES IN A GAS

Now equation (5.12) involves z which is the displacement of a point in the fluid. It is not therefore particularly useful, since we are not usually interested in how the longitudinal positions of points within the fluid vary due to the wave. On a molecular scale the position of a point in a fluid is a rather meaningless concept because, as the kinetic theory tells us, the molecules in a liquid or a gas are continuously moving about at very high velocities. What is of great importance is the variation of pressure due to waves in fluids — particularly gases. The partial differential equation governing pressure waves is obtained from equation (5.9). If we differentiate this twice partially with respect to time we get

$$\frac{\partial^2 p}{\partial t^2} = -K \, \frac{\partial^2}{\partial t^2} \left(\frac{\partial z}{\partial x} \right) \; .$$

When we carry out the differentiation of the right-hand side, we obtain the so-called mixed derivative, which is written in the form

$$\frac{\partial^2}{\partial t^2} \left(\frac{\partial z}{\partial x} \right) = \frac{\partial^3 z}{\partial t^2 \partial x} \; . \tag{5.14}$$

Note that the order in which the terms appear in the denominator of the right-hand side of (5.14) shows the order in which differentiation takes place. Thus

$$\frac{\partial^2 p}{\partial t^2} = -K \frac{\partial^3 z}{\partial t^2 \partial x} \ . \tag{5.15}$$

Differentiating (5.9) partially with respect to x gives

$$\frac{\partial p}{\partial x} = -K \frac{\partial^2 z}{\partial x^2} \ . \tag{5.16}$$

Eliminating $\partial^2 z/\partial x^2$ between (5.12) and (5.16) gives

$$\frac{\partial p}{\partial x} = -\rho \frac{\partial^2 z}{\partial t^2} \ , $$

and differentiating this partially with respect to x gives

$$\frac{\partial^2 p}{\partial x^2} = -\rho \frac{\partial}{\partial x} \left(\frac{\partial^2 z}{\partial t^2} \right) = -\rho \frac{\partial^3 z}{\partial x \partial t^2} \ . \tag{5.17}$$

It turns out that the order of differentiation in mixed derivatives such as $\partial^3 z/\partial x \partial t^2$ does not matter in the case of nearly all functions met in physics, so we may eliminate this quantity between (5.15) and (5.17) to obtain

$$\frac{\partial^2 p}{\partial x^2} = \frac{1}{K/\rho} \frac{\partial^2 p}{\partial t^2} \ , \tag{5.18}$$

so the pressure waves have the same speed $\sqrt{(K/\rho)}$ as the displacement waves. Note that p in (5.18) is not the actual pressure, but the *change* from ambient pressure produced by the wave.

The pressure waves in a gas of greatest interest here are sound waves. It turns out that changes in local conditions produced by the passage of a sound wave take place *adiabatically;* that is, no heat energy enters or leaves any given small region of the gas during the half period between, say, a compression and the following expansion. A popular, but wrong, explanation of this is that sound frequencies are so high that there is not time for the heat energy to get away. The correct explanation of why sound waves are adiabatic forms the basis for problem 5.9 at the end of this chapter.

When a fixed mass of ideal gas changes its state adiabatically, it turns out that

$$PV^\gamma = \text{constant} \tag{5.19}$$

where P is the pressure, V the volume, and γ the ratio of the principal heat capacities (C_p/C_v).

Taking logs of (5.19) we have

$$\ln P + \gamma \ln V = 0 \ . \tag{5.20}$$

Differentiation and tidying up produces

$$V \frac{dP}{dV} = -\gamma P ,$$
(5.21)

while substituting for $V \, dp/dV$ from (5.6) gives

$$K_A = \gamma P .$$
(5.22)

The suffix A in K_A shows that this is the bulk modulus for adiabatic conditions. Substituting this value for K_A into (5.13) gives the speed c for sound in a gas as

$$c = \sqrt{\left(\frac{\gamma P}{\rho}\right)}.$$
(5.23)

Still assuming an ideal gas, which obeys

$$P V_m = RT$$
(5.24)

where R is the molar gas constant, T the thermodynamic temperature, and V_m the volume of 1 mole, we may substitute this together with $V_m = M/\rho$, where M is the molar mass, into (5.23) to obtain

$$\boxed{c = \sqrt{\left(\frac{\gamma RT}{M}\right)}.}$$
(5.25)

This tells us that the speed of sound in a gas is independent of the pressure (at constant temperature), and increases with the square root of the absolute temperature; and also that the speed is greatest in gases of low molar mass, since $c \propto M^{-\frac{1}{2}}$ for fixed T.

Example 5.1
Calculate the speed of sound in air at $15°C$.

It will be appreciated that the speed of sound is different in different gases because both M and γ depend on the gas. Since air is a mixture of 80% nitrogen and 20% oxygen, for which the molar masses are 28 g and 32 g respectively, M can be taken as the weighted mean $(0.8 \times 28 + 0.2 \times 32) \times 10^{-3} = 28.8 \times 10^{-3}$ kg mol^{-1}. We ignore the presence of other gases such as carbon dioxide, water vapour, etc.

Now γ depends on the number of atoms in a molecule of the gas. For monatomic gases (e.g. He, Ne, A), $\gamma = 5/3 = 1.667$, while for diatomic gases (e.g. H_2, N_2, CO), $\gamma = 7/5 = 1.4$. Since nitrogen (N_2) and oxygen (O_2) are diatomic, γ can be taken with good accuracy as 1.4 for air.

Using the value $R = 8.31$ J K^{-1} mol^{-1}, we can calculate the speed of sound in air at $15°C$ ($= 288$ K),

$$c = \sqrt{\left(\frac{1.4 \times 8.31 \times 288}{28.8 \times 10^{-3}}\right)} = 341 \text{ ms}^{-1} . .$$

(It should be noted that M must be expressed in kg mol^{-1}).

An interesting observation is that the speed of sound in air — or indeed any gas — depends on the temperature, but *not on the pressure.* This might appear to be inconsistent with the equation $c = (\gamma P/\rho)^{\frac{1}{2}}$, until it is realized that if P is increased at constant T, then ρ also increases in proportion.

5.5 LONGITUDINAL WAVES IN A ROD

The reasoning of the previous section can be applied with very little modification to the case of longitudinal waves in a rod. Consider the small section PQ of the rod (Fig. 5.3) of cross-sectional area A, made of material of density ρ and Young modulus E; the section is displaced to P'Q', and is increased in length due to the passage of the longitudinal wave. Let the forces acting instantaneously on P'Q' be as shown in Fig. 5.3b.

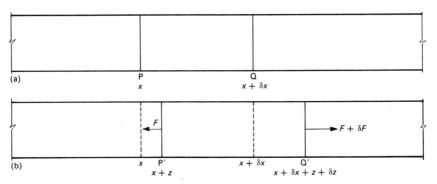

Fig. 5.3 — Longitudinal waves in a rod: (a) at rest, whilst in (b) the section PQ is displaced to P'Q' due to the passage of the wave.

Relating change in length to force acting, we have, from the definition of the Young modulus,

$$\frac{F}{A} = E \frac{\delta z}{\delta x} ,$$ (5.26)

ignoring δF in comparison with F. Applying Newton's second law of motion we have

$$\delta F = A\rho \, \delta x \, \frac{\partial^2 z}{\partial t^2} .$$

But $\qquad \delta F = \dfrac{\partial F}{\partial x} \, \delta x$

$$= AE \frac{\partial^2 z}{\partial x^2} \, \delta x \quad \text{by (5.26),}$$

Hence $$\frac{\partial^2 z}{\partial x^2} = \frac{1}{E/\rho}\frac{\partial^2 z}{\partial t^2} \; ,$$ (5.27)

which is the wave equation once again. The velocity for longitudinal waves in a rod is thus

$$\boxed{c = \sqrt{\frac{E}{\rho}}} \; .$$ (5.28)

This gives velocities of the order of 5000 m s^{-1} for typical values of E and ρ of common metals.

5.6 CURRENT AND VOLTAGE WAVES IN AN IDEAL TRANSMISSION LINE

A transmission line is a system of conductors, usually two, carrying electrical signals. In its simplest form, it consists of a pair of infinitely long, identical, parallel wires, separated by an insulating medium (for example, air or polythene). Another familiar example is a coaxial line, consisting of a solid central wire surrounded by a coaxial cylindrical conductor. If one end of the line is connected to an alternating current generator (Fig. 5.4), fluctuations in voltage and current are produced, which proceed along the line in the form of an electrical wave.

We will investigate the changes that take place in the small section of the line of length δx between PP$'$ and QQ$'$. We assume that the wires have zero resistance, and there is no leakage of current from one to the other. Such a line is said to be 'loss free'.

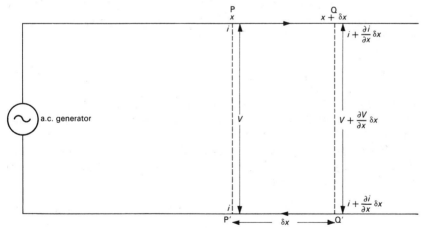

Fig. 5.4 – Ideal transmission line.

Now the two wires of the line act as a capacitor. It would appear that the problem of considering line capacitance is formidable, because PQ interacts not only with P$'$Q$'$, but with all elements of the lower line. However, it is clear that the electric field at PQ can have no component along PQ; otherwise there would be an infinite current in this element. The electric field is therefore transverse, and all such field lines originating from PQ must end on P'Q'. We are therefore justified in regarding PQ, P'Q' as an elemental capacitor, and can ignore the capacitance between PQ and other parts of the line.

Let the capacitance per unit length be C. Then the charge on PQ is $+ CV\delta x$ (and that on P'Q' is $- CV\delta x$). Now if V is increasing with time, the charge on PQ is increasing at a rate $C(\partial V/\partial t)\delta x$. This must therefore be equal to $i_P - i_Q = -(\partial i/\partial x)\delta x$, and so

$$\frac{\partial i}{\partial x} = -C\,\frac{\partial V}{\partial t} \,. \qquad (5.29)$$

We now consider in a similar manner the inductive effect of the line, but must be somewhat cautious. The inductance of a closed circuit can be defined as being (numerically) equal to the magnetic flux threading the circuit when unit current flows in it. But since the current flows along PQ and P'Q', but not along PP' and QQ', PQQ'P' does not form a closed circuit. Can we meaningfully talk about the inductance of the element PQQ'P'? Well, consider a very long line, terminated at both ends, carrying a *steady* unit current. The flux threading the line is uniformly distributed, and proportional to the length of the line. It is therefore meaningful to define an 'inductance per unit length', L, such that the flux threading the element PQQ'P' is $Li\delta x$. Like the electric field, the magnetic field is transverse.

Now if i is increasing, the voltages across PP' and QQ' are different. The induced voltage in the path PQQ'P' is $- dV = -(\partial V/\partial x)\delta x$. This equals the rate of change of flux threading the path, and so

$$\frac{\partial V}{\partial x} = -L\,\frac{\partial i}{\partial t} \,. \qquad (5.30)$$

(As readers familiar with electromagnetism will appreciate, Faraday's law may be applied round a closed *path* as we have done; it does not matter that it is not a complete *circuit*.)

It is easy now to show that voltage and current waves are propagated along the line. For if we differentiate (5.29) partially with respect to t, (5.30) with respect to x, and eliminate the mixed term, we obtain

$$\frac{\partial^2 V}{\partial x^2} = LC\,\frac{\partial^2 V}{\partial t^2} \,. \qquad (5.31)$$

Likewise, differentiating (5.29) partially with respect to x, and (5.30) with respect to t leads to

$$\frac{\partial^2 i}{\partial x^2} = LC\,\frac{\partial^2 i}{\partial t^2} \,. \qquad (5.32)$$

Equations (5.31) and (5.32) represent voltage and current waves, which exist simultaneously, and have speed c given by

$$\boxed{c = \sqrt{\left/\left(\frac{1}{LC}\right)\right.}}$$ (5.33)

Values of L and C for a specimen of ordinary household connecting flex are 7×10^{-7} H m^{-1} and 6×10^{-11} F m^{-1} respectively. The wave velocity is therefore 1.54×10^{8} m s^{-1}, which is rather more than half the velocity of light in vacuum $(3 \times 10^{8}$ m s$^{-1})$.

We can calculate the wavelength for 50 Hz alternating current in household flex from the relationship

Wave velocity = frequency × wavelength;

this gives λ to be 3080 km. The lengths of the lines over which alternating current is transmitted are very much smaller than this, so that the signals are transmitted practically instantaneously compared with the period of the signal; it is therefore unnecessary to speak of waves in this context, but, when the signal frequency is high, the wave nature of the transmission line can become important.

The wave velocity can be decreased by using cable with a higher value for the product LC; a complete analysis of this problem shows that the value of LC is determined solely by the nature of the insulation and is independent of the geometry of the conductors. The time taken for a wave to travel distances of the order of a metre (e.g. about 5×10^{-9} s for coaxial cable) is significant in electronic terms; this is the basis of the so-called delay line.

One example of the use of a delay line is in the trigger mechanism of good-quality cathode-ray oscilloscopes. When randomly occurring pulses are to be displayed, the leading edge of the pulse has to be used to trigger the sweep mechanism; that is, to start the spot off on its journey across the screen. The incoming pulse amplitude is split into two; the first part is used to trigger the sweep, whilst the second part is passed along a delay line timed so that its leading edge arrives at the plates immediately after the spot has begun to move. In this way, the whole of the pulse waveform is displayed upon the screen.

In this chapter we have seen how the equation

$$\frac{\partial^2 y}{\partial x^2} = \frac{1}{c^2}\frac{\partial^2 y}{\partial t^2}$$

arises in a variety of physical situations. It is by no means the only wave equation; any partial differential equation relating a displacement in a medium to the spatial coordinates and time is a wave equation. But the above equation is the simplest general description of the essentials of wave motion. It is known as the non-dispersive wave equation.

PROBLEMS

(5.1) Calculate the speed of sound in helium at $-100°C$. ($R = 8.31$ J K^{-1} mol^{-1}, molar mass of He $= 4$ g).

(5.2) Calculate the speed of longitudinal waves in steel. (Young's modulus $= 2.0 \times 10^{11}$ N m^{-2}, density $= 7.8 \times 10^3$ kg m^{-3}).

(5.3) An elastic string has mass 1 g and natural length 0.1 m. A mass 1 kg is attached to its lower end, and the string is stretched by 0.02 m. Calculate the speed of propagation of transverse waves along the string.

A transverse disturbance travels along the string, and is reflected at both ends. How many times will this disturbance pass a point on the string in one period of a small vertical oscillation of the mass?

(For simplicity, take the tension in the string to be uniform in this problem.)

(5.4) A wire of mass m and length l is fixed at one end, and hangs freely under its own weight. Deduce the time for a transverse wave to travel the length of the wire.

(5.5) A plane sinusoidal sound wave of displacement amplitude 1.2×10^{-3} mm and frequency 680 Hz is propagated in an ideal gas of density 1.29 kg m^{-3} and pressure 10^5 N m^{-2}. The ratio of principal specific heat capacities is 1.41. Find the pressure amplitude of the wave.

(5.6) It is believed by some people that a sinking ship never reaches the bottom of the ocean, but remains suspended in equilibrium at a certain depth. The 'reason' is that the pressures are enormous, even at modest depths. Using the data that at $25°C$, the speed of sound in sea-water is 1531 m s^{-1}, and the density of sea-water is 1.025×10^3 kg m^{-3}, show that the belief is incorrect as follows:

(a) calculate the bulk compressibility of sea-water;
(b) hence calculate the density at a depth of 8 km;
(c) show that an iron ship will certainly sink to the bottom of the ocean.

What assumptions have been made in the analysis?

(5.7) A length of coaxial cable is used to connect a television aerial to the receiving set. The inductance and capacitance per unit length of the cable are respectively 5×10^{-7} H m^{-1} and 8×10^{-11} F m^{-1}. If the frequency of the broadcast signal is 600 MHz, calculate (a) the wavelength in free space, (b) the wavelength in the cable.

(5.8) Show that if a sinusoidal wave is propagated along a transmission line in one direction, the voltage V and the current i are in phase at all points, and that $V/i = \sqrt{(L/C)}$. This quantity is called the characteristic impedance of the line Z_0.

Calculate Z_0 if $L = 7 \times 10^{-7}$ H m^{-1} and $C = 6 \times 10^{-11}$ F m^{-1}.

(5.9) (harder). Justify the assumption that the pressure changes in a gas carrying a sound wave are adiabatic as follows.

The regions of compression (at temperature T_1) and rarefaction (at T_2) can be thought of as occupying a length of, say, $\sim\lambda/4$, and as separated by $\sim\lambda/2$. Defining θ as $T_1 - T_2$, and K as the thermal conductivity, show that $d\theta/\theta = - dt/\tau_r$, where $\tau_r \sim \lambda^2 \rho c_p/K$ (c_p refers to unit mass). By integration, show that τ_r is the 'relaxation time' which determines how quickly the gas attains a uniform temperature.

Hence show that for a sound wave of frequency f and period τ, the ratio $\tau/\tau_r \sim Kf/c^2\rho c_p$. Show that this ratio for a typical frequency of 1 kHz in air is small, given that $K = 0.023$ $Wm^{-1}K^{-1}$, $c = 340$ m s^{-1}, $\rho = 1.2$ kg m^{-3}, $C_{p,M} = 7R/2$ (for 1 mole), $R = 8.31$ J K^{-1} mol^{-1}, and the molar mass of air $= 29$ g mol^{-1}.

(It is interesting to note that the adiabatic behaviour is better obeyed at the *lower* frequencies.)

CHAPTER 6

Boundary conditions and energy transfer

6.1 INTRODUCTION

This chapter is concerned with the general solution of

$$\frac{\partial^2 y}{\partial t^2} = c^2 \frac{\partial^2 y}{\partial x^2} \tag{6.1}$$

and the physical implications of the solution. We saw in Chapter 4 how 6.1 is obtained from the wave $y = f(x - ct)$. This means that $y = f(x - ct)$ is a solution of 6.1; we showed that $y = g(x + ct)$ is also a solution of the equation. (We call the function here g since it need not be the same function as the previous one.) Further, since the original wave equation is a *linear* partial differential equation, *any* linear sum of these two solutions is itself a solution. That is to say, a perfectly good solution of the wave equation 6.1 is

$$\boxed{y = f(x - ct) + g(x + ct)} \ . \tag{6.2}$$

In fact, it can be shown (but we shall not do so) that (6.2) is the *general solution* to the wave equation. This is commonly referred to as D'Alembert's solution.

There are two very striking things about this solution. The first is that it gives us a good deal of information about possible waves in a one-dimensional system governed by the wave equation (6.1). It tells us that either or both directions of wave propagation are possible (a superimposition of waves in both directions being the general case, and special cases of one direction only being when either f or g is zero). Static equilibrium is also consistent with the wave equation, since f and g can be zero. There is, of course, no wave at all in this trivial case, but it would be strange if the wave equation explicitly ruled out the possibility of the system existing in a state of static equilibrium. Another important fact that (6.2) tells us is that the speed has to be the same for both directions of propagation. As we have seen in the previous chapter, the value of c is determined solely by the physical properties of the wave system under consideration.

The second important feature about the solution (6.2) concerns the *lack* of information it gives. Not only can the waves travel (with equal speed) in either direction, but they can be of any form whatsoever, since there is no effective restriction on the nature of the functions *f* and *g*. So it becomes apparent that a waveform of *any* shape may be propagated in accordance with the wave equation. This, after all, ties up with our everyday experience. The air around us will transmit sound waves in accordance with the three-dimensional equivalent of the wave equation (6.1), and shows absolutely no preference to any particular signal. It will transmit Beethoven, Bartok and Bernstein with equal ease (and, indeed, at the same speed!); this enviable versatility is the prominent feature of D'Alembert's solution.

Although the solution (6.2) of the wave equation (6.1) is very general, this does not imply that the solution under any circumstances is so general. We shall now examine in some detail the factors which restrict the generality of the solution, and to illustrate this we shall take the case of a stretched string.

6.2 INITIAL CONDITIONS

Consider a very long stretched string, so long that it can be thought of as being of infinite length. We already know that any transverse wave propagated along the string must have a velocity $\sqrt{(T/\mu)}$ where T and μ are the tension, and mass per unit length, of the string respectively. Also, from the previous section, a wave of any shape may be propagated, subject to certain conditions, the most obvious one being that the shape must be represented by a *continuous* function – any discontinuity would correspond to a break in the string which would certainly not be propagated along its length.

Suppose initially we make the string take a certain shape, which we can describe by the function $\phi(x)$, and suppose that at time $t = 0$ we release the string. A wave will be propagated along the string according to the equation (6.2). We already know that the general shape of the string at any subsequent time t is given by

$$y = f(x - ct) + g(x + ct) . \tag{6.2}$$

We must interpret this equation in the light of our knowledge that at time $t = 0$

$$[y]_{t=0} = \phi(x) . \tag{6.3}$$

Equation (6.3) states the initial position of every particle of the string; the left-hand side is merely a convenient shorthand for the value of the function y at time $t = 0$. Since we are constraining the string until time $t = 0$, at which time we are 'letting go', the initial velocities of all particles in the string are zero. That is to say,

$$\left[\frac{\partial y}{\partial t}\right]_{t=0} = 0, \text{ for all } x . \tag{6.4}$$

The two equations (6.3) and (6.4) describe what are known as *initial conditions* which, as we shall now see, restrict the generality of (6.2). By making t zero in (6.2) we get

$$[y]_{t=0} = f(x) + g(x) .$$

But this, from (6.3), is equal to $\phi(x)$, i.e.

$$f(x) + g(x) = \phi(x) . \tag{6.5}$$

Let us now return to (6.2) and differentiate it partially with respect to t;

$$\frac{\partial y}{\partial t} = \frac{\partial}{\partial t} f(x - ct) + \frac{\partial}{\partial t} g(x + ct)$$

$$= \frac{df(x - ct)}{d(x - ct)} \frac{\partial(x - ct)}{\partial t} + \frac{dg(x + ct)}{d(x + ct)} \frac{\partial(x + ct)}{\partial t}$$

$$= -c \frac{df(x - ct)}{d(x - ct)} + c \frac{dg(x + ct)}{d(x + ct)} .$$

At time $t = 0$ this reduces to

$$\left[\frac{\partial y}{\partial t}\right]_{t=0} = -c \frac{df(x)}{dx} + c \frac{dg(x)}{dx} .$$

By cross-multiplying, we see that this becomes

$$\frac{1}{c} \left[\frac{\partial y}{\partial t}\right]_{t=0} dx = -df(x) + dg(x) ,$$

and by integrating with respect to x we obtain

$$\frac{1}{c} \int \left[\frac{\partial y}{\partial t}\right]_{t=0} dx = -f(x) + g(x) . \tag{6.6}$$

If we now subtract (6.6) from (6.5) we obtain

$$2f(x) = \phi(x) - \frac{1}{c} \int \left[\frac{\partial y}{\partial t}\right]_{t=0} dx \tag{6.7}$$

and if we add together (6.5) and (6.6) we obtain

$$2g(x) = \phi(x) + \frac{1}{c} \int \left[\frac{\partial y}{\partial t}\right]_{t=0} dx . \tag{6.8}$$

These last two equations define the general functions f and g of D'Alembert's solution in terms of the initial conditions we have imposed on the problem. In the particular case we are considering, we have assumed that the initial velocities of all particles of the string are zero, as stated in (6.4). We can immediately see that this effects a considerable simplification in (6.7) and (6.8) by getting rid of both integrals, and the equations become

$$f(x) = \tfrac{1}{2}\phi(x)$$

and $$g(x) = \tfrac{1}{2}\phi(x) \ .$$

Substituting these back into equation (6.2) we get

$$y = \tfrac{1}{2}\phi(x - ct) + \tfrac{1}{2}\phi(x + ct) \ . \tag{6.9}$$

To illustrate the meaning of (6.9), let us consider a particular initial shape $\phi(x)$, illustrated in Fig. 6.1. Here the uniform string, which is under tension T, is

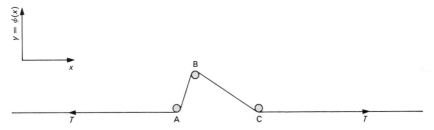

Fig. 6.1 – An example of initial conditions in a long string.

bent into the shape shown, by three pegs A, B and C. We can imagine the horizontal axis as x and the vertical as $\phi(x)$. The pegs are all removed at the same instant (time $t = 0$). What is the subsequent behaviour of the string? First of all, (6.9) very properly tells us that, at time $t = 0$, y is indeed equal to $\phi(x)$, the two terms on the right-hand side each contributing half. But at a later time the two halves will not be, as they were at the beginning, coincident in space. In fact the first term in (6.9) represents the initial shape (scaled down by a factor of two) travelling to the right with speed c, while the second term represents the

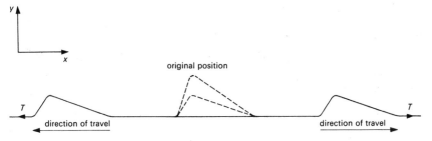

Fig. 6.2 – Appearance of the string of Fig. 6.1 at a later time.

same shape (similarly scaled down) travelling to the left with the same speed. At a subsequent time, therefore, the string would look as in Fig. 6.2.

As time goes on, the two disturbances in the string proceed away from each other at a constant relative velocity $2c$.

6.3 STANDING (STATIONARY) WAVES

As a special case of the initial conditions dealt with in the last section, let us suppose that the initial shape of the string is cosinusoidal (i.e. the shape of a cosine curve) throughout its length, with wavelength λ. That is to say,

$$\phi(x) = a \cos 2\pi \frac{x}{\lambda} \ . \tag{6.10}$$

As before, the initial velocities of all the particles in the string are zero and so equation (6.9),

$$y = \tfrac{1}{2}\phi(x - ct) + \tfrac{1}{2}\phi(x + ct) \ ,$$

is again valid. When we insert the form of ϕ given in (6.10), equation (6.9) becomes

$$y = \tfrac{1}{2}a \cos \frac{2\pi}{\lambda}(x - ct) + \tfrac{1}{2}a \cos \frac{2\pi}{\lambda}(x + ct) \ . \tag{6.11}$$

This equation describes the subsequent motion of the string. Now, we can rewrite (6.11) in the form

$$y = a \cos \frac{1}{2}\left[\frac{4\pi x}{\lambda}\right] \cos \frac{1}{2}\left[-\frac{4\pi ct}{\lambda}\right].$$

[The trigonometrical identity

$$\cos A + \cos B = 2 \cos \tfrac{1}{2}(A + B)\cos \tfrac{1}{2}(A - B)$$

has been used, and we can ignore the minus sign in the argument of the second cosine term since $\cos\theta = \cos(-\theta)$.] We can replace λ/c in this term by T, the period. So the last equation simplifies to

$$y = a \cos \left[\frac{2\pi x}{\lambda}\right] \cos \left[\frac{2\pi t}{T}\right]. \tag{6.12}$$

Now this is a rather peculiar result. Instead of a function of the $f(x \pm ct)$ type, we have the product of two cosine terms, one involving only x as a variable and the other only t. Consider what happens at the point on the string for which $x = 0$. Since

$$\cos \left[\frac{2\pi x}{\lambda}\right] = 1 \quad \text{for } x = 0 \ ,$$

equation (6.12) becomes

$$[y]_{x=0} = a \cos \left[\frac{2\pi t}{T} \right].$$

So the particle at $x = 0$ just bobs up and down, executing simple harmonic motion with period T. Consider another particle, say one eighth of a wavelength away from $x = 0$. Here

$$x = \frac{\lambda}{8} \ .$$

Thus

$$\frac{x}{\lambda} = \frac{1}{8}$$

and (6.12) gives us

$$[y]_{x=\frac{1}{8}\lambda} = a \cos \frac{\pi}{4} \cos \left[\frac{2\pi t}{T} \right] = \frac{a}{\sqrt{2}} \cos \left[\frac{2\pi t}{T} \right].$$

At this point along the string, therefore, the particle is executing simple harmonic motion with the same period but with reduced amplitude.

Let us proceed further and consider what happens at a point a quarter wavelength to the right of $x = 0$. This is the point $x = \frac{1}{4}\lambda$ or $x/\lambda = \frac{1}{4}$. Equation (6.12) now becomes

$$[y]_{x=\frac{1}{4}\lambda} = a \cos \frac{\pi}{2} \cos \left[\frac{2\pi t}{T} \right] = 0 \ ,$$

since $\cos \dfrac{\pi}{2} = 0$.

Therefore this point *does not move at any time*. In fact there is a series of such points, namely those for which

$$\cos \left[\frac{2\pi x}{\lambda} \right] = 0 \ ,$$

or $$\frac{2\pi x}{\lambda} = \pm \frac{\pi}{2}, \pm \frac{3\pi}{2}, \pm \frac{5\pi}{2}, \ldots \ ,$$

i.e. $$\frac{2\pi x}{\lambda} = (2n + 1) \frac{\pi}{2} \quad (n = \ldots, -2, -1, 0, 1, 2, \ldots) \ ,$$

i.e. $$x = (2n + 1) \frac{\lambda}{4} \ .$$

These points of no displacement are called *nodes*. Since any two adjacent nodes are a distance $\frac{1}{2}\lambda$ apart, half-way between the nth and $(n + 1)$th nodes the value of x will be given by

$$x = (2n + 1)\tfrac{1}{4}\lambda + \tfrac{1}{4}\lambda$$
$$= (2n + 2)\tfrac{1}{4}\lambda$$
$$= (n + 1)\tfrac{1}{2}\lambda$$

For this value of x,

$$\cos \frac{2\pi x}{\lambda} = \cos \left\{ 2\pi(n + 1) \frac{\lambda}{2\lambda} \right\}$$
$$= \cos[(n + 1)\pi] = \pm 1 \ .$$

Such points will therefore oscillate in accordance with the equation

$$y = \pm a \cos \left[\frac{2\pi t}{T} \right].$$

No point can have a greater amplitude than this (since unity is the maximum value of the cosine function). Thus, half-way between each adjacent pair of nodes we have a point of maximum vibration. These points are known as *antinodes*.

Figure 6.3 shows the profile of the string at different times. It is seen that there is apparently no wave travelling along the x-axis in either direction, the two constituent travelling waves in this case adding up to give a stationary effect. Such a superposition is called a *standing wave* or *stationary wave,* and is of great importance, as we shall see later.

We must stress an important mathematical feature of standing waves. We saw that the standing waves in this particular case are described by equation 6.12, i.e.

$$y = a \cos \left[\frac{2\pi x}{\lambda} \right] \cos \left[\frac{2\pi t}{T} \right].$$

This is no longer of the form

$$y = f(x \pm ct)$$

but is, rather, the *product* of two functions, $\cos(2\pi x/\lambda)$, which is a function of the position x only, and $\cos(2\pi t/T)$, which is a function of the time t only. Standing waves are always described in this way, and, in general, we can write

$$y = F_1(x) F_2(t) \ ,$$

where $F_1(x)$ and $F_2(t)$ are, respectively, functions of position and time only. Whenever we see a wave represented by an equation of this type, we know at once that a standing wave is indicated. It is doubtful whether this situation is, indeed, correctly describable as wave motion since there is no net flow of energy in any direction.

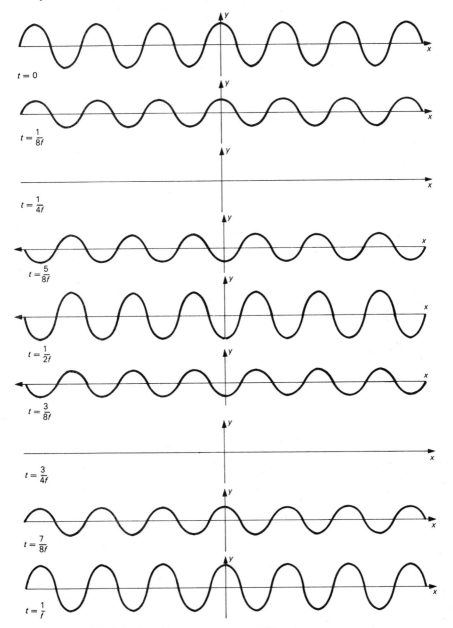

Fig. 6.3 – Standing-wave patterns at different times.

6.4 BOUNDARY CONDITIONS

Initial conditions specify the displacement, or rate of change of displacement, or some other time derivative of displacement of every particle of the system at a particular instant of time, and we have seen that they reduce the generality of the solution of the wave equation (6.1). In this section we are going to investigate the effect of what are known as *boundary conditions,* which occur in problems where we impose a restriction on what happens to a *particular* particle in the system as time goes on. These two different types of conditions are rather similar; in the one case we specify what happens at all values of x for a particular value of t, and in the other case we specify what happens at all values of t for a particular value of x.

To illustrate the ideas involved in boundary conditions, let us refer once more to the case of the uniform, tensioned string. Suppose we have such a string stretching from $x = 0$ to $x = \infty$. At the point $x = 0$ the string is firmly clamped so that it cannot move. Since the transverse displacement of a point at distance x from the origin at time t is $y(x,t)$, as before, the restriction placed by the clamping on the possible wave motions of the string can be stated as

$$y(0, t) = 0 \qquad\qquad (6.13)$$

for all time t. Equation (6.13) is a *boundary condition* that we are imposing in this particular problem.

Now suppose we are able to propagate a transverse wave of the form shown in Fig. (6.4), and described by a function $g(x,t)$, along the string towards the origin. Since the disturbance is travelling in the negative direction of x, the wave must be described by $y = g(x + ct)$.

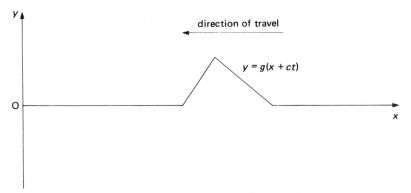

Fig. 6.4 – Transverse wave on a clamped string.

What happens when the disturbance arrives at the clamp at $x = 0$? A simple experiment can help us here. A length of cord (a clothes line would do nicely) is firmly tied at one end to some fixed object and the other end is held fairly taut.

If the held end is now given a sudden single flick, it is seen that the resulting disturbance travels down the cord to the tied end where it turns round and retraces its path back towards the hand-held end of the string.

What can we tell about this return wave? Firstly it must travel with same speed as the outward-going wave since, as we have seen, the speed is determined entirely by the tension, and mass per unit length, of the string. We shall make no assumptions about the shape of the return wave, and shall describe it by the function

$$y = f(x - ct) \ .$$

As the incident wave reaches the point of clamping at $x = 0$ it can cause no transverse motion of the string, because the string is not free to move. It follows, therefore, that the return wave is one of such a shape as to cancel out the lateral displacement of the incident wave at $x = 0$. In other words, the displacement of the incident wave at $x = 0$ is exactly equal and opposite to the displacement there due to the return wave at all times, so that when we add the two displacements together at $x = 0$ the result is always zero.

This is an example of the very important *principle of superposition,* which tells us that if waves are superposed the net displacement is the sum of the displacements due to each of the waves acting independently of the others. D'Alembert's solution

$$y = f(x - ct) + g(x + ct) \qquad\qquad [6.2]$$

is an example of the principle of superposition.

The diagrams in Fig. 6.5 show the incident wave at various stages after the arrival at the clamped point $x = 0$. With the knowledge that the return wave has to be of such shape as to cancel the displacement at $x = 0$ due to the incident wave, we can build up the shape of the return wave as shown, bearing in mind that both waves have the same speed. Since the displacement due to this particular incident wave is upwards, the displacement due to the return wave must be downwards. If we follow the sequences in Fig. 6.5 through, we see that the shape of the wave has also been reversed in the x-direction. In other words, the original wave has been turned back-to-front and upside down.

Mathematically, we can represent the process as follows. When we insert the boundary condition (6.13) into (6.2) for $x = 0$, we obtain

$$[y]_{x=0} = f(-ct) + g(ct) = 0 \ .$$

Thus $f(-ct) = -g(ct) \ .$

So, replacing the argument ct in the above equation in $x - ct$, we find that the relationship between f and g for this case is

$$g(ct - x) = -f(x - ct) \ .$$

Thus, from equation (6.2)

$$y = g(x + ct) - g(ct - x) \ . \tag{6.14}$$

The implication of equation (6.14) is that if we propagate a wave described by the function $g(x + ct)$ down the string, a second wave represented by $-g(ct - x)$

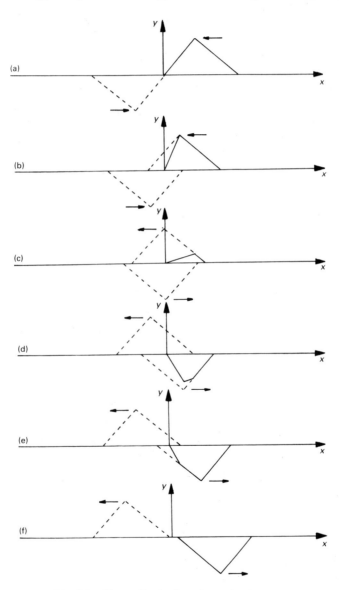

Fig. 6.5 — Wave reflection in a clamped string.

develops because of the restriction imposed at the origin. How is this latter function related to the original one? To understand this, we note that $g(x - ct)$

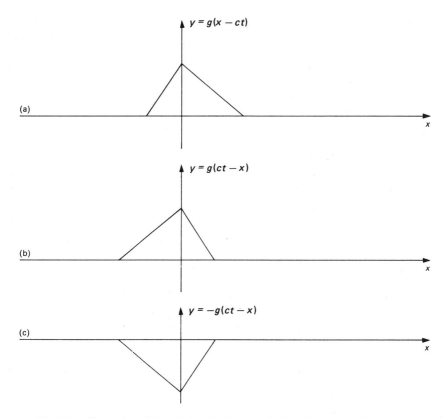

Fig. 6.6 – Illustration of the relationship between the functions $g(x - ct)$, $g(ct - x)$ and $-g(ct - x)$.

would be of exactly the same shape as $g(x + ct)$ but travelling in the opposite direction. It can also be noticed that $g(ct - x)$ is the same as $g(-\{x - ct\})$, so we are faced with the question of the relationship of $g(X)$ to $g(-X)$. A little thought will enable one to see that these functions are mirror images of one another, the line of reflection being the y-axis (Fig. 6.6b). Finally we note that there is a minus sign in front of $g(ct - x)$. This, of course, implies an additional reflection of the function about the x-axis (Fig. 6.6c).

Let us now summarize the consequences of the imposition of this boundary condition. The original wave incident on the boundary (namely $g(x + ct)$) is reflected back with an equal speed from the origin. Moreover the reflected wave is of the same shape as the incident wave, except that the shape is reversed left-to-right and has been turned upside down. This reflection process is very common in nature and, although we have taken as an example a particularly simple boundary condition, a great variety of such conditions have just this effect, that of producing a reflected wave. The details vary from one situation to another, but in most problems where the physical properties of the medium change, some form of reflection always takes place. It is the boundary condition at the surface of a mirror that causes it to reflect light waves, and it is a rather more complicated boundary condition at the bank of a river which causes the bank to reflect surface water waves. We shall examine several other kinds of boundary conditions later in the book.

6.5 PARTIAL REFLECTION

We have seen what happens when an incident wave arrives at a point on a stretched string which is securely clamped. In the ideal situation described, the profile is reflected without change of shape (apart from the inversion process). In this treatment, we implied that all energy in the incident wave appeared in the reflected wave — that is, there was no energy loss at the clamp. In practice, this would not, of course, be the case. Energy would be lost at the clamp (as well as during the progress of the wave along the string) and this would result in a change of shape in the reflected wave. The process becomes quite complicated to treat mathematically and this is why we have made the rather idealized assumptions in the previous section.

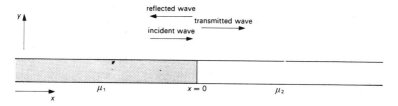

Fig. 6.7 — The junction of two stretched elastic strings. The arrows indicate the direction of travel of the transverse waves.

We will now go on to see what happens when the physical characteristics of the string change at some point. Suppose, for example, we have two stretched strings, both very long but of different mass per unit length, joined together as shown in Fig. 6.7. Let the join be at the point $x = 0$ and let the left- and right-hand strings have masses per unit length μ_1 and μ_2 respectively. Let us assume that a harmonic wave is sent along the left-hand string in the direction from left to right. We will use the exponential representation for harmonic waves which we discussed in section 4.3.

Let the incident wave be

$$y_i = A_i \exp i(\omega_i t - k_i x) \; . \tag{6.15}$$

Here, the suffix i indicates the incident wave, A_i is the amplitude (a real number); ω_i and k_i are, respectively, the circular frequency and the circular wavenumber of the wave.

What happens when this wave arrives at the junction at $x = 0$? Let us assume that part of the disturbance is transmitted into the second string, but that the other part is reflected back along the left-hand string. This is not begging the question as might at first appear. If, in fact, there is no wave reflected or no wave transmitted, our analysis will show this. We may, therefore, represent the transmitted and reflected waves quite generally as follows

$$y_t = A_t \exp i(\omega_t t - k_t x) \; , \tag{6.16}$$

$$y_r = A_r \exp i(\omega_r t + k_r x) \; , \tag{6.17}$$

where the suffixes t and r refer to the transmitted and reflected wave respectively (see Fig. 6.7). If it turns out that there are phase changes at the junction, A_t and A_r will prove to be complex quantities (or negative if the phase change is π).

Now by the principle of superposition, the total disturbance in the left-hand string will be the superposition of the incident and reflected waves. We can write this as

$$y_1 = y_i + y_r \; .$$

The total disturbance in the right-hand string is just the transmitted wave, so

$$y_2 = y_t \; .$$

Let us now examine the physical conditions which govern the values of y_1 and y_2 at the junction. Firstly, if the string does not come apart, the values of y_1 and y_2 must always be the same, so

$$(y_1)_{x=0} = (y_2)_{x=0}$$

or $$[y_i + y_r]_{x=0} = [y_t]_{x=0} \; . \tag{6.18}$$

The second condition is not so obvious. We saw in Chapter 5 that the transverse force acting at a point on a stretched string under tension T along which waves are travelling is $T(\partial y / \partial x)$. Now this latter quantity must be continuous along the string. Suppose for a moment that this is not so. Then for a given point on the string there would be a transverse force $T[\partial y / \partial x]_1$, say, due to the parts of the string to the left of the point, and a force $T[\partial y / \partial x]_2$, say, due to the parts of the string to the right of the point. So the net force on the point on the string would be $T\{[\partial y / \partial x]_2 - [\partial y / \partial x]_1\}$. But this force must be zero, otherwise infinite acceleration would be suffered by the infinitesimal mass comprised by the point. Therefore $[\partial y/\partial x]_1 = [\partial y/\partial x]_2$, and so $\partial y/\partial x$ is continuous along the string. So in addition to the boundary condition (6.18), we have the condition at the boundary

$$\left(\frac{\partial y_1}{\partial x}\right)_{x=0} = \left(\frac{\partial y_2}{\partial x}\right)_{x=0} . \tag{6.19}$$

Let us substitute the expressions for y_i, y_t and y_r (equations (6.15), (6.16) and (6.17)) into (6.18) putting $x = 0$. We get

$$A_i \exp i\omega_i t + A_r \exp i\omega_r t = A_t \exp i\omega_t t . \tag{6.20}$$

If we differentiate (6.15) with respect to x we get

$$\frac{\partial y_i}{\partial x} = - i k_i A_i \exp i(\omega_i t - k_i x) ,$$

with almost identical expressions for $\partial y_t/\partial x$ and $\partial y_r/\partial x$; if now substitute these into (6.19) putting $x = 0$, we get

$$- A_i k_i \exp i\omega_i t + A_r k_r \exp i\omega_r t = -A_t k_t \exp i\omega_t t . \tag{6.21}$$

Now equation 6.20 involves real and imaginary quantities, and it has to hold for all values of the time t. This can happen only if the exponential terms cancel out, which means that

$$\omega_i = \omega_r = \omega_t .$$

(We are here assuming that A_i, A_r and A_t are all finite).

This is a result that could be predicted physically, for it is clearly impossible for the frequency of the transmitted wave to be different from that of the incident wave, whilst ω_i and ω_r must be the same since they are determined by T and μ_1 only. We can now replace ω_i, ω_r and ω_t by the single quantity ω.

With this substitution, 6.20 becomes

$$A_i + A_r = A_t \tag{6.22}$$

and (6.21) becomes

$$A_i k_i - A_r k_r = A_t k_t . \tag{6.23}$$

Now we have seen that

$$c = \sqrt{\frac{T}{\mu}} = \frac{\omega}{k} .$$

Therefore $k_i = k_r$,

that is, the incident and reflected waves have the same circular wavenumber.

Also $\qquad k_i = \omega \sqrt{\dfrac{\mu_1}{T}}$ and $k_t = \omega \sqrt{\dfrac{\mu_2}{T}}$, (6.24)

We can rewrite (6.23) as

$$A_i k_i - A_r k_i = A_t k_t .$$ (6.25)

Solving the simultaneous equations (6.22) and (6.25) for A_t and A_r, we get

$$A_t = A_i \frac{2k_i}{k_i + k_t} ,$$ (6.26)

$$A_r = A_i \frac{k_i - k_t}{k_i + k_t} .$$ (6.27)

We now know the amplitudes of the reflected and transmitted waves in terms of the amplitude of the incident wave. Further, since the quantities on the right-hand sides of (6.26) and (6.27) are all real, A_t and A_r are both real numbers and there is no phase change involved, *except* when $k_t > k_i$ whereupon A_r has the opposite sign to A_i, indicating that the reflected wave has undergone a phase-change of π radians with respect to the incident wave.

Now we can introduce the tension and masses per unit length of the two parts of the string from equation (6.24).

When we do this we get

$$A_t = \frac{A_i \, 2\sqrt{\mu_1}}{\sqrt{\mu_1} + \sqrt{\mu_2}}$$

and $\qquad A_t = A_i \dfrac{\sqrt{\mu_1} - \sqrt{\mu_2}}{\sqrt{\mu_1} + \sqrt{\mu_2}}$,

so the change of phase on reflection occurs only when $\mu_2 > \mu_1$, that is, when the mass per unit length of the string on the right is greater than that on the left.

Example 6.1
Reflection of a wave on a transmission line terminated by a resistance R

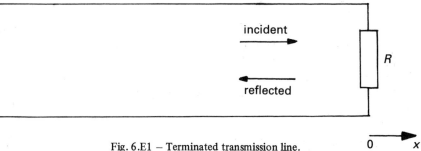

Fig. 6.E1 – Terminated transmission line.

In section 5.6 it was shown how a transmission line (for example, two parallel wires or a coaxial cable) carries voltage (and current) waves. The speed is $\sqrt{(1/LC)}$, where L and C are respectively the inductance and capacitance per unit length.

Consider a sinusoidal wave travelling along the line. The voltage can be represented by $V = A \exp j(\omega t \mp kx)$, the sign ($\mp$) depending on the direction of travel. Note that we have used j to denote $\sqrt{-1}$ to avoid confusion with i, which denotes current.

The reader will easily verify from (5.29) or (5.30) that

$$\sqrt{\frac{L}{C}} \; i = A \exp j(\omega t \mp kx)$$

since the wave speed $\omega/k = \sqrt{(1/LC)}$.

The quantity $\sqrt{(L/C)}$ is called the *characteristic impedance* of the line, denoted Z_0.

If the incident and reflected waves have amplitudes A and A' respectively, we have therefore

$$V = A \exp j(\omega t - kx) + A' \exp j(\omega t + kx)$$

$$Z_0 i = A \exp j(\omega t - kx) - A' \exp j(\omega t + kx) \; .$$

Now at the termination $x = 0$, the boundary condition is, from Ohm's law, $V = iR$, and therefore

$$\frac{A + A'}{A - A'} = \frac{R}{Z_0}$$

or $$\frac{A'}{A} = \frac{R - Z_0}{R + Z_0} \; .$$

Examination of this result illustrates some important points concerning wave motion, which are applicable in general and not merely to the particular case of waves on a transmission line.

(i) If $R < Z_0$, A' and A are of opposite sign, i.e. reflection is accompanied by a change in phase of $180°$. Indeed, this is the behaviour of any kind of wave which is incident upon a 'denser' medium.

Likewise, if $R > Z_0$, reflection occurs with no phase change, and this is found to be so for any wave incident upon a 'more rarefied' medium.

(ii) If $R = 0$ or $R = \infty$, the amplitude of the reflected wave equals that of the incident wave. This is not surprising since there is no dissipation of power in the resistance in either case; therefore all the incident power is reflected.

(iii) If $R = Z_0$, there is no reflected wave. The load resistance is said to be 'matched' to the line. Under this condition, maximum power is transferred from the line into the resistance.

(iv) The existence of two waves travelling in opposite directions gives rise to a standing wave. But it should be noted that since $|A'|$ is not in general equal to A, we do not in general have points of *no* disturbance, but rather a *minimum* disturbance. Clearly, there are points (Fig. 6.E2) where the two waves are in phase, and the voltage has its maximum amplitude $A + |A'|$. Midway between these, they are in antiphase, and the voltage has its minimum amplitude $A - |A'|$. At the termination $x = 0$, V is a maximum if $R > Z_0$, and a minimum if $R < Z_0$.

An important quantity in electrical engineering is the *voltage standing wave ratio*, which is $\dfrac{A + |A'|}{A - |A'|}$.

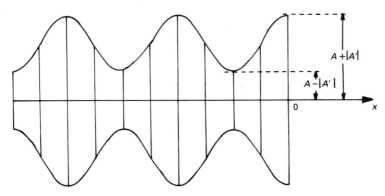

Fig. 6.E2 – Standing wave pattern.

6.6 ENERGY IN A TRAVELLING WAVE

We now consider briefly the propagation of energy in a wave, taking transverse waves on a string as our example.

In the absence of a wave, the kinetic energy is zero since no particle in the string has any velocity, and, since we can choose the zero of potential energy arbitrarily, we will assume that the potential energy is also zero. When a travelling wave of transverse displacement $y(x,t)$ is being propagated along the string, the latter is stretched locally, thus acquiring potential energy. Fig. 6.8 shows an infinitesimal length of the string, from which we see that a section of the string, which in the absence of a wave is of length dx, has now a length ds. The section has thus been stretched by a amount $ds - dx$. The constant force exerted during this stretching is T, the tension in the string, and thus the potential energy dE_P acquired by the length is

$$dE_P = T(ds - dx) \ ,$$

which, by reference to Fig. 6.8, becomes

$$dE_P = T[(dx^2 + dy^2)^{1/2} - dx]$$

$$= T \, dx \left[\left\{ 1 + \left(\frac{\partial y}{\partial x} \right)^2 \right\}^{1/2} - 1 \right].$$

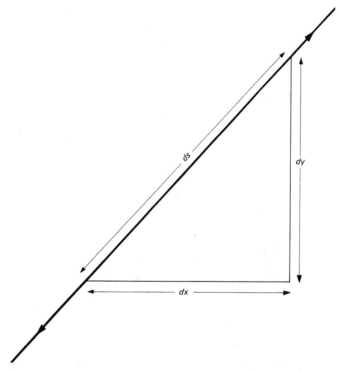

Fig. 6.8 – A section of stretched string while a transverse wave (upward displacement) is being propagated horizontally, showing the relationship between ds, dy and dx.

By the binomial theorem this finally becomes, approximately,

$$dE_P = \tfrac{1}{2} T \left(\frac{\partial y}{\partial x} \right)^2 dx .$$

(6.28)

The kinetic energy dE_K of the element is

$$dE_K = \tfrac{1}{2} \text{ (mass of element)} \times \text{(velocity of element)}^2$$

$$= \tfrac{1}{2} \mu \, dx \left(\frac{\partial y}{\partial t} \right)^2 .$$

(6.29)

If we denote the total energy of the element by dE, we see from (6.28) and (6.29) that

$$dE = \frac{dx}{2}\left[\mu\left(\frac{\partial y}{\partial t}\right)^2 + T\left(\frac{\partial y}{\partial x}\right)^2\right].$$

We now define the *energy density*, $D(x,t)$ as the energy per unit length. Thus

$$D(x,t) = \frac{1}{2}\left[\mu\left(\frac{\partial y}{\partial t}\right)^2 + T\left(\frac{\partial y}{\partial x}\right)^2\right]. \tag{6.30}$$

Let us calculate D for the harmonic wave represented by

$$y = A\cos(kx - \omega t) . \tag{6.31}$$

If we differentiate (6.31) partially and substitute into (6.30) we obtain

$$D(x,t) = \frac{A^2}{2}\sin^2(kx - \omega t)\,[\mu\omega^2 + Tk^2]$$

$$= \frac{\mu A^2}{2}\sin^2(kx - \omega t)\left[\omega^2 + \frac{T}{\mu}k^2\right].$$

Since $T/\mu = c^2$ the contents of the square bracket become $[\omega^2 + c^2 k^2]$, which, since $\omega^2 = c^2 k^2$ finally becomes $2\omega^2$. Thus

$$D(x,t) = \mu A^2 \omega^2 \sin^2(kx - \omega t) . \tag{6.32}$$

So we see that the energy in the wave is propagated as the function of $(kx - \omega t)$ described in the right-hand side of (6.32); it is thus propagated with the speed $\omega/k = c$ of the displacement wave.

Actually, the circular frequency ω and circular wavenumber k of the displacement wave are not those of the energy-density wave. Since

$$\sin^2\theta = \tfrac{1}{2}(1 - \cos 2\theta) ,$$

it follows that

$$D(x,t) = \frac{\mu A^2}{2}\omega^2[1 - \cos(2kx - 2\omega t)] . \tag{6.33}$$

Thus the energy-density wave propagates with a frequency twice that of the displacement wave and a wavelength of half that of the displacement wave, but, as mentioned above, the *velocity* is the same as that of the displacement wave. The spatial part of the energy-density and displacement waves are shown in Fig. 6.9.

The energy in length dx is $D(x,t)dx$, and therefore the energy in one wavelength is

$$\int_0^\lambda D(x,t)dx \ ,$$

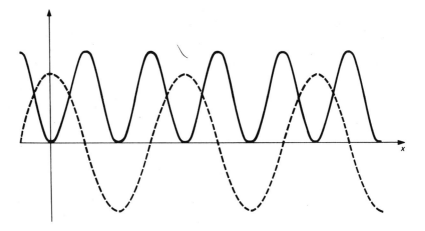

Fig. 6.9 — The dotted line represents the profile of the displacement wave (6.31), and the solid line the corresponding energy-density wave (6.32) for time $t = 0$. The scales of the ordinates are arbitrary.

which, from (6.33), becomes

$$\int_0^\lambda \frac{\mu A^2}{2}\, \omega^2[1 - \cos(2kx - 2\omega t)]\, dx \ .$$

The integral of the cosine term is zero; and the energy contained in a wavelength is thus

$$\int_0^\lambda \frac{\mu A^2}{2}\, \omega^2\, dx = \frac{\mu A^2 \omega^2 \lambda}{2} \ .$$

Now this energy takes a time equal to the period λ/c to pass a given point. Therefore the energy flowing per unit time (the power P) is given by

$$P = \frac{\mu A^2 \omega^2 c}{2} \ .$$

We see, therefore, that the power transmitted by the wave is proportional to the square of the amplitude and the square of the frequency. A similar result obtains for many other types of harmonic wave, including sound waves. That light intensity is proportional to the square of the amplitude of the disturbance is an analogous result which will be used in Chapter 11.

6.7 WAVEGUIDES

Chapter 5 concluded with some physical examples of wave transmission. Now that we have covered standing waves, we are in a position to consider another important example — namely the waveguide. The most usual meaning of the term 'waveguide' is a metallic tube having rectangular cross-section of the order of a few cm^2, through which electromagnetic waves in the microwave region flow. There are, however, other familiar examples of guided waves. Large houses built before the invention of the telephone were frequently equipped with 'speaking tubes'. A tube such as a hose-pipe provides a very efficient guide for acoustic waves and enables conversations to be conducted over a distance of many metres. The medical stethoscope is another example of an acoustic waveguide.

A modern example of guided waves is to be found in fibre optics; a light wave may be transmitted along a thin glass fibre over a distance of several km with little attenuation. Optical fibre transmission has several advantages over traditional electrical cable in the field of communications, and has recently begun to be used in the British telephone system.

In the present context, we use the term 'waveguide' to mean any kind of enclosure or container within which a wave may flow. The simplest example to treat mathematically is that of a pair of infinite parallel planes, the wave being contained entirely between them. Though hardly a convincing physical example, it does bring out the essential physics of waveguides, and the results we shall obtain are applicable to other forms of waveguide.

The waveguide is shown in Fig. 6.10 and consists of two infinite parallel planes a distance a apart; the upper plane is along $y = 0$ and lower along $y = -a$. A monochromatic plane wave of circular wavevector $\mathbf{k}$ is incident on the upper plane as shown. The axes are chosen so that $\mathbf{k}$ lies in the Oxy plane and therefore has no z component. The wave may be of any kind in which the disturbance can be described by a scalar quantity ϕ, for example a sound wave. We represent this incident wave by the exponential form of (4.36):

$$\phi_1 = A_1 \exp i(\mathbf{k} \cdot \mathbf{r} - \omega t) . \tag{6.34}$$

The wave produced by reflection at the plane at $y = 0$ can likewise be represented by

$$\phi_2 = A_2 \exp i(\mathbf{k}' \cdot \mathbf{r} - \omega t) . \tag{6.35}$$

We make no supposition about the direction of $\mathbf{k}'$ except that it has to be 'generally downward' as shown in Fig. 6.10. The resultant disturbance within the space between the two planes is given by the principle of superposition (section 6.4); we simply add (6.34) and (6.35) to obtain

$$\Phi = \phi_1 + \phi_2 = A_1 \exp i(\mathbf{k} \cdot \mathbf{r} - \omega t) + A_2 \exp i(\mathbf{k}' \cdot \mathbf{r} - \omega t) \ . \tag{6.36}$$

If we express $\mathbf{k}$ and $\mathbf{k}'$ in terms of their components as in section 4.4.2, (6.36) becomes

$$\Phi = A_1 \exp i[k_x x + k_y y - \omega t] + A_2 \exp i[k_x' x + k_y' y + k_z' z - \omega t] \ . \tag{6.37}$$

The plane at $y = 0$ imposes the boundary condition $\Phi = 0$ when $y = 0$ for all values of t — in particular $t = 0$. Applying these in (6.37) we have

$$A_1 \exp i[k_x x] + A_2 \exp i[k_x' x + k_z' z] = 0 \ . \tag{6.38}$$

Now (6.38) must be true for all values of z, which can be so only if

$$k_z' = 0 \ . \tag{6.39}$$

We see at once that $\mathbf{k}'$ must lie in the Oxy plane.

Again, since (6.38) must be true for all values of x, we must have

$$k_x = k_x' \tag{6.40}$$

therefore

$$A_1 = -A_2 \ . \tag{6.41}$$

Now $|\mathbf{k}| = |\mathbf{k}'|$ since the wavelength, and hence $|\mathbf{k}|$, are determined solely by the medium for a wave of given frequency. It follows from (6.39) and (6.40) that

$$k_y = -k_y' \ . \tag{6.41a}$$

We reject the solution $k_y = k_y'$ as being inconsistent with the physics of the problem — see Fig. 6.10.

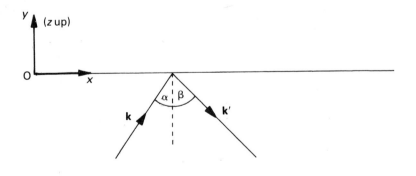

Fig. 6.10 — A waveguide consisting of two infinite parallel reflecting planes at $y = 0$ and $y = -a$.

Thus the component of the circular wavevector **k** parallel to the reflection plane is unaltered on reflection, but that perpendicular to the plane is reversed. This requires that both wave normals make the same angle with the plane normal, so that $\alpha = \beta$ in Fig. 6.10. This is the law of reflection, which is treated further in Chapter 11.

Substituting (6.39), (6.40), (6.41) and (6.41a) into (6.37) and writing $A_1 = A$, we have

$$\Phi = A \exp i(k_x x + k_y y - \omega t) - A \exp i(k_x x - k_y y - \omega t)$$

$$= 2Ai \sin k_y y \exp i(k_x x - \omega t) . \qquad (6.42)$$

So (6.42) describes in complex exponential form the resultant wave in the space between the two planes at $y = 0$ and $y = -a$; there is no need to take the real part of (6.42) for the interpretation we now make.

The presence of the plane at $y = -a$ imposes a further boundary condition on (6.42); when $y = -a$, $\Phi = 0$ so

$$\sin (k_y a) = 0$$

no matter what value x has.

Thus $k_y a = \pm n \pi$

or $k_y = \pm \dfrac{n \pi}{a}$ where $n = 0, 1, 2 \ldots$ \qquad (6.43)

The only allowed values of k_y are those given by (6.43).

We can now give a full physical interpretation of the wave given by (6.42). We recognise $\exp i(k_x x - \omega t)$ as describing a travelling wave propagating in the x direction. The amplitude of the disturbance propagated is given by $2A \sin(n\pi y/a)$ and therefore varies in the y direction. Sketches showing the form of this variation are given in Fig. 6.11, and these follow rather obviously from the above expression.

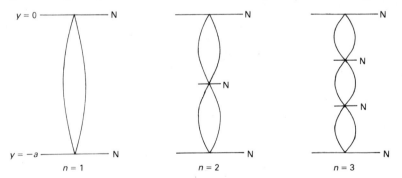

Fig. 6.11 – Variation of $\sin(n\pi y/a)$ with y for $n = 1, 2,$ and 3. The nodal planes (i.e. the planes of zero disturbance at all times) are indicated by N.

Thus we have a wave which is a *travelling* wave in the x direction but shows the characteristics of a *standing* wave in the y direction. An interesting feature of this wave is that not all frequencies may be propagated, for

$$k^2 = k_x{}^2 + k_y{}^2 ,$$

so, by (6.43), $\quad \dfrac{\omega^2}{c^2} = k_x{}^2 + \dfrac{n^2\pi^2}{a^2} \qquad\qquad (6.44)$

where $c = \omega/k$ is the wave speed

and hence $\quad k_x = \sqrt{\dfrac{\omega^2}{c^2} - \dfrac{n^2\pi^2}{a^2}}$.

Thus only waves of frequency greater than $c/2a$ may be guided.

A second interesting feature is that the wave travels with a speed greater than that of the original incident wave. The speed of the wave of (6.42) is $c' = \omega/k_x$; thus $c' > c$ since $k_x < k$, k_x being a component of **k**.

This is at first a somewhat puzzling result when applied to electromagnetic waves, since it would seem to imply a speed greater than that of light. But if we may anticipate a result from section 9.2, namely that the speed at which energy is propagated is given by the group velocity

$$c_g = d\omega/dk , \qquad\qquad [9.7]$$

we see by differentiating (6.44) that

$$c_g = \frac{d\omega}{dk_x} = \frac{c^2 k_x}{\omega} ,$$

hence $\qquad c' c_g = c^2 , \qquad\qquad (6.45)$

Thus while the phase velocity c' is greater than c, it follows from (6.45) that the group velocity c_g is less than c.

The above treatment can be adapted fairly readily for enclosed waveguides of rectangular cross-section, and with rather more difficulty for guides of circular cross-section. What is found in both cases is a progressive wave along the guide but with standing-wave characteristics in transverse directions. But the main essentials of waveguides are brought out by the simplified treatment we have given.

PROBLEMS

(6.1) By plotting rough sketches, investigate the behaviour of a disturbance of the same shape as that given in Fig. 6.5, which is reflected at a boundary *without* inversion. [(6.27), with $k_i \gg k_t$, shows that this can occur.]

(6.2) Use the computer program (appendix A) to display standing waves (A.8(e)). Experiment with various values of the circular wavenumber and wave speed. Note the existence of nodes and antinodes.

Observe the effect of changing the amplitude of one of the waves to half of that of the other. The resulting disturbance will look somewhat like a travelling wave, but it still shows points of maximum and minimum amplitude.

(6.3) Deduce, from equations (6.26), (6.27), and $P = 2\pi^2\mu A^2f^2c$, the fractional power transmitted (T) and reflected (R) at the junction in Fig. 6.7. Show that $T + R = 1$.

(6.4) Two stretched strings are joined, the masses per unit length being 0.01 kg m^{-1} and 0.04 kg m^{-1}. A sinusoidal wave of amplitude A is propagated along the first towards the join. Deduce the amplitude of (i) the transmitted wave, (ii) the reflected wave. What fraction of the incident energy is transmitted and reflected? Is there a phase change of the reflected wave?

Sketch the shape of the strings at the moment of maximum displacement of the join.

(6.5) Using the ideas developed in discussing the terminated transmission line, suggest a reason why a tuning fork vibrating in air transmits very little power to the air, but sounds loud if its stem is held rigidly against a large solid bench. (See also section 10.4).

(6.6) A coaxial cable has a characteristic impedance of 80 Ω. Assuming that waves travel along it with a speed 1.5×10^8 m s^{-1}, calculate the inductance and capacitance per unit length.

(6.7) A transmission line with characteristic impedance 50 Ω is terminated by a resistance 10 Ω. Is there a phase inversion on reflection? Determine the fraction of the incident power absorbed and reflected. Deduce the voltage standing wave ratio.

(6.8) Consider the problem of a longitudinal wave in a fluid impinging upon a boundary with a second fluid. If z is the displacement amplitude, show that $\rho c^2(\partial z/\partial x)$ is the same on both sides of the boundary, where ρ is the density and c is the wave speed. Hence write down the equations analagous to (6.26) and (6.27).

CHAPTER 7

Fourier's theorem

7.1 INTRODUCTION AND MATHEMATICAL DISCUSSION

The theorem of J. B. J. Fourier, in various guises, is an important proposition in physics. It is probably true to say that there is no branch of the subject which this theorem has not illuminated in some significant way or other. Although it finds its main use in studies involving wave motion, Fourier first introduced it (in 1822) in connection with the problem of heat conduction, in which subject is still occupies a prominent position. These two applications themselves illustrate the diversity of situations to which it has been applied.

Fourier's theorem is essentially a trigonometrical relationship which can be applied to a large class of mathematical functions, of which periodic functions provide the simplest examples. We will deal with periodic functions first, and later on in this chapter go on to non-periodic functions.

Mathematically, a periodic function of time $g(t)$, of period T, is a function which has the property that

$$g(t + T) = g(t) \ ,$$

for all values of t. By a simple iteration of this expression one can see that

$$g(t + NT) = g(t) \ ,$$

for all t, where N is any integer, positive, negative or zero. It necessarily follows that the function extends infinitely along the positive and negative t-axes.

Figure 7.1 illustrates some periodic functions, each of the same period T; in particular, Fig. 7.1a illustrates the function

$$y(t) = A \cos \left(\frac{2\pi t}{T} + \phi \right)$$

plotted against time. The profile of this is sinusoidal, the amplitude is A and the phase constant ϕ determines how far the first maximum is away from the origin.

If we substitute f_0 for $1/T$, the equation becomes

$$y(t) = A \cos(2\pi f_0 t + \phi) \tag{7.1}$$

Now Fourier's theorem states that *any* periodic function $g(t)$ can be expressed as the sum (to an infinite number of terms if necessary) of functions of the type appearing in equation (7.1), where the frequencies appropriate to each term in the sum are integral multiples, nf_0, of f_0 and the amplitudes A and phases ϕ are,

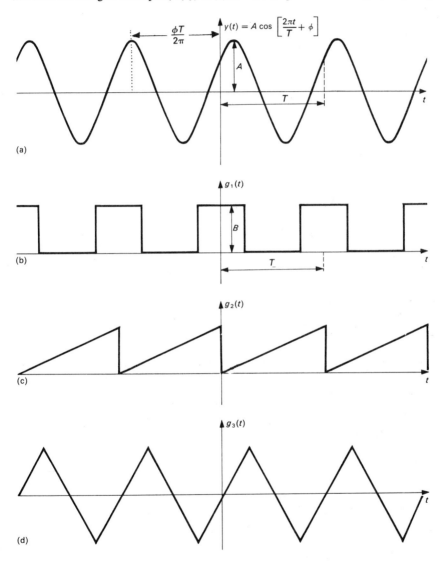

Fig. 7.1 – Some periodic functions of time.

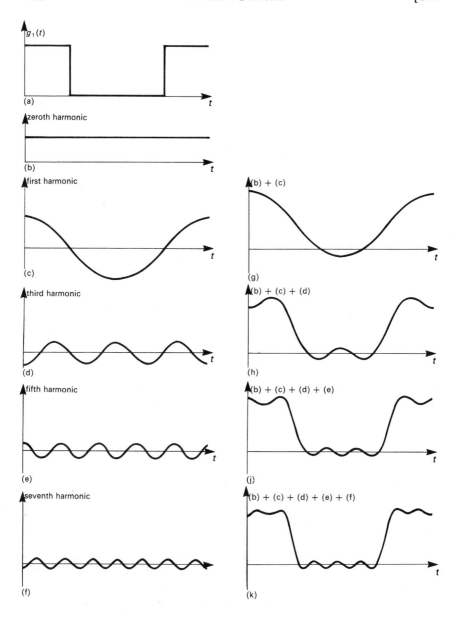

Fig. 7.2 – Illustration of Fourier's theorem. One period of the function illustrated in Fig. 7.1b appears in (a). The curves (b) – (f) on the left-hand side show the first five frequency components into which (a) is analysed. On the right-hand side, (g) – (k) are shown successive stages in the addition of the components in the synthesis of the original function. The last curve (k) is seen to be a reasonable approximation to (a) after the addition of only five terms.

in general, different for different values of n. The theorem implies that any periodic function of time can be *analysed* into *frequency components*; alternatively the original function can be *synthesized* by summing these frequency components. Fig. 7.2 illustrates these processes of analysis and synthesis for the periodic function shown in Fig. 7.1b.

Expressed in mathematical terms, Fourier's Theorem asserts that, for a periodic function of fundamental frequency f_0,

$$g(t) = \sum_{n=0}^{\infty} A_n \cos(2\pi n f_0 t + \phi_n) , \qquad (7.2)$$

where the suffixes on the As and the ϕs denote that these latter belong to a particular n.

If we wish to Fourier-analyse a given periodic function, our problem essentially is to determine the values of the amplitudes A_n, and phases ϕ_n, for each of its frequency components. We begin by expressing a typical term of the sum, namely

$$A_n \cos(2\pi n f_0 t + \phi_n) ,$$

as $\qquad A_n \cos(2\pi n f_0 t)\cos \phi_n - A_n \sin(2\pi n f_0 t)\sin \phi_n .$

This can be slightly rearranged to

$$(A_n \cos \phi_n)\cos 2\pi n f_0 t - (A_n \sin \phi_n)\sin 2\pi n f_0 t ,$$

where those terms which are independent of time have been collected together in brackets. For convenience we can replace these terms respectively by C_n and $- S_n$, so the expression becomes

$$C_n \cos 2\pi n f_0 t + S_n \sin 2\pi n f_0 t .$$

Thus, from 7.2,

$$g(t) = \sum_{n=0}^{\infty} C_n \cos 2\pi n f_0 t + \sum_{n=0}^{\infty} S_n \sin 2\pi n f_0 t . \qquad (7.3)$$

Our problem of finding the A_n and ϕ_n appropriate to a particular periodic function $g(t)$ has now become that of finding the C_n and S_n.

Now, concentrating our attention on a particular value of n, say m, we multiply (7.3) throughout by $\cos 2\pi m f_0 t$ and integrate with respect to t over a whole period, obtaining

$$\int_{-1/2f_0}^{+1/2f_0} \cos(2\pi m f_0 t)g(t)\, dt = \int_{-1/2f_0}^{+1/2f_0} \cos(2\pi m f_0 t)\left(\sum_{n=0}^{\infty} C_n \cos 2\pi n f_0 t \right) dt$$

$$+ \int_{-1/2f_0}^{+1/2f_0} \cos(2\pi m f_0 t)\left(\sum_{n=0}^{\infty} S_n \sin 2\pi n f_0 t \; dt \right) \qquad (7.4)$$

where the range of the integral (from $-1/2f_0$ to $+1/2f_0$) has been expressed in terms of f_0. Equation (7.4) appears very long and cumbersome, but we shall now see that remarkable simplifications can be effected on the right hand side. A typical term in the first integral on the right-hand side is

$$C_n \int_{-1/2f_0}^{+1/2f_0} \cos(2\pi m f_0 t) \cos 2\pi n f_0 t \, dt \qquad (7.5)$$

and similarly a typical term in the second integral is

$$S_n \int_{-1/2f_0}^{+1/2f_0} \cos(2\pi m f_0 t) \sin 2\pi n f_0 t \, dt \, , \qquad (7.6)$$

the quantities C_n and S_n being brought outside the integral sign because they are constants. Let us take (7.5) first, and suppose $m \neq n$. A little thought will reveal that the value of the integral is zero. Figure 7.3 illustrates this for the case $m = 4$ and $n = 3$, where the first two graphs are those of the two individual cosine

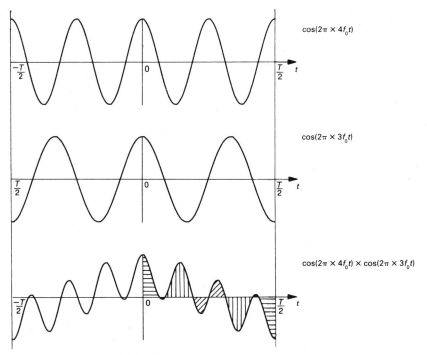

Fig. 7.3 – An illustration showing that

$$\int_{-1/2f_0}^{+1/2f_0} \cos(2\pi \times 3f_0 t) \cos(2\pi \times 4f_0 t) \, dt = 0 \, .$$

terms and the third graph is that of their product. Half the area of the third graph has been shaded with four different shadings; it will be noticed that each type of shading occurs twice, once for a positive area (above the time axis) and once for an equal negative area (below the axis). All the positive areas therefore have equal negative counterparts, producing a zero overall value.

Continuing with our consideration of the expression (7.5), and taking the case where $n = m$, we see that the expression now becomes

$$C_m \int_{-1/2f_0}^{+1/2f_0} \cos^2 2\pi m f_0 t \, dt$$

which can easily be shown to be equal to

$$\frac{1}{2f_0} C_m \; ,$$

provided m is not zero. If m is zero, then the expression becomes

$$C_0 \int_{-1/2f_0}^{+1/2f_0} dt \; ,$$

which is $\dfrac{1}{f_0} C_0$.

Coming now to expression (7.6) we have to evaluate

$$\int_{-1/2f_0}^{+1/2f_0} \cos (2\pi m f_0 t) \sin 2\pi n f_0 t \, dt \; ,$$

which can easily be shown to be equal to zero regardless of whether $m = n$ or not. (It is suggested that the reader try this.)

So (7.4) which initially looked rather formidable, has been reduced to

$$\int_{-1/2f_0}^{+1/2f_0} g(t) \cos (2\pi m f_0 t) \, dt = \frac{1}{2f_0} C_m$$

when $m \neq 0$, and to

$$\int_{-1/2f_0}^{+1/2f_0} g(t) \, dt = \frac{1}{f_0} C_0$$

when $m = 0$.

This gives us values for the C_m as follows:

$$C_m = 2f_0 \int_{-1/2f_0}^{+1/2f_0} g(t) \cos 2\pi m f_0 t \, dt, \quad m \neq 0 ,$$

$$C_0 = f_0 \int_{-1/2f_0}^{+1/2f_0} g(t) \, dt .$$

(7.7)

If we had started from (7.3) by multiplying by $\sin 2\pi m f_0 t$ instead of $\cos 2\pi m f_0 t$, we would, by a precisely similar argument, have arrived at the conclusion that

$$S_m = 2f_0 \int_{-1/2f_0}^{+1/2f_0} g(t) \sin 2\pi m f_0 t \, dt .$$

(7.8)

(So, unlike C_0, S_0 is always zero, since the integral vanishes for $m = 0$.) Equations (7.7) and (7.8) tell us how to find the coefficients C_n and S_n corresponding to a given periodic function $g(t)$, and hence enable us to perform the frequency analysis of any such function.

Example 7.1
Fourier analysis of a square wave
Let us take as a concrete example a function of period $T(= 1/f_0)$ which has a value of B in the range $-\alpha T/2 < t < + \alpha T/2$ and of zero elsewhere in the range $-T/2$ to $+ T/2$. Here, α is the proportion of the period for which the function has the non-zero value of B. The function is illustrated in Fig. 7.1b for $\alpha = \frac{1}{2}$. Equation (7.7) (for $m \neq 0$) becomes

$$C_m = 2f_0 \int_{-\frac{\alpha T}{2}}^{\frac{\alpha T}{2}} B \cos (2\pi m f_0 t) \, dt$$

$$= 2f_0 B \left[\frac{\sin 2\pi m f_0 t}{2\pi m f_0} \right]_{-\frac{\alpha T}{2}}^{\frac{\alpha T}{2}}$$

$$= \frac{2B}{\pi m} \sin(\pi m \alpha)$$

Taking, as an example, $\alpha = 3/4$ and substituting $m = 1, 2, 3, \ldots$ into this last result, we obtain

$$C_1 = \frac{2B}{\pi\sqrt{2}}$$

$$C_2 = -\frac{B}{\pi}$$

$$C_3 = \frac{2B}{3\pi\sqrt{2}}$$

$$C_4 = 0$$

$$C_5 = -\frac{2B}{5\pi\sqrt{2}}$$

$$C_6 = \frac{2B}{6\pi}$$

$$C_7 = -\frac{2B}{7\pi\sqrt{2}}$$

$$C_8 = 0 \ .$$

From the second of equations (7.7), C_0 is seen to be αB.

Having now found the C_m, let us turn our attention to finding the S_m, from (7.8). With the same limits of integration as before (7.8) gives

$$S_m = 2f_0 \int_{-\frac{\alpha T}{2}}^{+\frac{\alpha T}{2}} B \sin 2\pi m f_0 t \ dt$$

$$= -2f_0 B \left[\frac{\cos 2\pi m f_0 t}{2\pi m f_0} \right]_{-\frac{\alpha T}{2}}^{+\frac{\alpha T}{2}}$$

$$= 0 \quad \text{for all } m \ .$$

In the example just considered, the S_m were all zero. In fact this is so far *any* periodic function which is also *even* — that is to say, any function $g(t)$ where

$$g(-t) = g(t) \ .$$

The function we have taken, is clearly even. In a similar way, any odd function, i.e. any function for which

$$g(t) = -g(-t) \ ,$$

produces zero C_m. Figure 7.1(d) illustrates such a function.

The C_m for the function which is our example (with $\alpha = 3/4$) can now be displayed in graphical form by vertical lines plotted along an abscissa representing frequency, whose heights are proportional to the C_m. The result is shown in Fig. 7.E1.

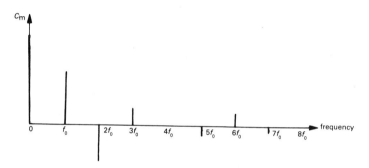

Fig. 7.E1 – Frequency sprectrum of the function of period T, of value B in the range $-\alpha T/2 < t < +\alpha T/2$ and zero elsewhere.

The frequency f_0 is termed the *fundamental frequency* or, alternatively, the *first harmonic*. The frequency $2f_0$ is termed the *second harmonic*; $3f_0$ is the *third harmonic* and so on. In the particular case of $\alpha = \frac{1}{2}$, it is interesting to note that even harmonics have zero amplitude; they are said to be 'missing'.

Before we leave the subject of the mathematical aspects of the Fourier analysis of periodic functions, there is one important step to be taken. It turns out that Fourier's theorem can be recast, with considerable advantage, into a form involving exponentials with imaginary exponents. We will now do this, and see the advantage it brings.

We started out with the representation of a periodic function (7.2):

$$g(t) = \sum_{n=0}^{\infty} A_n \cos(2\pi n f_0 t + \phi_n) \ . \tag{7.2}$$

Let us, instead, try the representation

$$\boxed{g(t) = \sum_{n=-\infty}^{\infty} G_n \exp(2\pi i n f_0 t)} \tag{7.9}$$

where the G_n are, in general, complex, and see if this is consistent with (7.2).

The terms in (7.9) may be grouped in the following way:

$$g(t) = G_0 + [G_1 \exp(2\pi i f_0 t) + G_{-1} \exp(-2\pi i f_0 t)]$$
$$+ [G_2 \exp(2\pi i 2 f_0 t) + G_{-2} \exp(-2\pi i 2 f_0 t)]$$
$$+ \ldots + [G_n \exp(2\pi i n f_0 t) + G_{-n} \exp(-2\pi i n f_0 t)] + \ldots$$

$$= G_0 + \sum_{n=1}^{\infty} [G_n \exp(2\pi i n f_0 t) + G_{-n} \exp(-2\pi i n f_0 t)] . \qquad (7.10)$$

Now suppose that, for all n, $G_n = \frac{1}{2} A_n \exp(i\phi_n)$ and $G_{-n} = \frac{1}{2} A_n \exp(-i\phi_n)$, where the A_n are real. Then (7.10) becomes

$$g(t) = G_0 + \frac{1}{2} \sum_{n=1}^{\infty} [A_n \exp 2\pi i(n f_0 t + \phi_n) + A_n \exp -2\pi i(n f_0 t + \phi_n)]$$

$$= G_0 + \sum_{n=1}^{\infty} A_n \cos(2\pi n f_0 t + \phi_n)$$

by virtue of the fact that

$$\cos\theta = \frac{1}{2} [\exp(i\theta) + \exp(-i\theta)] .$$

If we now make $G_0 = A_0 \cos\phi_0$ we finally obtain

$$g(t) = \sum_{n=0}^{\infty} A_n \cos(2\pi n f_0 t + \phi_n)$$

which is (7.2). Thus the trigonometrical (7.2) and exponential (7.9) represent-actions of a periodic function are identical, with G_n and A_n related as above, i.e. we interpret $|G_n|$ as half the amplitude of the nth harmonic in the trigonometrical representation and arg G_n as the phase angle.

It may be remarked that the use of complex numbers in (7.9) is different from that in Chapter 3. For a mathematically real signal $g(t)$, the right-hand side of (7.9) has, of course, to be real in order for it to equal the left-hand side. But how can it be real when each term in the series of (7.9) is complex? The answer lies in the fact that the sum of the nth and $-n$th terms is real for all non-zero n, and the term for $n = 0$ is also real. The right-hand side of (7.9) is therefore actually equal to the real quantity $g(t)$. This is in contrast to the applications of exponentials with complex exponents discussed in previous chapters, where the physical quantity being represented is a component (usually the real part) of the exponential.

Equation (7.9) is the complex form of Fourier's theorem, where the components are of negative as well as positive frequencies. The concept of negative frequencies may give some difficulty, but this is due to the way in which we are now analysing $g(t)$. Previously the frequency components were of the form $\cos 2\pi n f_0 t$ and $\sin 2\pi n f_0 t$ which, because n is non-negative, were always considered as of positive frequency. But each cosine (or sine) term can be regarded as having both a positive- and negative-frequency component since

$$\cos 2\pi n f_0 t = \tfrac{1}{2}[\exp 2\pi i n f_0 t + \exp(-2\pi i n f_0 t)]$$

(with a similar identity for $\sin 2\pi n f_0 t$), and now that we are *explicitly* using exponential functions we have to include components of negative frequencies.

To obtain the complex coefficients G_n we proceed much as we did previously to obtain S_n and C_n. We multiply (7.9) by

$$\exp(-2\pi i m f_0 t)\, dt \ ,$$

where m is an integer (this time positive, negative or zero), and integrate over a whole period of the function $g(t)$ to obtain

$$\int_{-1/2f_0}^{+1/2f_0} g(t)\exp(-2\pi i m f_0 t)\, dt = \int_{-1/2f_0}^{+1/2f_0} \exp(-2\pi i m f_0 t) \sum_{n=-\infty}^{\infty} G_n \exp 2\pi i n f_0 t\, dt \ .$$

$$(7.11)$$

A typical term on the right-hand side of (7.11) is

$$G_n \int_{-1/2f_0}^{+1/2f_0} \exp 2\pi i (n-m) f_0 t\, dt = G_n \left[\frac{\exp 2\pi i (n-m) f_0 t}{2\pi i (n-m) f_0} \right]_{-1/2f_0}^{+1/2f_0}$$

$$= \frac{G_n}{2\pi i (n-m) f_0}\, [\exp i\pi(n-m) - \exp\{-i\pi(n-m)\}]$$

$$= \frac{G_n}{\pi(n-m) f_0}\, \frac{\exp i\pi(n-m) - \exp\{-i\pi(n-m)\}}{2i}$$

and, since $\dfrac{\exp i\theta - \exp(-i\theta)}{2i} = \sin\theta$,

this becomes $\dfrac{G_n}{\pi(n-m) f_0} \sin \pi(n-m) = 0$ if $n-m \neq 0$.

So we see, as before, that if $n-m$ is not equal to zero a typical term on the right-hand side of (7.11) is zero. For the case $n-m = 0$, we note that, since $\sin\theta \to \theta$ as $\theta \to 0$,

$$\frac{G_n}{\pi(n-m) f_0} \sin \pi(n-m) \to \frac{G_n}{\pi(n-m) f_0} \pi(n-m) = \frac{G_n}{f_0} \ .$$

Thus (7.11) becomes

$$\int_{-1/2f_0}^{+1/2f_0} g(t) \exp(-2\pi i m f_0 t) \, dt = \frac{G_m}{f_0} \quad ,$$

so the mth coefficient is

$$\boxed{G_m = f_0 \int_{-1/2f_0}^{+1/2f_0} g(t) \exp(-2\pi i m f_0 t) \, dt \ .} \tag{7.12}$$

Equation (7.12) enables us to obtain all the Fourier coefficients for a given $g(t)$ by just one integration instead of the previous two. The reader may find it instructive to use (7.9) and (7.12) to Fourier-analyse the square wave treated previously.

7.2 THE PHYSICAL SIGNIFICANCE OF FOURIER'S THEOREM

Now that we have seen how to analyse a periodic function of time into its frequency components, we must enquire rather more deeply into the significance of the operation. Fourier theory has most of its applications to mechanical, electrical and other systems which have the properties of *linearity* and *time-invariance*. The response of the system (which may be displacement, current or some other quantity) to a stimulus (which may be a force or an e.m.f. varying with time) is governed, in general, by a differential equation connecting the response to the stimulus. If this equation is linear, the system is described as *linear* with respect to the quantities being considered; if the coefficients in the equation are constants, independent of time, the system is said to be *time-invariant*. Many systems studied in physics possess these two qualities to very good approximations. As an example, a mechanical system whose displacement can be characterized by a variable $y(t)$, impressed with a sinusoidally varying force

$$F \sin(2\pi f t + \epsilon)$$

might be described by the equation

$$a \frac{d^2 y}{dt^2} + b \frac{dy}{dt} + cy = F \sin(2\pi f t + \epsilon) \ ,$$

where a, b and c are constants. Such a system would be linear, because of the linearity of the dependent variable y, and time-invariant because of the constancy of the coefficients a, b and c.

It can be shown that the solution to the equation (assuming that the stimulus persists for all positive and negative values of t) is of the form

$$y = A \sin(2\pi \hat{f} t + \phi) \ ,$$

where A and ϕ are constants determined entirely by a, b, c, F and f. This is a most important result. It states that the response y to a force F varying sinusoidally with time *itself* varies sinusoidally with time at the same frequency. Suppose the input force were of the form

$$F_1 \sin(2\pi f_1 t + \epsilon_1) + F_2 \sin(2\pi f_2 t + \epsilon_2) \ ;$$

then, since the equation is linear, we can use the principle of superposition to show that y is of the form

$$y = A_1 \sin(2\pi f_1 t + \phi_1) + A_2 \sin(2\pi f_2 t + \phi_2)$$

and so on, for any number of frequency components in the stimulus.

Thus an input stimulus of a given frequency spectrum can only produce a response with a spectrum containing *the same frequencies*. No new frequencies can be generated. Each frequency component may be modified in both phase and amplitude, but the frequencies in the output are still those of the input. If we know the Fourier coefficients of the components in the stimulus and also know how the system modifies these, then we can determine the coefficients of the spectral components in the response, and, using equation 7.9, synthesize the waveform of the response. So, Fourier analysis of a periodic waveform turns out to be a very significant analysis in this case, since a sinusoidal variation has an *invariance*, with respect to a linear system, which no other wave shape possesses.

There are, of course, many other ways of analysing a periodic function. For many purposes a useful way is by expressing the function $g(t)$ as a power series

$$g(t) = a_0 + a_1 t + a_2 t^2 + \dots \ ,$$

or, in a more compact notation,

$$g(t) = \sum_{m=0}^{\infty} a_m t^m \ .$$

If an input stimulus were analysed in this way, the principle of superposition would still hold in that the response of the system to each individual component of the stimulus in the power series could be determined, and the effects of each term added to synthesize the final response. But the operation would be much more complex; one term in the power series, say $a_3 t^3$, would generate not only the cubic term in the response, but a whole power series, as would all the other components. On the other hand, if the original $g(t)$ had been *Fourier-analysed*, each component frequency in the stimulus would have produced that, and only that, frequency component in the response.

These processes of *frequency* analysis and synthesis are important in, for example, audio systems. When we buy our high-fidelity reproduction equipment, we demand of the manufacturer that the amplifier and loudspeaker be able to transmit the entire audio range of frequencies to our ears. Since we can hear sounds of frequencies up to 15 000 Hz, and our tapes and records contain frequencies up to that value, we require that the system does not modify the amplitude of the Fourier components in that range.

Fourier analysis is, then, a most useful concept in wave theory, and before passing on to more applications of it we must see how the theory can be generalized still further to include non-periodic signals.

7.3 THE FOURIER TRANSFORM

Many of the uses to which waves are put are in the field of communications; for example, light waves communicate information to our eyes, sound waves to our ears and radio waves allow information to be broadcast over large distances. It is immediately evident that the information being transmitted is not, in general, a periodically repeating function; this section will deal with the frequency analysis of those signals which are not of the simple periodic type so far described in this chapter.

There are many approaches to this problem; let it be said at the outset that a rigorous approach is mathematically very complex and far outside the scope of this book. Instead, we shall give an exposition which will indicate the plausibility of the theory, but which will probably not appeal to the mathematical purist.

We start with (7.9), which is the complex form of Fourier's theorem for periodic functions,

$$g(t) = \sum_{n=-\infty}^{\infty} G_n \exp 2\pi i n f_0 t \ , \qquad [7.9]$$

together with the equation (7.12), for determining the coefficients G_n of the series,

$$G_n = f_0 \int_{-1/2f_0}^{+1/2f_0} g(t) \exp(-2\pi i n f_0 t) \, dt \ , \qquad [7.12]$$

where n has been substituted for m. Let us consider (7.9). A non-periodic function can be thought of as a periodic function of infinitely long period (and therefore of infinitesimal fundamental frequency f_0). As the period gets longer and longer, the component frequencies become closer and closer together on the frequency scale. For example, if the period were as long as one second, the fundamental f_0 would be 1 Hz and each component would be 1 Hz apart from its neighbours. If the period is now extended to a hundred seconds, the fundamental would be 1/100 Hz and the components would be only 1/100 Hz apart in frequency. And so, as we let the period tend to infinity, the components become infinitely close together and in the limit merge to form a continuum. Instead of the discrete frequencies nf_0, we have a continuous variable f; likewise, the G_n in (7.9) are replaced by a quantity which describes the total amplitude within an elementary frequency band of width df. Let us call this quantity $G(f)df$, where $G(f)$ is the total amplitude per unit frequency range at the frequency f. The summation sign now becomes an integral and (7.9) becomes

$$g(t) = \int_{-\infty}^{\infty} G(f)\exp 2\pi ift \, df \; .$$

(7.13)

So the spectrum of a non-periodic function $g(t)$ is a *continuous* spectrum described by $G(f)$ and, if we know the spectrum, we can reconstruct the function $g(t)$ from it by the integral in (7.13).

But suppose that we know the original function $g(t)$ and wish to find its spectrum. To do this we must turn to (7.12) for periodic functions and modify it in a way similar to that which we have employed for (7.9). If we consider the right-hand side of (7.12) as the period of $g(t)$ tends to infinity, then nf_0 is replaced (as before) by the continuous variable f, f_0 becomes df and the limits of the integral, $+1/2f_0$ and $-1/2f_0$, tend to $+\infty$ and $-\infty$ respectively. Since G_n on the left-hand side of (7.12) is replaced by $G(f) \, df$, this equation now becomes

$$G(f) = \int_{-\infty}^{+\infty} g(t)\exp(-2\pi ift) \, dt \; .$$

(7.14)

This is the equation we employ to find the spectrum of a non-periodic function $g(t)$.

The two equations (7.13) and (7.14) represent a very general description of Fourier's theorem for functions of time. They also illustrate the essential symmetry which underlies the theorem, in that (7.14) is identical to (7.13) except that the variables t and f have been interchanged, the two functions G and g have likewise been interchanged, and the exponent is negative in one case and positive in the other. Any function $g(t)$ (with certain reservations which need not concern us here) when integrated to give its spectrum (7.14), which is then integrated again (7.13), will yield precisely the original function $g(t)$. This shows the very important point that if the spectrum $G(f)$ of a signal $g(t)$ is known completely, then the original signal $g(t)$ can be determined uniquely; if this were not so, then the process of integrating twice as described above would not be capable of generating the original function. All the *information* in the original signal is therefore preserved in its spectrum.

The function $G(f)$ is known as the *Fourier transform* (or *Fourier integral*) of the function $g(t)$. In some literature $g(t)$ and $G(f)$ are termed *Fourier mates* or *transform pairs* of each other.

Example 7.2
Fourier Transform of a truncated cosine wave
Let us find the Fourier transform of a signal

$$y = y_0 \cos 2\pi f_0 t \;\; ,$$

which starts at time $-T$ and stops at time $+T$, as illustrated in Fig. 7.E2.

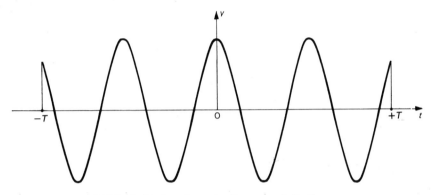

Fig. 7.E2 – Cosine function extending over a finite time.

One could imagine this signal as a pure sound of limited duration, such as one of the pulses which make up the Greenwich time signal. Such a signal is, of course, not periodic; it may, perhaps, be thought of as periodic between the finite time limits $-T$ and $+T$ but is certainly not so over the whole time scale. We know that if the value of T were infinity the function would extend over all time, and therefore would be truly periodic, there being only one frequency component at the frequency f_0. (Strictly speaking, of course, there would also be a component at a frequency $-f_0$, because we have chosen in our theory to include negative frequencies). The problem now is to determine the effect on the frequency spectrum of limiting the duration of the pure tone.

To do this, we must use Fourier transforms. The function $y(t)$ that we wish to transform is characterized mathematically by the following description:

$$y(t) = \begin{cases} y_0 \cos 2\pi f_0 t & \text{for } |t| \leqslant T \;\; , \\ 0 & \text{for } |t| > T \;\; , \end{cases} \tag{7.E1}$$

The Fourier transform of $y(t)$ – let us call it $Y(f)$ – is given by 7.14,

$$Y(f) = \int_{-\infty}^{\infty} y(t) \exp\left(-2\pi i f t\right) \, \mathrm{d}t \;\; .$$

Since $y(t)$ is zero for t less than $-T$ and greater than $+T$, the limits of the integral now assume these time values. So

$$Y(f) = \int_{-T}^{T} y_0 \cos 2\pi f_0 t \, \exp(-2\pi i f t) \, dt$$

$$= \int_{-T}^{T} y_0 \tfrac{1}{2} [\exp 2\pi i f_0 t + \exp(-2\pi i f_0 t)] \exp(-2\pi i f t) \, dt$$

$$= \tfrac{1}{2} y_0 \int_{-T}^{T} [\exp 2\pi i \{f_0 - f\} t + \exp(-2\pi i \{f_0 + f\} t)] \, dt$$

$$= \frac{y_0}{2} \left[\frac{\exp 2\pi i \{f_0 - f\} t}{2\pi i \{f_0 - f\}} + \frac{\exp(-2\pi i \{f_0 + f\} t)}{-2\pi i \{f_0 + f\}} \right]_{-T}^{+T} ,$$

which, after substitution of the limits, becomes

$$\frac{y_0}{2} \left[\frac{\exp 2\pi i \{f_0 - f\} T - \exp(-2\pi i \{f_0 - f\} T)}{2i} \cdot \frac{1}{\pi \{f_0 - f\}} \right.$$

$$\left. - \frac{\exp(-2\pi i \{f_0 + f\} T) - \exp 2\pi i \{f_0 + f\} T}{2i} \cdot \frac{1}{\pi \{f_0 + f\}} \right].$$

Since $\dfrac{\exp i\theta - \exp(-i\theta)}{2i} = \sin \theta$,

this becomes

$$Y(f) = \frac{y_0}{2} \left[\frac{\sin 2\pi (f_0 - f) T}{\pi (f_0 - f)} + \frac{\sin 2\pi (f_0 + f) T}{\pi (f_0 + f)} \right] ,$$

which, finally, can be put in the form

$$Y(f) = y_0 T \left[\frac{\sin 2\pi (f_0 - f) T}{2\pi (f_0 - f) T} + \frac{\sin 2\pi (f_0 + f) T}{2\pi (f_0 + f) T} \right] .$$

How do we interpret this Fourier transform? First of all, we notice that each of the two terms in the brackets is of the form

$$\frac{\sin \pi x}{\pi x}$$

(sometimes called sinc x) where x in the first case is $2(f_0 - f)T$ and in the second case $2(f_0 + f)T$. The last equation can now be written in the form

$$Y(f) = y_0 T[\text{sinc } 2(f_0 - f)T + \text{sinc } 2(f_0 + f)T] . \qquad (7.\text{E2})$$

The graph of sinc x against x is sketched in Fig. 7.E3.

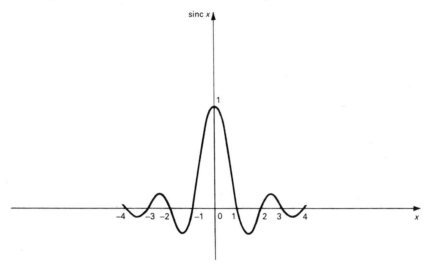

Fig. 7.E3 – Graph of sinc function.

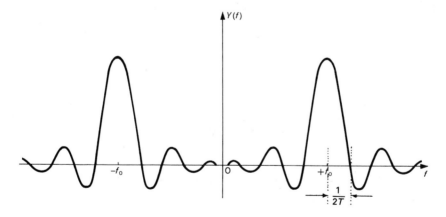

Fig. 7.E4 – Fourier transform of the function shown in Fig. 7.E2.

A little thought will reveal that the right-hand side of (7.E2) contains two functions of this type, the first centred on the frequency f_0 and the second on $-f_0$. The transform is sketched in Fig. 7.E4.   ∎

The Fourier transform in the above example shows a characteristic of non-periodic functions. It is a *band spectrum;* that is, unlike the spectrum in Fig. 7.E1, it exists continuously over a range of frequencies. Moreover, it is an even function. In fact, the Fourier transform of any even real function is even, as can quite easily be shown as follows. Suppose $x(t)$ is an even function of t. Then its Fourier transform, say $X(f)$, is related to $x(t)$ by

$$X(f) = \int_{-\infty}^{\infty} x(t)\exp(-2\pi i f t)\, dt \ .$$

which, because

$$\exp(-2\pi i f t) = \cos 2\pi f t - i \sin 2\pi f t \ ,$$

can be broken up into

$$X(f) = \int_{-\infty}^{\infty} x(t) \cos 2\pi f t\, dt - i \int_{-\infty}^{\infty} x(t) \sin 2\pi f t\, dt \ .$$

Since $\sin 2\pi f t$ is an odd function, and $x(t)$ is, by definition, even, the function $x(t) \sin 2\pi f t$ must be odd, and the integral over all t of this latter function must therefore vanish. Thus

$$X(f) = \int_{-\infty}^{\infty} x(t) \cos 2\pi f t\, dt \ .$$

If we now substitute $-f$ for f in the integral we obtain

$$X(-f) = \int_{-\infty}^{\infty} x(t) \cos(-2\pi f t)\, dt$$

$$= \int_{-\infty}^{\infty} x(t) \cos(+2\pi f t)\, dt$$

$$= X(f) \ .$$

Thus $X(f) = X(-f) \ ,$

showing that the Fourier transform of an even function is even.

By an extension of the above argument, it can be shown that the Fourier transform of *any* real function is *hermitian,* that is that

$$X(f) = X^*(-f) \ ,$$

where the asterisk denotes the complex conjugate. This means that the *amplitude spectrum* of any real function (where the magnitude, only, of the complex function is calculated) is always even. For this reason we can ignore the negative frequency range of a Fourier transform when we are interpreting it, since it provides no essentially new information.

The greatest amplitude occurs at the frequency f_0 of the pulse. However, the shortness of duration of the pulse has introduced more frequency components around the frequency f_0. In fact, examination of (7.E2) shows that the shorter the total duration, $2T$, of the pulse, the broader will be the sinc function. Conversely, the longer the duration (i.e. the closer $y(t)$ is to the ideal infinitely extending cosine function) the narrower the sinc function becomes. Figure 7.4 illustrates the positive frequency region of the spectrum of signals, each of frequency f_0 with different times, $2T$, of duration. The infinitely extending signal, illustrated in Fig. 7.4a, produces a 'line' spectrum — that is to say, the sinc function is infinitely narrow, centred on f_0 and infinitely high. (It may, however, be shown that the area under the graph in this case is finite.) As the duration of the signal decreases, Figs. 7.4b, c, d, e show that the maximum amplitude (which (7.E2) shows to be proportional to T) of $Y(f)$ decreases, and the broadness increases. The effect of the finite duration therefore is to 'broaden' the original 'line'. This illustrates an important principle, called the *uncertainty principle,* which states that the product of the duration of the signal and the frequency width of the spectrum of the signal is of the order of unity. In other words, the longer the signal lasts the narrower is its spectrum and vice versa. The validity of the uncertainty principle can be quite easily demonstrated mathematically for this particular signal. Suppose we define the duration as Δt and the width of the spectrum as Δf. Then clearly

$$\Delta t = 2T \ .$$

However, a little difficulty arises in defining the width Δf of the corresponding frequency spectrum. Since most of the amplitude is in the central peak of the sinc function, let us choose to define Δf as, say, half the spread in frequency of the central peak. The first zero of the sinc function below the frequency f_0 occurs, according to (7E.2), when

$$\sin 2\pi(f_0 - f)T = 0 \ ,$$

i.e. when $2\pi(f_0 - f)T = \pi$

or when $f_0 - f = \dfrac{1}{2T} \ .$

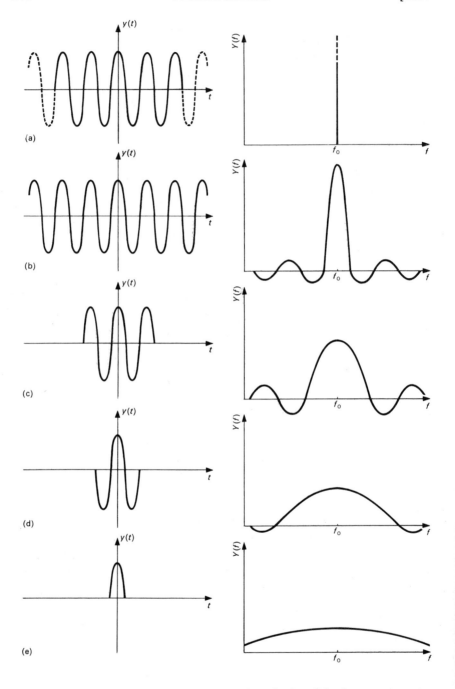

Fig. 7.4 – Effect on the Fourier transform of termination of signal.

Since we have defined Δf as $f_0 - f$, this means that

$$\Delta f = \frac{1}{2T} \ .$$

Thus $\Delta t \ \Delta f = 2T \ \dfrac{1}{2T} = 1 \ ,$

which verifies the original assertion. Of course, much depends upon how we choose to define the effective width of the spectrum, and different definitions will yield different values for $\Delta t \ \Delta f$. Mathematical analyses of different signals using a definition of effective width based on criteria of more general applicability yield a value of $1/2\pi$ for $\Delta f \ \Delta t$. So we can take it that a more thorough investigation shows the uncertainty principle to be described by

$$\boxed{\Delta t \ \Delta f \geqslant \frac{1}{2\pi} \ .} \tag{7.15}$$

However, the important point is that the number on the right-hand side of (7.15) is not zero, that there does exist, as a consequence of the nature of time and frequency, this connection between one and the other.

7.4 THE DELTA FUNCTION

In connection with the uncertainty principle and with many other topics related to Fourier transforms, an important concept is that of the *delta function*. The delta function may be considered as describing the spectrum of the cosine function as its duration $2T$ tends to infinity. The nearer this limit of duration is approached, the narrower the spectrum becomes (according to the uncertainty principle) until, when the cosine function is infinitely extended, the spectrum is of infinitesimal width and becomes an example of what is known as a *line spectrum* . The entity describing such a limiting situation is the delta function, which we may regard, therefore, as a limiting case of a sinc function. However, it turns out that a simpler (and equally valid) approach is to consider it as the limit of a different function which is illustrated in Fig. 7.5. This is a function $y(x)$ which is equal to zero for distances greater than some value X on either side of the origin of x, and to $1/2X$ for distances less than X. In other words,

$$y(x) = \begin{cases} 0 & |x| > X \ , \\ \dfrac{1}{2X} & |x| \leqslant X \ . \end{cases} \tag{7.16}$$

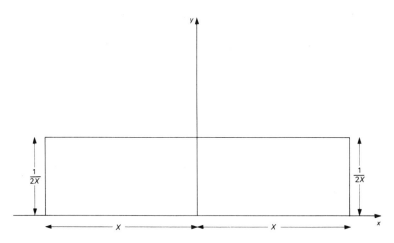

Fig. 7.5 – The function $y(x) = 0$ $|x| > X$
$$= 1/2X \quad |x| \leqslant X$$

These values have been chosen so that the integrated area,

$$\int_{-\infty}^{+\infty} y(x)\,\mathrm{d}x$$

is unity, since, clearly, this is equal to the product of the height $1/2X$ of the rectangle and its width $2X$. This integrated area is therefore independent of the value of X. Let us now investigate what happens when we let X tend to zero. The height of the function will increase, and its width will shrink until, in the limit, the width will be infinitesimal and the height infinite. The integrated area, however, will still be unity. Figure 7.6 shows how the limit is approached. We can define the delta function to be the limiting case of $y(x)$ as X tends to zero, and we denote the function by the symbol $\delta(x)$. Thus

$$\delta(x) = \lim_{X \to 0} y(x) \ .$$

The symbol $\delta(x)$ should not be confused with δx meaning a small finite increment of x. The brackets after the δ-symbol should eliminate this ambiguity. The symbol $\delta(x)$ is defined as describing a delta function situated at that point on the x-axis for which the quantity in brackets is equal to zero. So, for example, the symbol $\delta(x - a)$ is the mathematical description of a delta function at the point $x = a$, and, by the same reasoning, $\delta(x)$ represents a delta function at $x = 0$.

For certain applications we may wish to specify a delta function, at a particular value of x, of integrated area other than unity; all we need to do in this

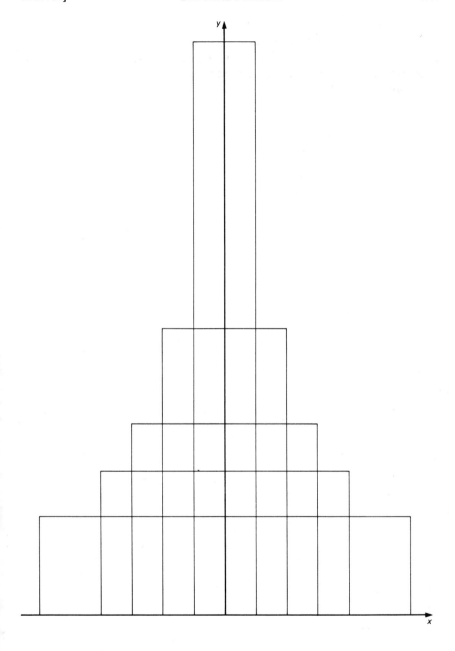

Fig. 7.6 — The function described by equations (7.16) for different values of X. Each rectangle is of unit area, but the width decreases as X decreases. In the limit of $X = 0$, the width is infinitesimal and the height infinite; the integrated area, however, is still unity.

case, of course, is to multiply the delta function by the appropriate amount. Thus, if we wish to specify a delta function of integrated area 2 and situated at $x = -3$, we write $2\delta(x + 3)$. A convenient method of representing delta functions graphically is by drawing a vertical line of height proportional to the integrated area. Some examples are given in Fig. 7.7.

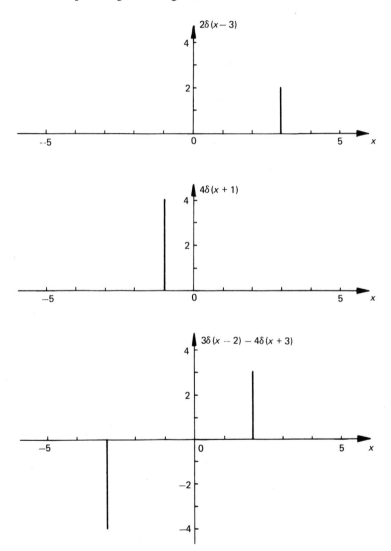

Fig. 7.7 – Some examples of delta functions and their graphical representation. The heights of the lines representing the delta functions are proportional to their integrated areas. In (c) there are two delta functions on one graph, and the one at $x = -3$ is of magnitude -4.

The method of defining the delta function as the limit, as $X \to 0$, of the function depicted in Fig. 7.6 is easy to visualize, and illustrates the idea of a 'spike' of infinitesimal width and infinite height, but with finite area, at the origin. The importance of the function does not reside in the details of its shape, which in this case is rectangular, but in its non-zero integrated area and its infinitesimal width. In fact, we can take limiting cases of a variety of functions to define the delta function. We could start with the so-called *gaussian* function

$$\sqrt{\frac{a}{\pi}} \exp(-ax^2) \ ,$$

which, in the form given, has unit integrated area, and define the delta function as the limit, as $a \to \infty$, of that. Alternatively, we could take the *lorentzian* function

$$\frac{a}{\pi(a^2 + x^2)}$$

and proceed to the limit as $a \to 0$. In fact, there is an infinite number of suitably chosen functions that we could use.

However, there is a more elegant way of defining the delta function, of general applicability, which does not rely on our proceeding to a limit of some function, such as those above, whose shape has essentially nothing to do with the delta function itself. We consider *any* function, $\phi(x)$, which is finite and continuous, and we define the delta function, $\delta(x)$, as that entity for which

$$\boxed{\int_{-\infty}^{\infty} \phi(x)\, \delta(x)\, \mathrm{d}x = \phi(0)} \qquad (7.17)$$

regardless of our choice of $\phi(x)$. A little thought will reveal that only if $\delta(x)$ is of the form of a spike at the origin with zero value everywhere else can the equation (7.17) be true for *any* $\phi(x)$.

We can derive from (7.17) a result we shall soon need. What is the value of

$$\int_{-\infty}^{\infty} \phi(x)\, \delta(x - x_0)\, \mathrm{d}x$$

where x_0 is a constant? Putting $x - x_0 = u$, we see that the expression becomes

$$\int_{-\infty}^{\infty} \phi(u + x_0)\, \delta(u)\, \mathrm{d}u$$

which, by (7.17) is equal to $\phi(x_0)$. Thus

$$\int_{-\infty}^{\infty} \phi(x)\, \delta(x - x_0)\, dx = \phi(x_0) \ . \tag{7.18}$$

Let us now see how the delta-function concept works in a simple, but very important, case. We suspect, from our previous discussion on the uncertainty principle, that the Fourier transform of $\cos 2\pi f_0 t$ (where the function has infinite duration for positive and negative time) consists of a delta function at the value f_0 along the f-axis and another of equal magnitude at the value $-f_0$. We do not know what the magnitude is; let us therefore call it A. Now if we tackled the problem directly by applying (7.14) we would see that the Fourier transform of $\cos 2\pi f_0 t$ is

$$\int_{-\infty}^{\infty} \cos 2\pi f_0 t\, \exp(-2\pi i f t)\, dt \ ,$$

but we cannot go further than this because the integral cannot be evaluated straightforwardly. However, assuming, as we have done, that the Fourier transform is

$$A\,[\delta(f - f_0) + \delta(f + f_0)] \ , \tag{7.19}$$

we can transform back into time from frequency and see if we obtain the function $\cos 2\pi f_0 t$. To do this we use (7.13), substituting the expression (7.19) for $G(f)$. So $g(t)$ is given by

$$g(t) = \int_{-\infty}^{\infty} A\,[\delta(f - f_0) + \delta(f + f_0)]\, \exp 2\pi i f t\, df \ ,$$

which can be expressed as the sum of two terms, so that

$$g(t) = A \int_{-\infty}^{\infty} \delta(f - f_0)\, \exp 2\pi i f t\, df + A \int_{-\infty}^{\infty} \delta(f + f_0)\, \exp 2\pi i f t\, df \ .$$

If we consider the first integral, we see that it is of the form (7.18) with f and f_0 for x and x_0, and $\exp(2\pi i f t)$ for $\phi(x)$. The value of the integral is therefore $A\,\exp(2\pi i f_0 t)$. Similarly, the second integral is $A\,\exp(-2\pi i f_0 t)$. Thus the full equation now becomes

$$g(t) = A\,[\exp(2\pi i f_0 t) + \exp(-2\pi i f_0 t)] \ .$$

Furthermore, since $\cos \theta = \frac{1}{2} [\exp(i\theta) + \exp(-i\theta)]$,

$g(t) = 2A \cos 2\pi f_0 t.$

Putting $A = \frac{1}{2}$, we see that $g(t)$ is, indeed, $\cos 2\pi f_0 t$. Thus the Fourier transform of $\cos 2\pi f_0 t$ is

$$\frac{1}{2} [\delta(f + f_0) + \delta(f - f_0)] \ .$$

The transform pair is illustrated in Fig. 7.8.

An interesting fact emerges when we make f_0 zero. The function $\cos 2\pi f_0 t$ becomes unity over all time and its Fourier transform becomes

$$\frac{1}{2} \delta(f - 0) + \frac{1}{2} \delta(f + 0) = \delta(f) \ ,$$

this is, a delta function at the origin. In other words, a steady d.c. voltage has a spectrum entirely at the zero of frequency. Furthermore, by using the symmetry of t and f in the transform relationship as described in an earlier section, we see that the Fourier transform of $\delta(t)$ is unity for all frequencies. In other words, the spectrum of a sharp pulse contains equal amplitude at all frequencies.

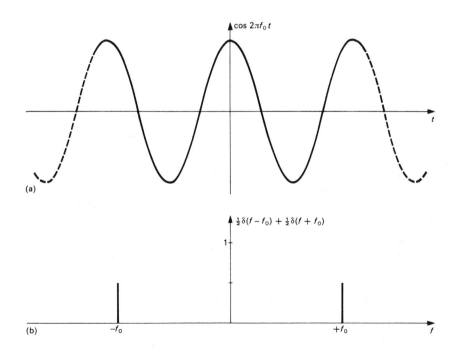

Fig. 7.8 — (a) The function $\cos 2\pi f_0 t$, and (b) its Fourier transform.

We now see more clearly the nature of the delta function. It is not a description of anything that could exist in nature but it is a very useful idealization. No signal of the description cos $2\pi f_0 t$ can be produced by any apparatus, since such apparatus would need to have been made (and switched on) an infinite time ago, and moreover would have to continue to operate for an infinite time to come. Consequently, there can be no spectra consisting of delta functions. Nevertheless, in practice we can get very close to the line-spectrum situation which makes the concept important.

The delta-function is by no means limited to discussions on Fourier transforms; it is unconsciously built in to our thinking at an early age. The particle of classical mechanics is introduced as a body having a finite mass but no size. It is the limiting case of a finite-sized body of mass m as the size tends to zero, the density meanwhile tending to infinity in such a way as to keep the total mass m a constant. In other words, the particle is none other than a three-dimensional version of a delta function of magnitude m. In the same way we can treat point electric charges, and many other physical concepts, as delta functions.

PROBLEMS

(7.1) Prove that $\int_{T_0}^{T_0+T} \cos 2\pi m f_0 t \cos 2\pi n f_0 t \, dt$ is equal to $T(m = n = 0)$, or $\frac{1}{2}T \, (m = n \neq 0)$ or $0 \, (m \neq n)$, where T is the period, T_0 is any 'starting point' of the cycle and m and n are integers.

Prove likewise that $\int_{T_0}^{T_0+T} \sin 2\pi m f_0 t \sin 2\pi n f_0 t \, dt$ equals $\frac{1}{2}T \, (m = n \neq 0)$ or $0 \, (m \neq n)$, and that $\int_{T_0}^{T_0+T} \cos 2\pi m f_0 t \sin 2\pi n f_0 t \, dt = 0$ for all m, n.

(7.2) Prove that for any even function of t, [that is, $g(t) = g(-t)$], which is periodic, $S_m = 0$ for all m. Prove that for any odd function of t, [that is, $g(t) = -g(-t)$], which is periodic, $C_m = 0$ for all m (including $m = 0$).

(7.3) A function $g(t)$ of period T is defined between $t = 0$ and $t = T$ as follows:

$$g(t) = \quad A \text{ for } 0 < t \leqslant T/4$$
$$g(t) = -A \text{ for } T/4 < t \leqslant 3T/4$$
$$g(t) = \quad A \text{ for } 3T/4 < t \leqslant T .$$

Perform a Fourier analysis of $y(t)$ using the exponential form of Fourier's theorem, and display the results for the first ten harmonics graphically. Repeat this for the function $g(t - T/4)$. Compare the amplitudes of the first ten harmonics in the two cases, and comment on the result.

Develop a method of exponential Fourier analysis of *any* periodic function $g(t - t_0)$, where t_0 is a constant, and the Fourier components of $g(t)$ are already known. Comment on the result when t_0 equals the period T.

(7.4) Perform a Fourier analysis, using the trigonometrical form of Fourier's theorem, of a 'saw-tooth' function of period T, defined by $g(t) = 2 a t/T$ for $-T/2 < t \leqslant T/2$. (It is helpful to consider the symmetry of this function.)

(7.5) Use a calculator to plot the sum of (i) the first two terms, (ii) the first three terms of the series in Problem 7.4 from $t = -T/2$ to $T/2$.

(7.6) Perform a Fourier analysis, using the trigonometrical form of Fourier's theorem, of a 'triangular wave' function of period T, defined by $g(t) = 2 a t/T$ for $0 < t \leqslant T/2$, and $g(t) = 2 a(1 - t/T)$ for $T/2 < t \leqslant T$.

(7.7) Show that the Fourier transform $X(f)$ of any real function $x(t)$ is Hermitian, that is, $X(f) = X^*(-f)$. Hence show that the amplitude spectrum of any real function is even.

(7.8) Sketch the gaussian function $g(t) = 1/(T\sqrt{2\pi}) \exp(-t^2/2T^2)$. Show that its Fourier transform is $G(f) = \exp(-2\pi^2 f^2 T^2)$, and sketch $G(f)$. In what respect, therefore, might the gaussian function be considered special?

(7.9) Sketch the function $f(t) = 1/2T \exp(-|t|/T)$, and show that its Fourier transform is $G(f) = (1 + 4 \pi^2 f^2 T^2)^{-1}$. Sketch $G(f)$.

(7.10) Using the result of problem 7.9, evaluate the integral $\displaystyle\int_{-\infty}^{\infty} \frac{e^{i\omega t}}{1 + \omega^2} \, d\omega$.

(7.11) A burst of 10 cycles from a 5 kHz sinusoidal oscillator is fed into an amplifier. What frequency bandwidth must the amplifier possess to give a reasonably undistorted output?

CHAPTER 8

Further topics in Fourier theory

8.1 SOME THEOREMS

It may be thought at first that, in order to obtain a Fourier transform (F.T.) of interest, one would have to perform some integration, in view of the form of (7.14). In fact, however, it is often possible to transform a function without integrating, because of the existence of certain theorems to be described below. As we shall see, the theorems allow one to see the relationship between the F.T. of a function and that of others which are related to it in certain ways. From a few basic functions (whose F.T.s may have to be obtained by integration) we can build up a 'library' − without further integration − of F.T.s, with the use of these theorems.

8.1.1 The addition theorem

This merely states that the F.T. of the sum of two functions is the sum of the individual F.T.s. Suppose we know the F.T.s $G_1(f)$ and $G_2(f)$ of the functions $g_1(t)$ and $g_2(t)$ respectively. Then the F.T. of

$$h(t) = g_1(t) + g_2(t) \text{ is } H(f) = G_1(f) + G_2(f) \ . \tag{8.1}$$

The proof, which is trivial, will not be given.

8.1.2 The shift theorem

Suppose the F.T. of $g(t)$ is $G(f)$. Then, we ask, what is the F.T. of $g(t-t_0)$ (where t_0 is a constant) in terms of $G(f)$? The function $g(t - t_0)$ is, of course, the function $g(t)$ shifted bodily an amount t_0 in the direction of positive t. To obtain its F.T. say $H(f)$, we start with (7.14), except that now we wish to transform $g(t - t_0)$ instead of $g(t)$. Therefore

$$H(f) = \int_{-\infty}^{\infty} g(t - t_0) \exp(-2\pi i f t) \, \mathrm{d}t \ .$$

We proceed by putting $u = t - t_0$, so that $du = dt$. The integral then becomes

$$H(f) = \int_{-\infty}^{\infty} g(u) \exp[-2\pi i f(u + t_0)]\ du\ .$$

The factor $\exp(-2\pi i f t_0)$ is a constant which may be taken outside the integral. So

$$H(f) = \exp(-2\pi i f t_0) \int_{-\infty}^{\infty} g(u) \exp(-2\pi i f u)\ du\ .$$

Therefore, from (7.14),

$$H(f) = \exp(-2\pi i f t_0)\ G(f)\ . \tag{8.2}$$

This is the so-called Shift Theorem; if a function of t is translated along the time axis (shifted), then its F.T. is multiplied by $\exp(-2\pi i f t_0)$. It will be noted that this latter factor has a modulus of unity. So $|H(f)| = |G(f)|$; that is, if we shift a function of t, then there is no change whatsoever in its amplitude spectrum. That this is so is not difficult to see. If a sound is played on two separate occasions (so that if the signal is $g(t)$ on the first occasion then it is $g(t - t_0)$ on the second occasion t_0 later) then it is clear that its amplitude spectrum must be the same on both occasions.

The shift theorem provides us with general information about the spectrum of a sound together with an echo of itself. Suppose, for simplicity, that the original sound is $g(t + \frac{t_0}{2})$ and that its echo is an exact replica of the original except that it is delayed by a time t_0, so that it is $g(t - \frac{t_0}{2})$. Then the complete signal, say $h(t)$, is

$$h(t) = g(t + \frac{t_0}{2})\ +\ g(t - \frac{t_0}{2})\ .$$

By the addition (8.1) and shift (8.2) theorems,

$$H(f) = [\exp(2\pi i f t_0/2) + \exp(-2\pi i f t_0/2)]\ G(f)\ ,$$

where $G(f)$ is the F.T. of $g(t)$.

Since $\cos\theta = [\exp(i\theta) + \exp(-i\theta)]/2\ ,$

we have

$$H(f) = 2 \cos(\pi f t_0)\ G(f)\ .$$

So the spectrum is that of $g(t)$, multiplied by a cosine function which causes certain regularly spaced frequencies, namely $1/2t_0, 3/2t_0, 5/2t_0, (2n + 1)/2t_0 \ldots$ to be absent.

8.1.3 The similarity theorem

This theorem concerns the relationship between the F.T. of a function $g(t)$ and that of $g(at)$, where a is a constant. We will, for the moment, think of a as positive, but will remove this restriction later. To see the relationship between $g(t)$ and $g(at)$, let us fix our ideas by supposing a to be 2. The function $g(2t)$ plotted against $2t$ will look exactly the same as $g(t)$ plotted against t. So if $g(2t)$ is plotted against t instead of $2t$, it will appear to be 'squashed', by a factor of 2, along the t axis. In other words, any given feature of $g(2t)$ will occupy half as much time as the same feature in $g(t)$. In still other words, a sound signal $g(t)$ played by a tape recorder at normal speed will become $g(2t)$ if the tape recorder is played at double the speed. The relationship between $g(t)$ and $g(2t)$ is displayed in the left-hand side of Fig. 8.1.

If the F.T. of $g(t)$ is $G(f)$, what is the F.T. of $g(at)$? We start, again, with (7.14) and suppose that the F.T. of $g(at)$ is $H(f)$. Then

$$H(f) = \int_{-\infty}^{\infty} g(at) \exp(-2\pi ift) \, dt \ .$$

We put $u = at$, so that $du = a \, dt$.
Thus

$$H(f) = \int_{-\infty}^{\infty} g(u) \exp(-2\pi ifu/a) \, du/a$$

$$= \frac{1}{a} \int_{-\infty}^{\infty} g(u) \exp\left[-2\pi i \left(\frac{f}{a}\right) u\right] du \ . \tag{8.3}$$

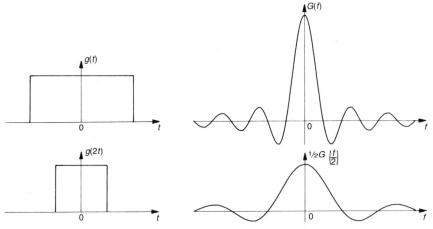

Fig. 8.1 – Illustration of the similarity Theorem. The left-hand diagrams show the relationship between $g(t)$ and $g(2t)$; the right-hand diagrams are the F.T.s of those on the left.

Now, the integral in (8.3) is exactly of the form of (7.14), except that t in (7.14) is replaced by u (which does not matter since it disappears on application of the limits of the integral) and f is replaced by f/a. So (8.3) becomes

$$H(f) = \frac{1}{a} G\left(\frac{f}{a}\right).$$

This is the so-called similarity theorem. Before we interpret it, let it be mentioned that if a is negative, an analysis identical to the above would yield

$$H(f) = -\frac{1}{a} G\left(\frac{f}{a}\right).$$

Thus two results may be subsumed, for *any* real, non-zero a, into a single result

$$H(f) = \frac{1}{|a|} G\left(\frac{f}{a}\right). \tag{8.4}$$

We interpret the similarity theorem as follows. If the original signal $g(t)$ is 'squashed' by a factor of a to produce $g(at)$, then its F.T., $G(f)$ is 'stretched' in frequency space to produce $\frac{1}{|a|} G\left(\frac{f}{a}\right)$. (The overall magnitude of the F.T. is also changed by a factor of $|a|$, but this is not generally of as much interest as the 'stretching'.) In particular, if $a = 2$, then the F.T. of $g(2t)$ is $\frac{1}{2} G\left(\frac{f}{2}\right)$, the $f/2$ in the argument of G showing that the F.T. of $g(t)$ has been 'stretched' by a factor of 2 to produce the F.T. of $g(2t)$.

In other words, if a tape recorder gives out the signal $g(2t)$, all the features in its spectrum will be at twice the frequencies that they would be at if the signal were $g(t)$.

A particular case of the similarity theorem is given by $a = -1$, where we see immediately from (8.4) that the F.T. of $g(-t)$ is $G(-f)$. So reversal of $g(t)$ implies reversal of $G(f)$, and, since the amplitude spectrum of a real function $g(t)$ is even, there is no change in the amplitude spectrum on reversal of $g(t)$. In other words, the amplitudes at various frequencies are the same if we play a tape backwards as forwards.

Example 8.1
Show that the F.T. of the Gaussian function $g(t) = \exp(-t^2/2T^2)$ is consistent with the Similarity Theorem.

The F.T. of this function can readily be shown (Problem 7.8) to be $G(f) = T\sqrt{(2\pi)} \exp(-2\pi^2 f^2 T^2)$.

Consider now the function $g_1(t) = \exp(-t^2/2T_1^2)$, where $T_1 \neq T$. This is simply another Gaussian function of the same peak height, but a different width (Fig. 8.E1). We see that the scaling factor $a = T/T_1$, since then

$$g(at) = \exp(-a^2t^2/2T^2) = \exp(-t^2/2T_1^2) = g_1(t)$$

as required.

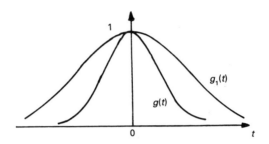

Fig. 8.E1 – Gaussian function.

The Similarity Theorem therefore gives that the F.T. of $g_1(t)$ is

$$\frac{1}{|a|} G\left(\frac{f}{a}\right) = \frac{T_1}{T} T\sqrt{(2\pi)} \exp\left(-2\pi^2f^2T^2 \cdot \frac{T_1^2}{T^2}\right)$$

$$= T_1\sqrt{(2\pi)} \exp - 2\pi^2f^2T_1^2 \quad .$$

But this is exactly the result we would have expected merely by replacing T by T_1 in the expression for $G(f)$. It follows therefore that this expression for $G(f)$ is consistent with the Similarity Theorem. This should cause no surprise to the reader.

8.1.4 The derivative theorem
As its name implies, the derivative theorem connects the F.T. of $dg(t)/dt$ with that of $g(t)$. We suppose that the F.T. of the derivative is $H(f)$; (7.14) then gives

$$H(f) = \int_{-\infty}^{\infty} \frac{dg(t)}{dt} \exp(-2\pi ift) \, dt \quad .$$

We cancel the dt's and obtain

$$H(f) = \int_{t=-\infty}^{\infty} \exp(-2\pi ift) \, dg(t) \quad .$$

Now, from the theory of integration by parts, we know that

$$\int_a^b u\,dv = [uv]_b^a - \int_a^b v\,du \quad,$$

and so, putting $u \equiv \exp(-2\pi ift)$ and $v \equiv g(t)$,

we have

$$H(f) = [\exp(-2\pi ift)\, g(t)]_{t=-\infty}^{\infty}$$

$$- \int_{-\infty}^{\infty} g(t)\, (-2\pi ift)\, \exp(-2\pi ift)\, dt \quad.$$

We now assume that $g(t)$ is a function which tends to zero as t tends to $\pm\infty$; in other words we assume that $g(t)$ is physically realizable.

So $$H(f) = 2\pi if \int_{-\infty}^{\infty} g(t)\, \exp(-2\pi ift)\, dt \quad.$$

The integral itself being the F.T., $G(f)$, of $g(t)$, we have

$$H(f) = 2\pi if\, G(f) \quad. \tag{8.5}$$

This is the *derivative theorem,* that if a function of t is differentiated, then its F.T. is multiplied by $2\pi if$. By a simple extension of the above argument, we can see that if a function of t is differentiated n times, then its F.T. is multiplied by $(2\pi if)^n$. There are many obvious uses of the theorem for generating a variety of F.T.s of functions which are the derivatives with respect to time of a function whose F.T. is known. In addition, however, the theorem is particularly useful in illuminating certain aspects of linear differential equations.

Example 8.2
Fourier-transform analysis of an RLC circuit
Let us consider, as an example, the electrical circuit depicted in Fig. 3.8b. Here, a time-varying voltage is applied to an *RLC* series circuit. The voltage need not be sinusoidal; indeed, it can be any suitable signal, for example the output from a microphone or tape recorder. Let us call it $v(t)$. As a result of the application of $v(t)$, a time-varying current, $i(t)$, will flow in the circuit. What is the relationship between $v(t)$ and $i(t)$?

Applying equation (3.28), and bearing in mind that $i = dq/dt$, we have

$$v(t) = R\,i(t) + L\,\frac{d\,i(t)}{dt} + \frac{q(t)}{C}\,.$$

Differentiation with respect to t yields

$$\frac{dv(t)}{dt} = R\,\frac{di(t)}{dt} + L\,\frac{d^2 i(t)}{dt^2} + \frac{i(t)}{C}\,. \qquad (8.\text{E}1)$$

The technique we will now adopt is to obtain the F.T. of (8.E1) which may be transformed term by term by the addition theorem (8.1). We let the F.T.s of $v(t)$ and $i(t)$ respectively be $V(f)$ and $I(f)$. Then by the derivative theorem, the F.T.s of $dv(t)/dt$, $di(t)/dt$ and $d^2 i(t)/dt^2$ are, respectively, $2\pi i f\,V(f)$, $2\pi i f\,I(f)$ and $(2\pi i f)^2 I(f)$. So the F.T. of (8.E1) is

$$2\pi i f\,V(f) = 2\pi i f\,RI(f) + (2\pi i f)^2\,LI(f) + \frac{I(f)}{C}\,. \qquad (8.\text{E}2)$$

We see immediately that the process of Fourier transformation of (8.E1) has converted that equation from a differential equation into an ordinary algebraic one. Dividing (8.E2) throughout by $2\pi i f$ we obtain

$$V(f) = [R + 2\pi i f L + \frac{1}{2\pi i f C}]\,I(f) \qquad (8.\text{E}3)$$

which is an equation well known to those readers who are familiar with alternating-current theory. In fact the Fourier-transform approach is essentially nothing more than generalization of phasor methods applied to circuits fed with sinusoidally-varying voltages. The point of the generalization lies, of course, in the fact that *any* time-varying voltage, $v(t)$, may be dealt with. To find $i(t)$ for a given $v(t)$, we solve (8.E3) for $I(f)$ and then perform an inverse F.T. (7.13) on the resulting equation. For a general $v(t)$ this can be quite tricky, and we will not go into details here.

8.2 CONVOLUTIONS

Convolution is a certain mathematical operation involving two (or, sometimes more) functions. The convolution $f(x)*g(x)$ of two functions $f(x)$ and $g(x)$ is defined as

$$\boxed{\; f(x)*g(x) = \int_{-\infty}^{\infty} f(u)g(x-u)\,du \;} \qquad (8.6)$$

where u is a dummy variable in x space. The first function is considered as being plotted out as a function of u, and the second is reflected about the vertical axis and displaced a distance x. These two functions are then multiplied, and the value of the convolution for the particular value of x chosen is the integrated area of the product. By choosing, in turn, different values of x, we may build up a picture of the convolution as a function of x.

If the functions are of finite width in x space it is generally true that the convolution is broader than either $f(x)$ or $g(x)$; indeed its width is of the order of the sum of the original widths. For this reason, convolution is sometimes called a 'smearing' of one function by the other. It turns out, in many cases, that the degradation of information in the form of a signal $f(x)$ that takes place in the passage of the signal through a channel may be expressed as the convolution of $f(x)$ with a function, say $g(x)$, which is a property of the channel.

In this section, we will study some of the properties of convolutions, but will leave a discussion of their relevance to Fourier theory until the next section.

Firstly, we will prove the surprising result that $f(x)*g(x) = g(x)*f(x)$, that is, that convolution is commutative. The right-hand side of (8.6) looks, at first glance, to be alarmingly asymmetrical in f and g. However, if we put $v = x - u$, and remember that x is a constant in this integral, then (8.6) becomes

$$f(x)*g(x) = \int_{+\infty}^{-\infty} f(x - v)\, g(v)\, (-\,dv)$$

$$= \int_{-\infty}^{\infty} f(x - v)\, g(v)\, dv = \int_{-\infty}^{\infty} g(v)\, f(x - v)\, dx$$

$$= g(x)*f(x) \ ,$$

which proves the commutativity of f and g with respect to convolution.

We next state that convolution is *associative,* i.e. that

$$[f(x)*g(x)]*h(x) = f(x)*[g(x)*h(x)] \ , \tag{8.7}$$

so that the convolution of three functions may be expressed as $f(x)*g(x)*h(x)$. The proof of this is delayed till the next section. Clearly, any number of functions to be convolved may be strung together with asterisks and (in view of the commutativity discussed above) may be written in any order.

A function may be convolved with one or more delta functions, and two or more delta functions may be convolved. Let us consider the simplest case, that of $\delta(x)*f(x)$. It will be useful to recall (7.17):

$$\int_{-\infty}^{\infty} \phi(u)\, \delta(u)\, du = \phi(0) \tag{[7.17]}$$

where $\phi(u)$ is *any* finite and continuous function, and we have (for our later convenience) substituted u for x. Now

$$\delta(x)*f(x) = \int_{-\infty}^{\infty} \delta(u) f(x-u)\, du$$

by definition (8.6). This is exactly of the form (7.17) with $f(x-u)$ substituted for $\phi(u)$. So, by (7.17)

$$\boxed{\delta(x)*f(x) = f(x)}.$$ (8.8)

In other words, convolution with a delta function at the origin of x leaves the original function $f(x)$ unaltered; thus $\delta(x)$ is to convolution what unity is to multiplication.

What, then, is the value of the convolution of $f(x)$ with a delta function, $\delta(x-x_0)$, situated at the point $x=x_0$? By definition (8.6) it is

$$\delta(x-x_0)*f(x) = \int_{-\infty}^{\infty} \delta(u-x_0)f(x-u)\, du \ .$$

We put $u-x_0 = v$, and the convolution becomes

$$\int_{-\infty}^{\infty} \delta(v) f(x-x_0-v)\, dv$$

which, by (7.17) is $f(x-x_0)$. So

$$\delta(x-x_0)*f(x) = f(x-x_0) \ .$$ (8.9)

We see, then, that convolution with a delta function is equivalent to shifting the origin of $f(x)$ to the point x_0 where the delta function is situated, producing $f(x-x_0)$.

In our discussion of the shift theorem in section 8.1.2 we considered a signal $g(t+\frac{t_0}{2})$ and its echo t_0 later, $g(t-\frac{t_0}{2})$ giving a total signal

$$h(t) = g(t+\frac{t_0}{2}) + g(t-\frac{t_0}{2}) \ .$$

From the above result (8.9) concerning convolutions of functions with delta functions we can now see that $h(t)$ may be represented by a convolution,

$$h(t) = g(t)*[\delta(t+\frac{t_0}{2}) + \delta(t-\frac{t_0}{2})] \ .$$ (8.10)

So we have a representation of $h(t)$ which separates the form of the signal $g(t)$ from details of the echo. This is a simple example of the way in which the convolution representation can separate sharply the information being conveyed [$g(t)$] from the degradation being performed on it [in this case

$$\delta(t + \frac{t_0}{2}) + \delta(t - \frac{t_0}{2})]$$

by a system. The representation (8.10) has a further significance as we shall see in the next section.

Finally, in this section, we turn our attention to the convolution representation of periodic functions.

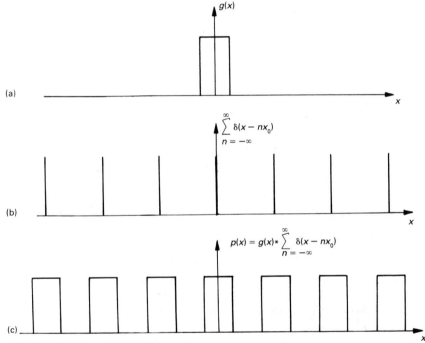

Fig. 8.2 -- Illustration of the convolution representation of a periodic function. (a) is the basic motif of the periodic function, (b) is a series of equally-spaced unit-integrated-area delta functions, and (c) is the convolution of (a) and (b), producing the final periodic function.

We can consider a periodic function as consisting of a motif laid out at periodic intervals along the x axis. If the motif (the contents of one period) is $g(x)$, and identical motifs are to be situated at distance x_0 apart, then the periodic function, $p(x)$, may be represented by the function

$$p(x) = \sum_{n=-\infty}^{\infty} g(x - nx_0) \ .$$

But, by (8.9)

$$g(x - nx_0) = g(x)*\delta(x - nx_0) \ .$$

So

$$p(x) = \sum_{n=-\infty}^{\infty} g(x)*\delta(x - nx_0) \ ,$$

and, since $g(x)$ is common to all terms in the summation,

$$p(x) = g(x)* [\ \sum_{n=-\infty}^{\infty} \delta(x - nx_0)] \ . \tag{8.11}$$

Here, we have, in the convolution representation of a periodic function, a separation made between the details of the motif $[g(x)]$ and those of the periodicity $[\sum_n \delta(x - nx_0)]$. For a given periodicity, only the first term in the convolution gives any information concerning what it is that is being repeated. It is as if two aspects of a periodic function have been 'factorized' into two separate 'factors'. An illustration is given in Fig. 8.2.

A perfect crystal, which is a periodic arrangement of a motif in three dimensions, may be represented in a way similar to (8.11). Here, we are able to represent the crystal as the convolution of the contents of the so-called *unit cell* (the motif) with a triply-periodic set of delta functions, called the *lattice*. Crystallographers find this separation very useful, and when they are investigating a crystal structure, usually determine the details of the lattice dimensions and symmetry before concentrating on those of the motif.

8.3 THE CONVOLUTION THEOREM

In the last section, we dealt with the nature of the convolution, without discussing its role in Fourier theory. We now proceed with this discussion and start by asking the question: what is the Fourier transform of the convolution of a pair of functions? In other words, what is the value, $H(f)$, of the integral

$$H(f) = \int_{-\infty}^{\infty} [g_1(t)*g_2(t)] \exp(-2\pi i f t) \ \mathrm{d}t \ ?$$

We first expand the integral according to (8.6) and obtain

$$H(f) = \int_{-\infty}^{\infty} \int_{-\infty}^{\infty} g_1(u) \, g_2(t - u) \exp(-2\pi i f t) \ \mathrm{d}u \ \mathrm{d}t$$

$$= \int_{-\infty}^{\infty} g_1(u)[\int_{-\infty}^{\infty} g_2(t - u) \exp(-2\pi i f t) \ \mathrm{d}t] \ \mathrm{d}u \ .$$

We work out the inner integral first, and put $y = t - u$. Noting that u is a constant in this integral because we are integrating with respect to t, we have $dy = dt$. So

$$H(f) = \int_{-\infty}^{\infty} g_1(u) \left[\int_{-\infty}^{\infty} g_2(y) \exp\left[-2\pi i f (y + u)\right] dy \right] du$$

$$= \int_{-\infty}^{\infty} g_1(u) \exp(-2\pi i f u) \left[\int_{-\infty}^{\infty} g_2(y) \exp(-2\pi i f y) dy \right] du \ .$$

But the inner integral is the F.T., $G_2(f)$, of $g_2(y)$ by (7.14). So

$$H(f) = \int_{-\infty}^{\infty} g_1(u) \exp(-2\pi i f u) \, G_2(f) \, du$$

$$= G_2(f) \left[\int_{-\infty}^{\infty} g_1(u) \exp(-2\pi i f u) \, du \right] \ .$$

Now the contents of the square bracket are, by (7.14), the F.T., $G_1(f)$ of $g_1(u)$. So

$$H(f) = G_1(f) \, G_2(f) \ . \tag{8.12}$$

Equation (8.12) is a statement of the *convolution theorem,* that the F.T. of a convolution of two functions is the product of the individual transforms. If we convolve two functions in time, then we multiply the two transforms in frequency space.

The equation (8.12) can easily be extended to give the F.T. of

$$g_1(t)*g_2(t)* \ldots *g_n(t)$$

(i.e. the convolution of n functions) which is

$$G_1(f) \, G_2(f) \ldots G_n(f) \ . \tag{8.13}$$

The commutativity and associativity of the convolution operation, discussed in the last section, is now very obvious. Since in (8.12) $G_1(f) \, G_2(f)$ is equal to $G_2(f) \, G_1(f)$, it follows that $g_1(t)*g_2(t) = g_2(t)*g_1(t)$. Similarly, since, in (8.13), $[G_1(f) \, G_2(f)] \, G_3(f) = G_1(f) \, [G_2(f) \, G_3(f)]$ then we must have $[g_1(t)*g_2(t)] *g_3(t) = g_1(t)* [g_2(t)*g_3(t)]$.

There is another form of the convolution theorem that can be useful. In view of the great similarity in form of the two equations (7.13) and (7.14), we may start in frequency space instead of time, and ask what function of time would when Fourier transformed, give a convolution of two functions in frequency space. By an analysis identical to the above except that we start in frequency space and proceed to time, we can show that the inverse F.T. of $G_1(f)*G_2(f)$ is

$g_1(t) g_2(t)$, where $g_1(t)$ and $g_2(t)$ are the inverse F.T.s of $G_1(f)$ and $G_2(f)$ respectively. So the convolution theorem displays a symmetry between time and frequency spaces. If we convolve two functions in time space, we multiply their F.T.s in frequency space; if we multiply two functions in time space, we convolve their F.T.s in frequency space.

Let us take a simple example of the application of the convolution theorem. For this, we will need the F.T. of a delta function situated at the time t_0. The expression for this delta function is of course, $\delta(t - t_0)$. Its F.T. is

$$\int_{-\infty}^{\infty} \delta(t - t_0) \exp(-2\pi i f t) \, dt \ ,$$

by (7.14), which, by virtue of (7.18) becomes

$$\exp(-2\pi i f t_0) \ . \tag{8.14}$$

Now the example that we take is the calculation of the F.T. of a signal $g(t - t_0)$, which, of course, is a shifted version of a signal $g(t)$. Since, by (8.9), $g(t - t_0) = \delta(t - t_0)*g(t)$, its F.T. is, by the convolution theorem (8.12), the product of the F.T.s of each function in the convolution. Because (by (8.14)) the F.T. of $\delta(t - t_0)$ is $\exp(-2\pi i f t_0)$, we have that the F.T. of $g(t -t_0)$ is

$$\exp(-2\pi i f t_0) \, G(f) \ , \tag{8.2}$$

a result identical to the shift theorem (8.2). We see, therefore, that the shift theorem is merely a special case of the convolution theorem in which one of the two functions convolved is the $\delta(t - t_0)$ which supplies the information concerning the amount (t_0) by which the function $g(t)$ has been shifted.

Returning to expression (8.14), and putting $t_0 = 0$, we see that the F.T. of a delta function at the origin of time, $\delta(t)$, is 1. So an infinitesimally wide pulse has an F.T. which is a constant at all frequencies. Therefore, in order to reproduce such a sound signal we would need an amplifier which would amplify equally all frequencies. Neither such a sound signal nor such an amplifier could exist in practice, and the situation described represents an idealisation.

Since any signal $g(t)$ can be represented as $\delta(t)*g(t)$, its F.T. is, by the convolution theorem (8.12), $1 \times G(f) = G(f)$, giving us an obvious truth. Trivial though this example may be, it illustrates, once again, that a delta function at the origin is to convolution what unity is to multiplication.

We turn our attention now to the convolution representation of a signal with its echo

$$h(t) = g(t)* \left[\delta(t + \frac{t_0}{2}) + \delta(t - \frac{t_0}{2}) \right] \ . \tag{8.10}$$

The F.T. of the contents of the square bracket is, by (8.14)

$$\exp(+ 2\pi i f \frac{t_0}{2}) + \exp(-2\pi i f \frac{t_0}{2})$$

$$= 2 \cos(\pi f t_0) \; .$$

So, by the convolution theorem (8.12), the F.T. of equation (8.10) is

$$H(f) = 2\, G(f) \cos(\pi f t_0) \; ,$$

a result which we obtained earlier from the shift theorem.

Finally in this chapter, we consider the F.T. of a periodic function. We have already seen that a periodic function $p(t)$ may be represented as a convolution of a motif $g(t)$ with a series of delta functions, $\sum\limits_{n=-\infty}^{\infty} \delta(t - nT)$ spaced equally apart at the periodic time T:

$$p(t) = g(t)* \sum_{n=-\infty}^{\infty} \delta(t - nT) \; .$$

So $P(f)$, the F.T. of $p(t)$, is, by convolution theorem (8.12), equal to the product of $G(f)$ and the F.T. of the sum of the delta functions. We therefore require to find the latter F.T. Unfortunately, this is not a particularly easy problem, and is outside the scope of this book. The result, however, is simple and will now be quoted. The F.T. of

$$\sum_{n=-\infty}^{\infty} \delta(t - nT) \text{ is } \frac{1}{T} \sum_{m=-\infty}^{\infty} \delta(f - \frac{m}{T}).$$

So the F.T. of a sequence of identical equally-spaced delta functions is itself a sequence of identical equally-spaced delta functions. Such a sequence is often called a *comb,* by reason of its appearance when plotted (see Fig. 8.2b). The F.T. of a comb is therefore another comb. The 'teeth' of the comb in t space are a time T apart, and those of the comb in f space are $1/T$ apart. So the coarser the comb in t space is, the finer is that in f space, and *vice versa.* A proof of this result is given in *The Fourier transform and its applications* by R. Bracewell (McGraw-Hill, 2nd edition 1978).

The F.T. of $p(t)$ is shown pictorially in Fig. 8.3. Here we see in (c) the periodic function $p(t)$ expressed as the convolution of $f(t)$ (a) with the comb (b). The latter defines the periodicity of the function $p(t)$. On the right-hand side of the figure we see the F.T.s of the functions on the left-hand side. $G(f)$ is the F.T. (d) of the motif; (e) is the comb which is the F.T. of the comb (b) on the left-hand side. The final $P(f)$ is depicted in (f). We see in (f) that the positions of the delta functions define the frequencies at which components are situated, and the amplitudes of those components are determined by the local value of $G(f)$ the F.T. of the basic motif.

A three-dimensional version of Fig. 8.3 is that which prevails in crystallography. Here we have space (say, x) instead of t on the left-hand side, and wavenumber σ instead of f on the right. (Crystallographers call σ space *reciprocal space*). When the crystallographer investigates the structure of crystals by irradiating them with X-rays or other forms of radiation, he can obtain directly only information in σ space. So for a hypothetical one-dimensional crystal, which we may suppose is $p(x)$ depicted in (c), he would observe the amplitudes (but not the phases) of the components of $P(\sigma)$ illustrated in (f). He would first measure the inter-component distance in σ space and so determine the lattice spacing. Then by observing the amplitudes of the components in (f), he would surmise what $G(\sigma)$ would be and hence determine the details of the unit cell (the motif) $g(x)$.

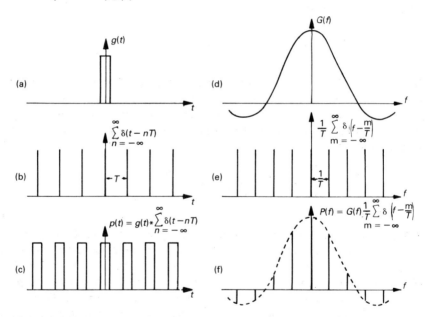

Fig. 8.3 — An illustration of the F.T. of a periodic function $p(t)$. (d), (e) and (f) are the F.T.s of (a), (b) and (c) respectively. (a) shows the motif to be repeated, (b) is a comb defining the periodicity, and (c) is the convolution of (a) with (b). (d) is the F.T. of the motif, (e) is the comb in f space defining the component frequencies present, and (f) is the product of (d) and (e).

PROBLEMS

(8.1) Prove the addition theorem, namely that the Fourier transform of $g_1(t) + g_2(t)$ is $G_1(f) + G_2(f)$, where $G_1(f)$ and $G_2(f)$ are the Fourier transforms of $g_1(t)$ and $g_2(t)$ respectively.

(8.2) Use the results of Problems 7.8 and 7.9, together with the shift theorem, to deduce the Fourier transforms of

$$\frac{1}{T\sqrt{(2\pi)}} \exp\left(-\frac{(t-t_0)^2}{2T^2}\right) \text{ and } \frac{1}{2T} \exp\left(-\frac{|t-t_0|}{T}\right).$$

(8.3) An oscillator gives N successive bursts of oscillation, each of the shape shown in Fig. 7.E2. They are centred on $t = 0, T_1, 2T_1 \ldots$. Using equation (7.E2), show that the Fourier transform of the whole signal is

$$y_0 T e^{-i\pi(N-1)fT_1} \frac{\sin \pi NfT_1}{\sin \pi fT_1} \left\{ \text{sinc } 2(f_0-f)T + \text{sinc } 2(f_0+f)\,T \right\}.$$

(8.4) Following Example 8.1, and using the result of Problem 7.9, show that the Fourier transform of $\exp(-|t|/T)$ is consistent with the similarity theorem.

(8.5) A business-man needs to transmit a large quantity of verbal information by long-distance telephone. To save money, he records this information on a tape recorder, and plays it back at ten times the speed over the telephone. The recipient records this, and plays it back at one tenth of the speed. If the bandwidth for intelligible speech is f_1 to f_2, what bandwidth must be possessed by the recorders and telephone line?

Suggest why one might expect a worse than usual degrading of the signal by noises inherent in the telephone line itself.

(8.6) Using the derivative theorem and the result of Problem 7.8, deduce the Fourier transforms of $t \exp(-\alpha t^2)$ and $t^2 \exp(-\alpha t^2)$, where α is a positive constant.

(8.7) Deduce the current $i(t)$ in the RLC circuit of Example 8.2, for the case $v(t) = v_0 \cos 2\pi f_0 t$, $(-\infty < t < \infty)$.

(8.8) Prove from the defining equation (8.6) for convolutions that

$$\{f(x)*g(x)\} * h(x) = f(x) * \{g(x)*h(x)\}.$$

(8.9) Prove from the defining equation (8.6) for convolutions that

$$\exp\left(-\alpha x^2\right) * \exp\left(-\beta x^2\right) = \sqrt{\left(\frac{\pi}{\alpha+\beta}\right)} \exp\left(-\frac{\alpha\beta}{\alpha+\beta}x^2\right)$$

(Hint: show that the convolution equals

$$\int_{-\infty}^{\infty} \exp\left\{-(\alpha+\beta)\left(u^2 - \frac{2\beta x}{\alpha+\beta}u\right) - \beta x^2\right\} du.$$

Re-express the exponent by 'completing the square' in u. Finally, use the identity

$$\int_{-\infty}^{\infty} \exp\left(-\gamma y^2\right) dy = \sqrt{\frac{\pi}{\gamma}} \ .$$

(8.10) Prove the result of Problem 8.9 from the convolution theorem. Use the result for the Fourier transform of $\exp\left(-\alpha x^2\right)$ obtained in Problem 7.8.

Similarly, using the result of Problem 7.9, show that

$$\frac{1}{a^2 + x^2} * \frac{1}{b^2 + x^2} = \frac{\pi(a + b)}{ab} \frac{1}{(a + b)^2 + x^2} \ .$$

(8.11) Show that the Fourier transform of a function which is unity for all time t is $\delta(f)$. (Hint: consider the inverse Fourier transform of $\delta(f)$.)

Interpret this result physically, e.g. for a steady current flowing in a circuit.

CHAPTER 9

Some wave phenomena

9.1 THE DOPPLER EFFECT

Consider a source of sinusoidal waves and an observer remote from the source. If the source is moving, the observer receives a wave of frequency different from that generated by the source. If, on the other hand, the observer is moving, the source being stationary, the observer again receives a wave of frequency different from that generated. This phenomenon is known as the *Doppler effect*, and a common acoustical example of it is the change in the pitch of the note of the horn sounded by a passing vehicle.

We shall deduce expressions for the magnitude of the effect. Consider first a source S, initially at rest, emitting a wave of frequency f, which propagates with wavelength λ and wave velocity c, and which is received by an observer O, also initially at rest (Fig. 9.1). We assume that the medium is at rest, and consider motion in only one dimension (i.e. along SO in Fig. 9.1).

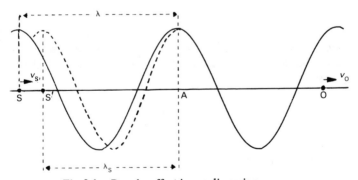

Fig. 9.1 – Doppler effect in one dimension.

When both S and O are at rest, the number of wave crests received by O in unit time is equal to the frequency f of the wave. Suppose now that O moves away from S with a constant speed v_O; the number of crests received by O in unit time will be decreased by the number of crests that are contained in a length equal to the distance travelled by O in unit time.

Since this distance is v_O, and the distance between adjacent crests is the wavelength λ, the decrease in the number of crests received by O is v_O/λ. Thus if f_O is the apparent frequency received by O, we have

$$f_O = f - \frac{v_O}{\lambda} \; .$$

But, since $c = f\lambda$,

we have $\quad f_O = f - \dfrac{v_O f}{c} \; .$

Thus $\quad f_O = f \dfrac{c - v_O}{c} \; .$ $\hspace{4cm}$ (9.1)

[We note that this equation predicts that $f_O = 0$ when $v_O = c$, as we would expect.]

Next we examine the effect of the motion of the source. When the source is at rest, successive wave crests emitted by it are one wavelength λ apart, but when the source is moving towards the observer, the distance between adjacent crests is decreased by the distance the source travels in one cycle. The situation is shown in Fig. 9.1 in which S is moving to the right with constant speed v_S; the distance travelled by S in one cycle is SS′ and the wavelength is decreased from SA ($=\lambda$) for stationary S to S′A ($=\lambda_S$). The time taken for one cycle is $1/f$ and the velocity of S is v_S; the distance SS′ is thus v_S/f. Therefore

$$\lambda_S = \lambda - \frac{v_S}{f} \; .$$

But since the medium in which the wave is being propagated is at rest, the wave velocity is unchanged, so that the frequency of the signal received by the stationary observer is

$$f_S = \frac{c}{\lambda_S} \; .$$

Replacing λ_S and λ by c/f_S and c/f respectively, we have

$$\frac{c}{f_S} = \frac{c}{f} - \frac{v_S}{f} \; ;$$

thus $\quad f_S = \dfrac{cf}{c - v_S} \; .$ $\hspace{4cm}$ (9.2)

These results can be combined as follows to give the frequency f_{O+S} received by the observer when both source and observer are in motion. The moving source gives rise to a wave whose apparent frequency is given by (9.2). If we take f_S to be the frequency of the wave itself, we need not concern ourselves further with the source. The moving observer will receive a wave whose apparent frequency, f_{O+S}, is obtained by substituting f_S for f in the right-hand side of 9.1 giving

$$f_{O+S} = f \frac{c - v_O}{c - v_S} \, . \tag{9.3}$$

Perhaps the most interesting example of the Doppler effect is in astronomy. When the light from a star is examined spectroscopically, it is found to contain the spectra of common terrestrial elements, but the spectral lines are shifted towards the red end of the spectrum (i.e. the values of λ are all greater than those emitted by atoms in a light source in the laboratory). This 'red shift' can be explained by (9.2), for if the star is travelling away from the earth, it is evident that $\lambda_S > \lambda$. However, the truth is rather more complex than this since, firstly, (9.2) is only approximately true for light waves and, secondly, there are other agencies which cause a red shift.

Example 9.1

Beats arising from the Doppler effect

A source emitting a sinusoidal sound wave of frequency 500 Hz travels towards a wall at a speed 10 ms^{-1}. What is the beat frequency perceived by an observer travelling away from the wall at a speed 20 ms^{-1}, if the speed of sound is 340 ms^{-1}?

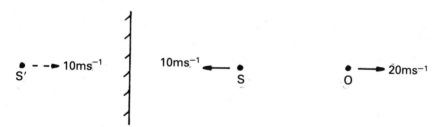

Fig. 9.E1 – Sound source moving towards a wall.

Consider the sound travelling directly from S to O. The frequency perceived by O is given by (9.3), where $v_S = -10$ ms^{-1} and $v_O = 20$ ms^{-1}. Hence $f_{O+S} = 500 \times 320/350$ Hz.

Now the observer will also receive the sound reflected from the wall. How is this to be taken into account? Clearly, the reflection at the wall cannot depend on the motion of the source S; therefore the reflected wavelength must equal the incident wavelength. But the incident wavelength is, from the argument given earlier, $\lambda + v_S/f = (c + v_S)/f$. The apparent frequency, if O were stationary, would therefore be $fc/(c + v_S)$. Since O is moving, the frequency observed by O is $f(c - v_O)/(c + v_S) = 500 \times 320/330$ Hz.

Although the analysis in the last paragraph is correct, there is a quicker way of arriving at the same result; the observer 'sees' an image S' of the source, behind the wall, moving at a speed 10 ms^{-1} from left to right. The observed frequency from S' is obtained therefore by putting $v_{S'} = 10$ ms^{-1}, $v_O = 20$ ms^{-1} into (9.3), whence $f_{O+S'} = 500 \times 320/330$ Hz, as previously obtained.

The observer therefore receives two slightly different frequencies, and will therefore perceive an audible 'beat'. The beat frequency is $500 \times 320 \times (1/330 - (1/350) = 27.7$ Hz.

9.2 DISPERSION AND GROUP VELOCITY

Each physical system treated in Chapter 5 gave a unique wave speed determined solely by the physical constants of the medium concerned. We found that

$$c = \sqrt{\frac{T}{\mu}}$$

for a string, and

$$c = \sqrt{\frac{K}{\rho_0}}$$

for a fluid, where ρ_0 is the ambient density, so that waves can be propagated with these speeds and with no others.

There are, however, examples in physics in which the wave velocity turns out to be dependent upon the wavelength, but these are considerably more difficult to treat than those of Chapter 5. One example is that of surface waves on a liquid of depth h, density ρ, and surface tension γ for which

$$c^2 = \left[\frac{g}{k} + \frac{\gamma k}{\rho} \right] \tanh(kh) \ ,$$

where g is the acceleration due to gravity and k is the circular wavenumber. Another example is that of light waves in a transparent medium, where the relationship between the velocity and wavelength is rather complicated. This property of velocity dependence upon wavelength is called *dispersion*; a medium possessing this property is called a *dispersive medium.*

We now proceed to examine the collective behaviour of a number of waves of different wavelength propagated simultaneously through a medium. We saw in Chapter 6 how two or more waves may be superposed according to the principle of superposition. There we superposed two waves of the same circular frequency and circular wavenumber; let us now see what happens when we superpose two waves of slightly different circular frequency and circular wavenumber, but of the same amplitude.

Let the two waves be

$$y_1 = a \sin(\omega_1 t - k_1 x)$$

and

$$y_2 = a \sin(\omega_2 t - k_2 x) \ .$$

Then, according to the principle of superposition, the combined effect of these two waves is given by

$$y = y_1 + y_2$$
$$= 2a \sin\left[\tfrac{1}{2}(\omega_1 + \omega_2)t - \tfrac{1}{2}(k_1 + k_2)x\right] \cos\left[\tfrac{1}{2}(\omega_1 - \omega_2)t - \tfrac{1}{2}(k_1 - k_2)x\right]. \ (9.4)$$

The sine term represents a wave whose circular frequency and circular wavenumber are the averages of those of the original wave, and whose wave velocity is

$$\frac{\omega_1 + \omega_2}{k_1 + k_2} \ .$$

Since we have assumed that ω_1 differs only slightly from ω_2, and k_1 only slightly from k_2, $\tfrac{1}{2}(\omega_1 + \omega_2)$ will differ only slightly from ω_1 or ω_2, and $\tfrac{1}{2}(k_1 + k_2)$ only slightly from k_1 or k_2. Thus the sine term represents a wave whose phase is very similar to those of both the original waves.

The cosine term represents a wave whose circular frequency and circular wavenumber are, respectively, $\tfrac{1}{2}(\omega_1 - \omega_2)$ and $\tfrac{1}{2}(k_1 - k_2)$, and whose wave velocity is therefore

$$\frac{\omega_1 - \omega_2}{k_1 - k_2} \ ;$$

this term varies more slowly with both time and distance than does the sine term. Figure 9.2 shows how a sketch of the function (9.4) is obtained for fixed t; the ordinates of the sine term (a) and the cosine term (b) are multiplied together, point by point, to produce the heavy curve in (c) which is seen to be contained within an envelope defined by the cosine curve of (b) and its image in the x-axis. It may be seen from the symmetry between the x- and t-terms in (9.4) that a plot of y against t for constant x would give a curve of the same form as that in Fig. 9.2c. The successive building up and dying away of amplitude with time is the phenomenon of beats which has already been referred to at the end of Chapter 2.

A combination of two or more waves in this manner is known as a *wave group*. We will examine now how wave groups behave in non-dispersive and dispersive media. In a non-dispersive medium, the wave velocity is constant, so

$$c = \frac{\omega_1}{k_1} = \frac{\omega_2}{k_2} = \frac{\omega_1 + \omega_2}{k_1 + k_2} = \frac{\omega_1 - \omega_2}{k_1 - k_2} \ .$$

This means that the sine part and the cosine part of (9.4) have exactly the same wave velocity, so that as the heavy curve and the envelope of Fig. 9.2c move to the right with increasing time, the position of each relative to the other remains constant. This means that a signal propagated in a non-dispersive medium suffers no change of form.

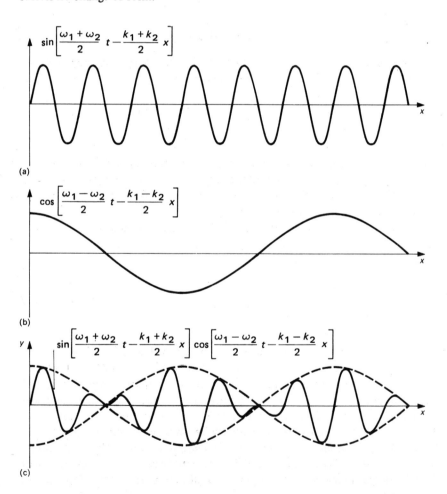

(a)

(b)

(c)

Fig. 9.2 – Superposition at constant t of two waves of slightly different ω and k: (a) shows the sine term of 9.4, (b) the cosine term, and (c) the product of the two terms (heavy line).

In the case of a dispersive medium, we have seen that wave velocity varies with wavelength so that

$$\frac{\omega_1}{k_1} \neq \frac{\omega_2}{k_2}$$

and therfore $\dfrac{\omega_1 - \omega_2}{k_1 + k_2} \neq \dfrac{\omega_2 - \omega_2}{k_1 - k_2}$.

This means that the heavy curve and the envelope in Fig. 9.2c move forward with *different* velocities. The situation is illustrated in Fig. 9.3, where the curves of Fig. 9.2c are shown at two successive times. It can be seen in Fig. 9.3

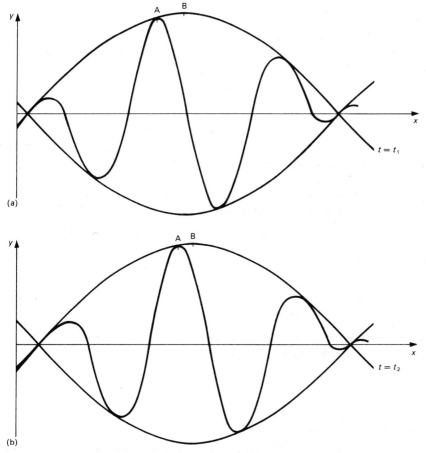

Fig. 9.3 — Wave group in a dispersive medium. The sketches (a) and (b) show the curves of Fig. 9.2c at two successive instants of time. It can be seen that the crest A of the inner curve has advanced a greater distance along the x-axis than has the maximum B of the envelope.

that the inner curve is moving forward at a faster rate than that of the envelope, which means that in this example

$$\frac{\omega_1 - \omega_2}{k_1 - k_2} < \frac{\omega_1 + \omega_2}{k_1 + k_2} \; . \tag{9.5}$$

It happens that in the great majority of cases in physics (9.5) holds so that this type of dispersion is referred to as *normal dispersion*; an example is deep-sea waves with wavelengths so large that surface-tension effects can be neglected. On the other hand, if the envelope moves faster than the heavy curve, we have

$$\frac{\omega_1 - \omega_2}{k_1 - k_2} > \frac{\omega_1 + \omega_2}{k_1 + k_2} \; .$$

This happens less frequently in physics and is referred to as *anomalous dispersion*; examples of it are transverse waves in a solid rod and electromagnetic waves near what is known as an 'absorption edge'.

An extremely important quantity, which we must now examine, is the velocity with which energy is carried forward when two waves are superposed to form a group. When we have a single wave, the energy is carried forward with the velocity at which an amplitude maximum moves forward, which, of course, is the wave velocity. In the case of a wave group, however, we can see from a study of Fig. 9.3 that the velocity with which an amplitude maximum moves forward is that of the *envelope*. It follows that the energy is borne forward with the velocity of the envelope. This velocity is known as the *group velocity* c_g. We saw earlier that the envelope moves with velocity

$$\frac{\omega_1 - \omega_2}{k_1 - k_2} \; ,$$

so
$$c_g = \frac{\omega_1 - \omega_2}{k_1 - k_2} \; . \tag{9.6}$$

We assumed at the outset that ω_1 differed from ω_2, and k_1 from k_2, by small amounts; we may therefore rewrite (9.6) as

$$c_g = \frac{\Delta\omega}{\Delta k}$$

where $\Delta\omega = \omega_1 - \omega_2$ and $\Delta k = k_1 - k_2$.
In the limit, as $\Delta k \to 0$ we have

$$\boxed{c_g = \frac{d\omega}{dk}} \; . \tag{9.7}$$

Since $k = 2\pi/\lambda$, this may be rewritten as

$$c_g = \frac{df}{d(1/\lambda)} = -\lambda^2 \frac{df}{d\lambda} \cdot \text{ i.e. } c_g = \frac{1}{2\pi} \frac{d\omega}{d(1/\lambda)} = -\frac{\lambda^2}{2\pi} \frac{d\omega}{d\lambda} \cdot \qquad (9.8)$$

Equation (9.8) is one of three useful equivalent expressions for the group velocity; the others can be obtained as follows. Firstly, if we replace ω in (9.7) by kc, where c is the *wave* velocity (the waves which are superposed to form the group have velocities so near to one another than the single value c can be used), then (9.7) becomes

$$c_g = \frac{d(kc)}{dk} = c + k \frac{dc}{dk} \cdot \qquad (9.9)$$

Secondly, if we replace k by $2\pi/\lambda$ in the right-hand side of (9.9) we obtain another useful expression,

$$c_g = c + \frac{2\pi}{\lambda} \frac{dc}{d(2\pi/\lambda)} \text{ i.e. } \boxed{c_g = c - \lambda \frac{dc}{d\lambda}} \cdot$$

The above results have been deduced from the superposition of only two waves, but they are valid for a group comprising a superposition of any number — even an infinite number — of waves.

9.3 MODULATION

In the transmission of information by radio waves the original signal is not sent out directly, but is first modified by a process called *modulation*. At the receiving end the incoming wave is *demodulated*, producing a replica of the original signal. There are various types of modulation, the three most common of which, namely *amplitude modulation, phase modulation,* and *frequency modulation,* will be described briefly in this section.

9.3.1 Amplitude modulation
This is a common technique used in the radio broadcasting of audio signals. It would in principle be possible to convert an audio signal into an electromagnetic wave with the use of an appropriate transducer, but since we require an aerial of length of the order of λ to deliver a significant amount of power in propagating the wave, an impracticably long aerial would be needed at these frequencies. For example, to radiate efficiently a signal of 1000 Hz as a radio signal, we would need an aerial of length of the order of

$$\frac{\text{velocity of light}}{\text{frequency}} \approx \frac{3 \times 10^8}{1000} = 3 \times 10^5 \, \text{m} - \text{about two hundred miles!}$$

It is evident, therefore, that it is prohibitively difficult to transmit audio signals as electromagnetic waves; the technique of *amplitude modulation* is one in which the audio signal is processed in such a way as to change its frequency spectrum so that only much higher frequencies are in the transmitted signal.

When no information is being transmitted, the transmitter gives out a pure sinusoidal electromagnetic wave known as the *carrier*. Different broadcasting stations operate at different *carrier frequencies*, each of which is characteristic of a particular station. When the input stage of the receiving set is adjusted to be at resonance with the carrier frequency, the set is said to be 'tuned' to that station. The carrier frequencies are (by audio standards) extremely high, typically in the range 0.1 MHz–100 MHz. Now suppose it is desired to send an audio signal (the spectrum of which lies between about 30 Hz and 15 kHz) $y(t)$ by radio. It is first necessary that the magnitude of the signal $|y(t)|$ never exceeds a certain value. Let us suppose, for simplicity, that this value is unity. So $|y(t)| \leqslant 1$. The initial part of the process of amplitude modulation is to add a d.c. component to the signal, so that it is always positive. This can, of course, be achieved by adding such a component of unit amplitude. The signal has therefore now become $1 + y(t)$. The next part of the process is to feed this latter signal into a circuit which gives, as output, the product of the signal with the function describing the carrier wave, namely

$$[1 + y(t)] \cos 2\pi f_c t , \tag{9.10}$$

where f_c is the frequency of the carrier. Expression (9.10) is the form of the transmitted wave (see Fig. 9.4).

To understand why this should be a desirable modification of the original signal $y(t)$ before transmitting it, it is necessary to know the spectrum of expression (9.10). Before we find this, let us take a simple example. Suppose we wish to transmit a pure tone of frequency f_p; that is, suppose

$$y(t) = \cos 2\pi f_p t .$$

Then (9.10) becomes

$$[1 + \cos 2\pi f_p t] \cos 2\pi f_c t , \tag{9.11}$$

which, by a little rearrangement involving familiar trigonometric identities, further becomes

$$\tfrac{1}{2}\cos 2\pi(f_c - f_p)t + \cos 2\pi f_c t + \tfrac{1}{2} \cos 2\pi(f_c + f_p)t .$$

The spectrum of this, obtained by Fourier transformation, is

$$\tfrac{1}{4}\delta(f - f_c + f_p) + \tfrac{1}{4}\delta(f + f_c - f_p) + \tfrac{1}{2}\delta(f - f_c) + \tfrac{1}{2}\delta(f + f_c) +$$
$$+ \tfrac{1}{4}\delta(f - f_c - f_p) + \tfrac{1}{4}\delta(f + f_c + f_p) ,$$

by equation (7.19), and is illustrated in Fig. 9.4 together with the spectra of $\cos 2\pi f_p t$, $1 + \cos 2\pi f_p t$ and $\cos 2\pi f_c t$.

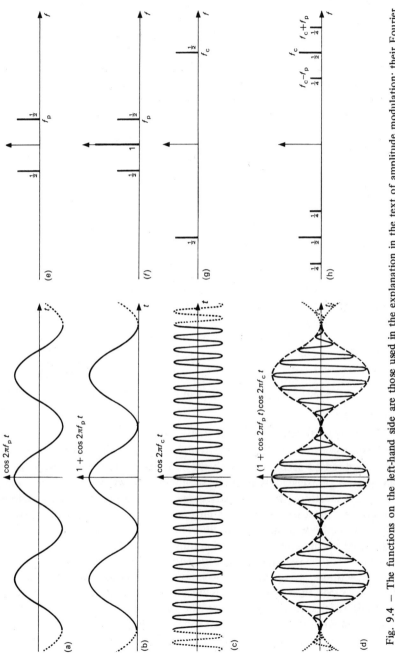

Fig. 9.4 – The functions on the left-hand side are those used in the explanation in the text of amplitude modulation; their Fourier transforms are shown on the right-hand side.

The above analysis, together with Fig. 9.4, illustrates many of the essential properties of the amplitude-modulated carrier. We see immediately from the spectrum (h) of the transmitted signal (d) (expression (9.11)) that there is no amplitude at audio frequencies, although the original signal modulating the wave is of audio frequency. This reveals the importance of modulation techniques; frequencies are *changed* from their original values to any value we care to specify, the new frequencies being determined by that of the carrier.

Consider the detailed structure of the spectrum in Fig. 9.4h. The amplitude appears to be concentrated symmetrically about the carrier frequency. This in fact is generally true, as we shall shortly show. The components represented by the delta functions at frequencies $f_c - f_p$ and $f_c + f_p$ are known as *sidebands*. The process of demodulating at the receiving end is essentially one of recovering the original spectrum from the information contained around the region of the carrier frequency. We will, however, not go into details here.

Let us now consider the Fourier transform of the function

$$[1 + y(t)] \cos 2\pi f_c t \; , \tag{9.10}$$

where $y(t)$ is a general function of time (Fig. 9.5d). We note that the function to be transformed is a product of two functions $1 + y(t)$ and $\cos 2\pi f_c t$. So, by the convolution theorem discussed in Chapter 8, the F.T. of the function must be the convolution of the F.T. of $1 + y(t)$ and that of $\cos 2\pi f_c t$. If we let the F.T. of $y(t)$ be $Y(f)$, then the F.T. of $1 + y(t)$ is $\delta(f) + Y(f)$.

The F.T. of $\cos 2\pi f_c t$ is $\frac{1}{2}[\delta(f - f_0) + \delta(f + f_0)]$ (equation (7.19)). So the F.T. of $[1 + y(t)] \cos 2\pi f_c t$ is $[\delta(f) + Y(f)] * \frac{1}{2}[\delta(f - f_0) + \delta(f + f_0)]$

$$= \tfrac{1}{2}[\delta(f - f_0) + Y(f - f_0) + \delta(f + f_0) + Y(f + f_0)] \; . \tag{9.12}$$

by (8.9).

The relevant functions and their transforms are shown in Fig. 9.5.

From the nature of the Fourier transform, Fig. 9.5h, we see that the band-width required to accommodate all the information in the original $y(t)$, when that signal is propagated as an amplitude-modulated wave, is twice the extent of the original spectrum. One of the advantages of the technique is that, by choosing appropriate carrier frequencies, the information can be propagated in whatever frequency range we choose. No interference with other information being transmitted on the same, or a neighbouring, transmitter can occur if the carrier frequencies for the two signals are sufficiently far apart in frequency.

Furthermore, it is possible to accommodate twice as many signals in a given frequency range than the above discussion would indicate by suppressing the sidebands of frequencies lower than (or higher than) that of the carrier, the information from the remaining sideband still being extractable. This is because the amplitude spectrum is symmetrical about the carrier frequency; there is therefore no essential information about the signal in the lower sideband that is not already contained in the upper sideband. This *single-sideband* transmission

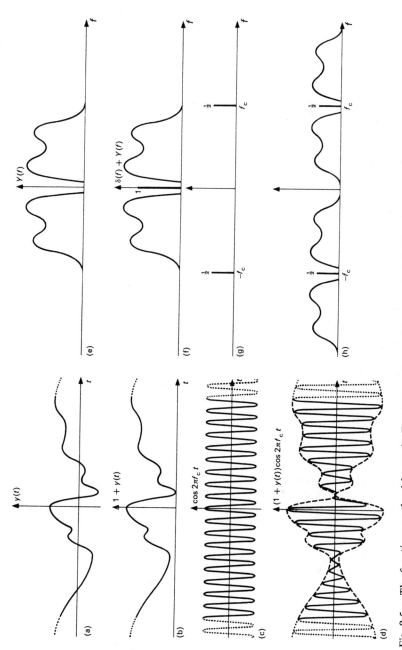

Fig. 9.5 — The functions on the right are the Fourier transforms of those on the left. The transmitter signal (d) is the product of (b) and (c); the F.T., (h), of the transmitted signal is the convolution of (f) and (g).

occupies only half the bandwidth taken by the double-sideband modulation, and therefore we can put other information in the suppressed sideband region provided, of course, that the receiving set is constructed accordingly.

9.3.2 Phase modulation and frequency modulation

These are both examples of what is known as *angle modulation*. The signal $y(t)$, instead of modifying the amplitude of the carrier wave, as in the previous case, modifies the angle which is the argument of the cosine function representing the carrier. Without any signal, the carrier can be represented as $\cos 2\pi f_c t$; this is modified, when a signal $y(t)$ phase modulates the carrier, to $\cos[2\pi f_c t + y(t)]$. So we see that the amplitude of the carrier remains constant regardless of the presence or absence of a signal, and the information in the signal is contained in the deviation of the argument of the cosine from what it would be if $y(t)$ were zero. In a very similar way the representation of a carrier wave *frequency modulated* by a signal $y(t)$ is

$$\cos\left[2\pi f_c t + \int_{\infty}^{t} y(u)\,du\right]. \qquad (9.13)$$

where u is a dummy variable in units of time. The reason for calling (9.13) a frequency-modulated wave is as follows. We can define the *instantaneous frequency* f_i as

$$\frac{1}{2\pi}\frac{d}{dt}\,(\text{argument of the cosine}) .$$

This yields a constant value f_c for an unmodulated cosine wave $\cos 2\pi f_c t$, since the argument of the cosine here is $2\pi f_c t$, giving f_i as

$$f_i = \frac{1}{2\pi}\frac{d}{dt}\,(2\pi f_c t) = f_c .$$

In a similar way, we find the instantaneous frequency for the expression (9.13) is

$$f_i = \frac{1}{2\pi}\frac{d}{dt}\left[2\pi f_c t + \int_{\infty}^{t} y(u)\,du\right]$$

$$= f_c + \frac{1}{2\pi}\,y(t) .$$

Thus $$f_i - f_c = \frac{1}{2\pi}\,y(t) ,$$

and we see that the instantaneous deviation in frequency from that of the carrier is directly proportional to the magnitude of the signal at that time. Hence the wave (9.13) is described as a frequency-modulated wave.

We do not propose to go into the question of the spectra of these waves; these are much more complicated than for amplitude-modulated waves and we refer the reader who may be interested in the matter to the list for further reading (for example *Analysis, Transmission and Filtering of Signals* by M. Javid and E. Bronner (McGraw-Hill 1963)).

PROBLEMS

(9.1) A car is travelling along a road on which there is a speed limit of 70 m.p.h. (= 31.3 ms^{-1}). A stationary policeman notices that the pitch of the horn falls by an interval of a major third (i.e. a frequency ratio of 5/4) when the car passes. To what conclusion might he come? (Speed of sound in air = 340 ms^{-1}).

(9.2) Show that it is possible for zero frequency to be perceived if the observer is in motion, but not if the source is in motion with the observer stationary.

(9.3) How would equation (9.3) be modified if there were a wind moving from observer to source with velocity v_W?

(9.4) Show that if v_S and v_O are both small compared with c, the fractional change in frequency due to the Doppler effect depends on the *relative* velocity, and is in the fact $(v_S - v_O)/c$.

(9.5) Using the result of problem (9.4), and assuming (correctly!) that it also applies to the Doppler effect for light, estimate the Doppler spread in wavelength from hydrogen atoms which, if stationary, would emit light with wavelength 650 nm, but are in fact moving randomly with speeds $\sim 3 \times 10^3$ ms^{-1}. (Speed of light = 3×10^8 ms^{-1}).

(9.6) (longer) Consider the meaning of the 'apparent wavelength of a stationary source to a moving observer'. This is less well-defined than the frequency, which is unambiguous. Consider two ways in which the wavelength may be measured:
(a) by taking an instantaneous 'photograph' of the medium with its troughs and crests.
(b) by performing an acoustic Young's slits experiment (Chapter 11).
No solution is given, but the interested reader is referred to Physics Education **16**, 366–8, (1981).

(9.7) Deep-water waves are defined as being such that λ is much smaller than the depth of water, but large enough for surface tension effects to be negligible. Show that for such waves, $c^2 = g\lambda/2\pi$. [(N.B. tanh $\theta = (e^\theta - e^{-\theta})/(e^\theta + e^{-\theta})$].
Calculate the wave velocity if $\lambda = 10$ m.
Show that the group velocity of deep-water waves is half the wave velocity.

(9.8) Show that for shallow water waves (i.e. λ is much greater than the depth h, and surface tension effects are negligible), $c^2 = gh$. Are such waves dispersive? What is the group velocity?

(9.9) Surface ripples on water are such that λ is much smaller than the depth, and also so small that surface tension effects dominate (i.e. $2\pi\gamma/\rho\lambda \gg g\lambda/2\pi$). What range of wavelengths would satisfy this condition for water? ($\gamma = 0.073$ Nm^{-1}).

Show that for such waves, $c^2 = 2\pi\gamma/\rho\lambda$. Calculate the wave velocity if $\lambda = 1$ mm.

Show that the group velocity is $3/2$ times the wave velocity. (Note that this is a case of anomalous dispersion.)

(9.10) Deduce an expression for the wave velocity c as a function of λ for a hypothetical medium in which the group velocity is a constant V at all wavelengths. Show that the only physically acceptable solution is one in which the medium is non-dispersive.

(9.11) Use the computer program (Appendix A, section A.8(g)) to demonstrate group velocity.

(9.12) Use the computer program (Appendix A, section A.8(h)) to demonstrate amplitude modulation.

CHAPTER 10

Sound

10.1 INTRODUCTION

This chapter is concerned with some features of sound waves. The word 'sound' has two distinct meanings. The first meaning is 'longitudinal waves in matter' — that is, the actual disturbance and its propagation in the medium; the second meaning is 'those longitudinal waves in a fluid which evoke a percept in the auditory system'. Now, as we shall discuss later in this chapter, the auditory system (i.e. the combination of ears and brain) can perceive only a limited range of frequencies. The range varies from person to person and is also dependent upon the age of a person, but is usually from about 16 Hz–16000 Hz. It is therefore evident that there can exist 'sound' in the sense of the first meaning which is certainly not sound according to the second. For this reason, physicists and others have, in recent years, referred to sounds of very low, inaudible frequencies as *infrasonic* and sounds of very high, inaudible frequencies as *ultrasonic*. But audibility is not determined solely by frequency, because, even though a sound has a spectrum within the audible frequency range, it does not necessarily mean that it can be heard. In fact for amplitudes below a certain 'threshold' the sound is too faint to be heard – i.e. the wave is not sufficiently energetic to evoke a percept.

The first observation to be made about sound in air (in its first meaning) is that it is a longitudinal wave motion that must be described by a solution of the three-dimensional equivalent of the one-dimensional wave equation

$$\frac{\partial^2 z}{\partial t^2} = c^2 \frac{\partial^2 z}{\partial x^2} \qquad (10.1)$$

discussed in section 5.3. Sound waves in air (or, indeed, in any fluid) have to be longitudinal because a fluid is unable to sustain a torsional or shear force.

In this equation, z is the displacement at a position x and at a time t, and c, the velocity of the sound waves, is $\sqrt{(\gamma P/\rho)}$, where γ is the ratio of principal specific heats for air, P is the ambient pressure and ρ is the density. The velocity of sound is about 340 ms^{-1} (760 m.p.h.); that is, a sound wave travels roughly one third of a kilometre in one second. Since this velocity is so much less than that of light, distant events producing simultaneous optical and acoustical disturbances (such as in an electrical storm) do not evoke simultaneous visual and aural percepts.

10.2 SOUND WAVES IN A PIPE

Sound waves within a pipe of fixed length must, of course, be described by solutions of (10.1); however, the presence of the pipe imposes boundary conditions on the problem which restrict the possible solutions, as was described in Chapter 6. Before embarking on an analysis of sound waves in pipes we make two assumptions, of which the first is that the length L of the pipe is much larger than its radius. This assumption enables us to consider the pipe as essentially a one-dimensional entity, in which the air can vibrate only along its length. We therefore are able to use the one-dimensional wave equation (10.1). We also assume that the pipe is of uniform cross-section.

We shall consider in detail the pipe closed at one end and open at the other. The x-axis is taken along the pipe. There are two boundary conditions that must be applied. The first is very simple; at no time can there be any displacement at the closed end of the pipe, at $x = 0$, because this is considered to be rigidly fixed. Our first boundary condition therefore is

$$[z]_{x=0} = 0 \quad \text{for all values of } t \ . \tag{10.2}$$

The second boundary condition is concerned with the magnitude of vibrations at the open end of the pipe, and is by no means as simple as the first. It will be recalled from Chapter 5 that the displacement variations in a sound wave are accompanied by pressure variations. Indeed the sound wave can be specified either by the pressure or the displacement variations, as desired. As was shown in section 5.3, the acoustic pressure p and the displacement z are related by

$$p = -K \frac{\partial z}{\partial x} \ . \tag{5.9}$$

Now, because of the presence of the rigid wall of the pipe, there is no opportunity for any excess pressure caused by the displacement to dissipate in a direction perpendicular to the length of the pipe. However, beyond the open end of the pipe there is such an opportunity and, consequently, the acoustic pressure falls away very quickly. So to a first approximation we can say that there is no acoustic pressure outside the pipe. This, as we shall discuss later on, is an assumption we can make only with reservations, but it is not unreasonable. So our second boundary condition is that

$$[p]_{x=L} = 0$$

for all values of t, which, because of equation (5.9) can be re-expressed as

$$\left[\frac{\partial z}{\partial x}\right]_{x=L} = 0 \quad \text{for all values of } t \ . \tag{10.3}$$

The wave equation (10.1), together with the boundary conditions (10.2) and (10.3), enable us to deduce a complete description of the wave motion within the pipe. Whatever the most general motion is, we can say from our experience in Chapter 2 that it must be some linear combination of the normal modes. Since the air in the pipe can be regarded as a continuous medium, there must be an infinite number of normal modes of vibration. Let us therefore find a typical normal mode solution. It will be recalled that a normal mode solution is one for which the air vibration throughout the whole pipe takes place at a single frequency, say f_n (the suffix n indicates the nth normal mode). The amplitude of vibration will vary along the length of the pipe but will, of course, be constant with time; we will describe its variation by the function $\phi_n(x)$. So a typical normal-mode solution is

$$z_n(x,t) = \phi_n(x) \cos(2\pi f_n t + \alpha_n) \ , \tag{10.4}$$

where α_n is a constant phase angle which belongs to the nth normal mode. Differentiating partially the equation (10.4) we obtain

$$\frac{\partial^2 z_n}{\partial t^2} = -4\pi^2 f_n^2 \, \phi_n(x) \cos(2\pi f_n t + \alpha_n) \quad \text{and}$$

$$\frac{\partial^2 z_n}{\partial x^2} = \cos(2\pi f_n t + \alpha_n) \frac{d^2\phi_n(x)}{dx^2} \ .$$

Substituting these derivatives into the original wave equation (10.1) we obtain

$$-4\pi^2 f_n^2 \, \phi_n(x) \cos(2\pi f_n t + \alpha_n) = c^2 \cos(2\pi f_n t + \alpha_n) \frac{d^2\phi_n(x)}{dx^2} \ ,$$

which, after some cancellation and rearrangement, becomes

$$\frac{d^2\phi_n(x)}{dx^2} = -\frac{4\pi^2 f_n^2}{c^2} \phi_n(x) \ . \tag{10.5}$$

Equation (10.5) is an ordinary differential equation in the one independent variable x, and we see immediately that it is identical in form to the simple-harmonic motion equation, except that the latter has t as its independent variable. The general solution of this has the form given by equation (2.2), namely

$$\phi_n(x) = a_n \sin \left[\left(\frac{4\pi^2 f_n^2}{c^2} \right)^{\frac{1}{2}} x + \epsilon_n \right]$$

$$= a_n \sin \left[\left(\frac{2\pi f_n}{c} \right) x + \epsilon_n \right] ,$$

where a_n and ϵ_n are arbitrary constants which are, in general, different for different values of n. Thus the amplitude variation $\phi_n(x)$ repeats periodically at intervals of

$$\lambda_n = \frac{2\pi}{2\pi f_n/c} = \frac{c}{f_n} .$$

So $c = f_n \lambda_n$.   (10.6)

The normal mode solution is, therefore, one of sinusoidal form (although we have not yet determined its phase) and we have shown that the wavelength λ_n is related to the frequency f_n by the simple, familiar relationship 10.6. Since the amplitude a_n is completely arbitrary, any amplitude of vibration is possible. In other words the wave equation determines only the *form* of the wave, not its *scale*.

The typical normal mode solution (10.4) can now be written as

$$z_n(x,t) = a_n \sin \left[\left(\frac{2\pi f_n}{c} \right) x + \epsilon_n \right] \cos(2\pi f_n t + \alpha_n) .$$ (10.7)

This will also be reconsized as being of the form of a standing wave (compare (10.7) with (6.12)) as expected, since there are two waves moving in opposite directions.

Let us now apply the boundary condition (10.2), namely

$$[z_n]_{x=0} = 0 \quad \text{for all } t ;$$

$$z_n(0,t) = a_n \sin \epsilon_n \cos(2\pi f_n t + \alpha_n) .$$

For this to be zero for all values of t, $a_n \sin \epsilon_n$ must be zero. Since $a_n = 0$ represents the trivial case of no vibration at all, we are forced to conclude that $\sin \epsilon_n$ is zero. This implies that

$$\epsilon_n = m\pi ,$$

where m is an integer. The only physically distinct values of m are 0 and 1, since the angles 2π, 4π, ... are identical to 0, and 3π, 5π, ... to π. The case $\epsilon_n = \pi$ merely changes the sign of the amplitude a_n, so, without any loss of generality, we may take ϵ_n as zero. Thus (10.7) may be rewritten as

$$z_n(x,t) = a_n \sin \left(\frac{2\pi f_n}{c} \right) x \cos(2\pi f_n t + \alpha_n) .$$ (10.8)

To apply the second boundary condition (10.3),

$$\left[\frac{\partial z_n}{\partial x}\right]_{x=L} = 0 \qquad [10.3]$$

we must differentiate (10.8) partially with respect to x. This gives us

$$\frac{\partial z_n(x,t)}{\partial x} = a_n 2\pi \frac{f_n}{c} \cos\left(2\pi \frac{f_n}{c} x\right) \cos(2\pi f_n t + \alpha_n) \ ,$$

which, for $x = L$, becomes

$$\left[\frac{\partial z_n(x,t)}{\partial x}\right]_{x=L} = a_n 2\pi \frac{f_n}{c} \cos\left(2\pi \frac{f_n}{c} L\right) \cos(2\pi f_n t + \alpha_n) \ .$$

But this must be zero for all values of t, by equation (10.3), and so

$$\cos 2\pi \frac{f_n}{c} L = 0 \ .$$

This implies that

$$2\pi \frac{f_n}{c} L = (n + \tfrac{1}{2})\pi \ ,$$

where n is an integer, i.e.

$$\frac{f_n}{c} = \frac{(n + \tfrac{1}{2})}{2L}$$

$$= \frac{(2n + 1)}{4L} \ . \qquad (10.9)$$

Thus the functions $\phi_n(x)$ are

$$\phi_n(x) = a_n \sin \frac{2\pi(2n + 1)x}{4L} \ ,$$

which are sine functions of wavelengths

$$\lambda_0 = 4L, \ \lambda_1 = \tfrac{4}{3}L, \ \lambda_2 = \tfrac{4}{5}L, \ \lambda_3 = \tfrac{4}{7}L, \text{ etc.}$$

The first four of these functions are sketched in Fig. 10.1, from which it will be seen that an antinode of displacement exists at $x = L$ for all the functions ϕ_n. This is a direct consequence of the pressure node at the open end of the pipe which was the second of our boundary conditions. The displacement nodes at

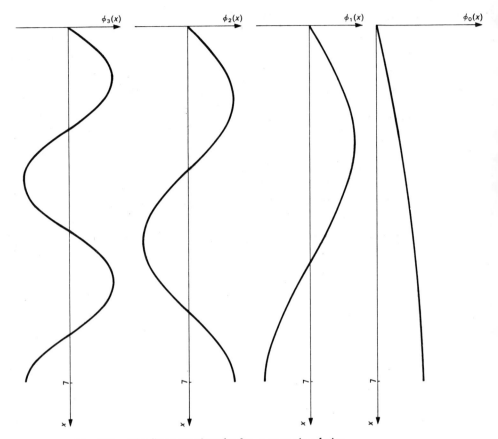

Fig. 10.1 – The first normal modes for an open-closed pipe.

$x = 0$ for all the ϕ_n are, of course, a result of the boundary condition of no displacement at the closed end. The values of the different f_n are seen from (10.9) to be

$$f_n = \frac{(2n+1)}{4L} \, c \; ;$$

substituting $n = 0$ in this equation we obtain

$$f_0 = \frac{c}{4L} \, .$$

Similarly $f_1 = 3 \, \dfrac{c}{4L}$, $f_2 = 5 \, \dfrac{c}{4L}$, etc .

The relationship between the natural frequencies is therefore

$$f_1 = 3f_0, f_2 = 5f_0, f_3 = 7f_0, \text{ and so on} .$$

These frequencies are thus seen to be very simply related to each other; in fact if we had analysed the wave motion in pipe open at both ends, we would have found an even simpler relationship, namely that the frequencies would have been related in the ratios of the natural numbers 1, 2, 3, 4, . . . ; that is,

$$f_2 = 2f_1, f_3 = 3f_1, \text{ and so on} .$$

The reason why we did not analyse this case was that it did not give an opportunity to apply the two different kinds of boundary condition provided by the pipe closed at one end and open at the other.

We are now in a position to see why the pipe is such an important constituent part of some musical instruments. Taking the open–open pipe as our example, we have already seen that the normal mode frequencies are f_1, $2f_1$, $3f_1$, $4f_1$, etc. This is the *harmonic* series with f_1, the *first harmonic* (or *fundamental*), f_2 the *second harmonic* and so on. If the first eight of these could be successively sounded in ascending order of harmonics, and if the fundamental happened (for example) to be C below the bass stave, the musical effect would be as follows:

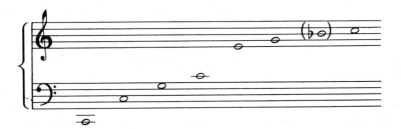

With the exception of the seventh harmonic, which is an excruciatingly flat B♭ (for which reason we have put the note in brackets) the first eight harmonics are all notes to be found on the western scale; in fact, the musical reader will immediately recognize them as forming the common chord of C major.

Since the general state of motion of the air in any pipe must be the sum of all the normal-mode solutions in varying strengths, depending on the method of exciting the motion, a given pipe can give out only frequencies in the harmonic sequence. These frequencies (for reasonably small harmonic number, at any rate) sound harmonious when heard in conjunction with each other. The musical nature of the sound from a pipe depends entirely on the fact that the natural frequencies for this acoustic system happen to be harmonically related to each other. The reason why a drum does not sound as musical as a pipe is that the natural frequencies of vibration of the drum head are related to each other in a very complicated way (in fact it may be shown that

$$f_2 \cong 1.5933f_1, f_3 \cong 2.1355f_1, f_4 \cong 2.2954f_1, \text{ and so on})$$

and the effect of these when heard simultaneously is nowhere near as harmonious as that from a pipe.

A little more should be said about the boundary condition (10.3) for the open end of a pipe. Strictly speaking, the problem is much more complex than was apparent from our analysis. There is some acoustic pressure just outside the open end, and our justification for assuming there was none was that the acoustic pressure outside was much less than that inside. More accurate (and complicated) analysis shows that the approximation is such that the pipe appears to be operating with an effective length slightly larger than its physical length. The extra length to make the frequencies observed fit the theory has been shown from experimentation and theoretical analysis to be about $0.6R$ where R is the radius of the pipe. This is known as the *end-correction*. Further, the end-correction has been shown to depend very slightly on the wavelength, with the consequence that the harmonics are progressively more out of tune with an integral multiple of the fundamental as the harmonic number increases. But this is not, in most cases, a large enough deviation to worry the listener.

Another way in which the theory is approximate is that we have tacitly assumed that no acoustical energy is lost from the pipe, so that, once we have excited the air in the pipe, the vibrations will go on for an infinite time, even if we terminate the excitation. That this is not so is a matter of common observation; organ pipes, for example, cease to speak as soon as the organist takes his fingers (or feet) off the keys. The reason for this lack of *motus perpetuus* is that the pipe radiates acoustic energy from its open end, and also, in practice, through the walls.

A final word should perhaps be said about the open–closed pipe. These are found, as well as open–open pipes, in organs, and they produce a tone which is significantly different from that given by the open–open pipe, since only the odd harmonics are present. The clarinet's distinctive tone is connected with the fact that, to a good approximation, it behaves as a closed pipe.

10.3 WAVES ON STRINGS

We have said a great deal about transverse waves on strings as easily visualized examples of wave motion; our reason for discussing them still further is that strings, as well as pipes, form the bases of many musical instruments such as the pianoforte, harp, members of the violin family and so forth. They are thus very relevant to a discussion of sound.

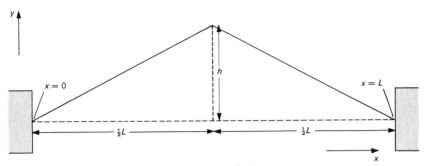

Fig. 10.2 – An example of initial conditions for a stretched string.

Let us consider a string of mass per unit length μ, length L, under a tension T, fixed at both ends as shown in Fig. 10.2. The wave equation (10.1) is valid for the stretched string, as we saw in Chapter 5, the velocity c, of transverse waves, in this case being $\sqrt{(T/\mu)}$. Our analysis will proceed much as that for waves in a pipe. First we need the boundary conditions; clearly, these are that the displacement y at each end of the string must be zero at all times. That is,

$$y(0,t) = 0 \qquad\qquad\qquad\qquad\qquad\qquad (10.10)$$

and $y(L,t) = 0$.   (10.11)

We take a typical normal-mode solution of (10.1) to be

$$y(x,t) = \phi_n(x) \cos(2\pi f_n t + \alpha_n) \qquad\qquad\qquad (10.12)$$

and, by an argument precisely the same as that in the last section we can obtain that $\phi_n(x)$ is the solution to the ordinary differential equation

$$\frac{d^2\phi_n(x)}{dx^2} = - \frac{4\pi^2 f_n^2}{c^2} \phi_n(x) .$$

As before, therefore, the most general solution is

$$\phi_n(x) = a_n \sin\left(\frac{2\pi f_n}{c} x + \epsilon_n\right) , \qquad\qquad (10.13)$$

and substitution of the boundary condition (10.10) yields the result $\epsilon_n = 0$. But the second boundary condition (10.11) differs from that in the previous section, and its implications can be seen by equating $\phi_n(L)$ in (10.13) to zero. This gives

$$a_n \sin \frac{2\pi f_n}{c} L = 0 ,$$

$$\text{i.e. } \frac{2\pi f_n}{c} L = 0, \pi, 2\pi, \ldots, n\pi, \ldots .$$

Thus the natural frequencies f_n are

$$f_n = \frac{nc}{2L} .$$

Since $c = \sqrt{(T/\mu)}$, the natural frequencies of the string are finally

$$f_n = \frac{n}{2L} \sqrt{\frac{T}{\mu}} . \tag{10.14}$$

Equation (10.14) is an expression of *Mersenne's law*; we see immediately from it that the natural frequencies are a harmonic series, since

$$f_1 = \frac{1}{2L} \sqrt{\frac{T}{\mu}} ,$$

and therefore $f_n = nf_1$.

The general motion of the string is a linear combination of all the normal modes, and therefore a string of given mass per unit length, under a given tension and of fixed length, can give only a combination of all its harmonics and no other frequency. This property, as we saw in the case of the pipe in the last section, is that which makes the string so suitable as the primary vibrator in a musical instrument.

Mersenne's law determines to a considerable extent the design, and in some cases the shape, of stringed musical instruments. By substituting $n = 1$ in (10.14), which gives

$$f_1 = \frac{1}{2L} \sqrt{\frac{T}{\mu}} , \tag{10.15}$$

we see that the fundamental frequency is determined exclusively by T, μ and L. Equation (10.15) determines, for example, the combination of the basic shape of the grand pianoforte, and the gradation in mass per unit length from string to string along the compass of the instrument. Suppose the lengths of all the strings in the pianoforte were the same, and further suppose all the strings were from one reel of wire. Then μ and L would be constants for the instrument, and the only way in which we could produce all the different notes over the instrument's seven-octave range would be having the strings at different tensions.

Now, each octave rise in pitch means a doubling of the frequency; this means that the highest note on the instrument is of frequency 2^7 times that of the lowest note seven octaves lower. If the frequencies of the top and bottom note are denoted by f_t and f_b respectively, with corresponding string tensions T_t and T_b, then (10.15) tells us that, for constant L and μ,

$$\frac{f_t}{f_b} = \sqrt{\frac{T_t}{T_b}} \ .$$

Thus $\quad \dfrac{T_t}{T_b} = \left(\dfrac{f_t}{f_b}\right)^2 = (2^7)^2 = 2^{14} = 16\ 384$.

So, whatever other defects this arrangement may have, the frame of the instrument would have an absurdly uneven distribution of tension. Clearly, some other way has to be found to give us the seven octave range. In practice, all the possible variables, T, μ and L, are used to this end, but the gradations of μ and L are the most obvious. The strings are shorter for higher frequencies than for lower, giving the grand pianoforte its harp-like shape (the harp's shape is, of course, determined by the same reasoning). In addition the strings of the lower notes are thicker than those of the higher notes, having the effect of reducing the enormous length the instrument would otherwise have.

The increased mass per unit length for the lower strings is achieved in a rather interesting way. The strings are not simple thick strings; they are comparatively thin strings which are overspun — that is, a second wire is coiled tightly round the original wire over its whole length. The effect of this is to make the string flexible; a simple thick string would have somewhat rod-like characteristics so that transverse waves along it would, as was pointed out briefly in Chapter 1, be dispersive, causing the natural frequencies of the string not to be harmonically related to each other. In fact, even with overspun strings and simple strings for the higher notes, the natural frequencies are not harmonic because of stiffness (i.e. non-flexibility), but this defect is not sufficiently large to be noticed directly by the ear. Nevertheless it is a fact that a pianoforte, tuned so that the fundamental frequencies of all the notes are in tune, sounds badly out of tune, particularly at the higher end, and it may well be that the ear is taking as its criterion of pitch the upper harmonics of notes in the middle and lower ranges, rather than the fundamentals.

Mersenne's law (10.14) also determines some of the characteristics of instruments of the violin family. In these instruments, as in the case of the guitar and some other instruments, the different notes of the scale are obtained not by having a different string for each note, but by having a limited number of strings (only four in the case of the violin) whose effective lengths L are varied by 'stopping' the strings with the fingers of the left hand. The range of the instrument would be somewhat limited if only one string were used, and one of the purposes of the other three strings is to increase it. (Another reason for having more than one string is that several notes can be sounded simultaneously; this facility is extensively used in guitar music.) Furthermore, since the basic design is such that the four strings be of the same length, either the tension or the mass per unit length must be different for each string. Since it is undesirable that the tension be significantly different, causing the bridge of the instrument to be unevenly stressed, it is the mass per unit length that is different in practice. It is therefore necessary to buy a G-, D-, A- or E-string for the instrument, all of which are of different masses per unit length. The G-string is usually overspun with fine silver wire to increase μ, for the same reason as for the lower notes on the pianoforte. The D- and A-strings are usually made of gut (of different thicknesses) and the E-string, which has the highest fundamental, is usually made of fairly fine steel wire which combines the necessity for a small value of μ with that of mechanical strength.

We see, therefore, that Mersenne's law is basic to many aspects of the design of stringed instruments in that it determines the conditions which must be satisfied to obtain a desired fundamental frequency.

We will return to some other aspects of musical instruments later in this chapter, but let us for the present discuss some further properties of vibrating strings. We know that the general motion of a string must be some linear combination of its normal modes, and that, given the initial conditions, the strengths of the various harmonics can be determined. The typical normal-mode solution is (from (10.12) and (10.13))

$$y_n(x,t) = a_n \sin\left(2\pi \frac{f_n}{c} x\right) \cos(2\pi f_n t + \alpha_n) \ ,$$

$$\text{and since } \frac{f_n}{c} = \frac{n}{2L} \text{ and } f_n = nf_1$$

from Mersenne's law (10.14),

$$y_n(x,t) = a_n \sin \frac{\pi n x}{L} \cos(2\pi n f_1 t + \alpha_n) \ .$$

The general motion of the string is

$$y(x,t) = \sum_{n=1}^{\infty} a_n \sin \frac{\pi n x}{L} \cos(2\pi n f_1 t + \alpha_n) \tag{10.16}$$

We can re-express (10.16) as

$$y(x,t) = \sum_{n=1}^{\infty} a_n \sin \frac{\pi n x}{L} (\cos 2\pi n f_1 t \cos \alpha_n - \sin 2\pi n f_1 t \sin \alpha_n) \ .$$

We can replace $a_n \cos \alpha_n$ by C_n and $-a_n \sin \alpha_n$ by S_n, which gives

$$y(x,t) = \sum_{n=1}^{\infty} \sin \frac{\pi n x}{L} (C_n \cos 2\pi n f_1 t + S_n \sin 2\pi n f_1 t) \ . \tag{10.17}$$

The coefficients C_n and S_n depend on the initial conditions of the string, that is, on the positions and velocities of each point on the string at time $t = 0$. These vary, of course, according to the particular problem. For example, for a piano-forte string, the initial displacements $y(x,0)$ are zero, but the initial velocities depend on the shape, size and elastic properties of the hammer, and the velocity with which it hits the string. We will, however, not attempt to analyse this difficult problem; instead we shall take the problem of a string constrained into some shape described by the function $y(x,0)$, and then, at time $t = 0$, released. Our problem is to find the subsequent motion of the string with the aid of (10.17).

The initial velocity of every point on the string is zero; our initial conditions can therefore be summarized by the fact that the initial shape is $y(x,0)$ and that

$$\left[\frac{\partial y}{\partial t}\right]_{t=0} = 0 \, , \tag{10.18}$$

for all x.

Let us first find the effect of the initial condition 10.18 upon 10.17. If we differentiate this latter equation partially with respect to time we obtain

$$\frac{\partial y}{\partial t} = \sum_{n=1}^{\infty} \sin \frac{\pi n x}{L} (-2\pi n f_1 C_n \sin 2\pi n f_1 t + 2\pi n f_1 S_n \cos 2\pi n f_1 t) \, ,$$

which, for time $t = 0$, becomes

$$\left[\frac{\partial y}{\partial t}\right]_{t=0} = \sum_{n=1}^{\infty} 2\pi n f_1 S_n \sin \frac{\pi n x}{L} \, .$$

Since this must be zero for all values of x, by (10.18), it follows that all the coefficients S_n must be zero. So (10.17) assumes the simpler form

$$y(x,t) = \sum_{n=1}^{\infty} C_n \sin \frac{\pi n x}{L} \cos 2\pi n f_1 t \, . \tag{10.19}$$

To find the C_n we apply our knowledge of the initial shape $y(x,0)$ to (10.19). At time $t = 0$, this equation becomes

$$y(x,0) = \sum_{n=1}^{\infty} C_n \sin \frac{\pi n x}{L} \, . \tag{10.20}$$

Suppose we wish to find a particular coefficient C_m; following the methods developed in section 7.1 we merely multiply (10.20) by

$$\sin \frac{\pi m x}{L} \, dx$$

and integrate over the whole length of the string, obtaining

$$\int_0^L y(x,0)\sin\frac{\pi mx}{L}\ dx = \int_0^L \sin\frac{\pi mx}{L}\ \sum_{n=1}^{\infty} C_n\sin\frac{\pi nx}{L}\ dx\ .$$

Just as in our discussions on Fourier series, the nth term on the right-hand side is zero unless $n = m$, and the equation therefore reduces to

$$\int_0^L y(x,0)\sin\frac{\pi mx}{L}\ dx = C_m\int_0^L \sin^2\frac{\pi mx}{L}\ dx\ .$$

The integral on the right-hand side of the latter equation can easily be shown to be $\frac{1}{2}L$, reducing the equation still further to

$$\int_0^L y(x,0)\sin\frac{\pi mx}{L}\ dx = \frac{1}{2}C_m L\ .$$

Finally, reverting to the nomenclature C_n rather than C_m, we have

$$C_n = \frac{2}{L}\int_0^L y(x,0)\sin\frac{\pi nx}{L}\ dx\ . \tag{10.21}$$

So in the case of zero initial velocity, all we need do to calculate the C_n of (10.19) is to use our knowledge of the initial shape of the string, $y(x,0)$, together with the integral in (10.21). It may seem surprising that Fourier series enter into this problem, and also that they arise in a spatial rather than a temporal way. This is so because the x part of the normal-mode solution contains the function $\sin \pi nx/L$ so central to Fourier theory; all we have then done is to multiply the equation by another suitable sine function which, upon integration, has yielded a zero result except for one term in the infinite series. The sine functions we have been using have the important mathematical property called *orthogonality*, which is that the integral of the product of any two of these functions over the appropriate limits is zero unless the two functions chosen are identical. It is this orthogonality property which is basic to analyses of this kind. If, for example, the string had not been of uniform mass per unit length, the normal-mode solutions would not have been sinusoidal in x and, in general, multiplication by a sine term and integration would not have solved our problem for us since there would be no orthogonality. However, sine functions are not the only orthogonal set, and functions orthogonal to the x-part of the normal-mode solutions can be used in the same way as the sine function in our analysis above.

Example 10.1
The motion of a stretched string with specified initial conditions.
　　To take a specific example of initial conditions, suppose the string is initially

displaced in the manner illustrated in Fig. 10.2. This profile, $y(x,0)$ has to be described by the two equations

$$y(x,0) = \begin{cases} \dfrac{2h}{L}\,x & 0 \leqslant x \leqslant \tfrac{1}{2}L \ , \\[2ex] 2h\left(1 - \dfrac{x}{L}\right) & \tfrac{1}{2}L \leqslant x \leqslant L \ . \end{cases} \tag{10.E1}$$

To find the motion of the string after the midpoint has been released (at time $t = 0$), we use (10.19), in which the C_n are given by (10.21). The integral on the right-hand side of the latter equation must be expressed as two integrals, one for the region between 0 and $\tfrac{1}{2}L$ (using the first function in equations (10.E1) and the other for the region between $\tfrac{1}{2}L$ and L (using the second function). From equation (10.21) we thus obtain

$$C_n = \frac{2}{L}\left[\int_0^{L/2} \frac{2h}{L}\,x \sin \frac{\pi n x}{L}\,\mathrm{d}x + \int_{L/2}^{L} 2h\left(1 - \frac{x}{L}\right) \sin \frac{\pi n x}{L}\,\mathrm{d}x \right] ,$$

which, after some rearrangement, becomes

$$\frac{LC_n}{4h} = \int_0^{L/2} \frac{x}{L}\,\sin \frac{\pi n x}{L}\,\mathrm{d}x + \int_{L/2}^{L} \left(1 - \frac{x}{L}\right) \sin \frac{\pi n x}{L}\,\mathrm{d}x \ .$$

Since x/L occurs frequently, we can simplify further by letting $x/L = z$, in which case $\mathrm{d}x = L\,\mathrm{d}z$. The last equation therefore becomes

$$\frac{C_n}{4h} = \int_0^{1/2} z \sin \pi n z\,\mathrm{d}z + \int_{1/2}^{1} (1 - z) \sin \pi n z\,\mathrm{d}z \ . \tag{10.E2}$$

These two integrals may be evaluated by parts. Suppose u and v are both functions of x. Then, as is well known,

$$\int_a^b u\,\mathrm{d}v = [uv]_a^b - \int_a^b v\,\mathrm{d}u \ . \tag{10.E3}$$

Applying (10.E3) to the first integral, I_1 in (10.E2), with $u = z$ and $v = \cos \pi n z$, we obtain

$$I_1 = \frac{1}{\pi^2 n^2}\,\sin \tfrac{1}{2}\pi n - \frac{1}{2\pi n}\,\cos \tfrac{1}{2}\pi n$$

By exactly similar reasoning we evaluate the second integral, I_2, in (10.E2) as

$$I_2 = \frac{1}{2\pi n} \cos \tfrac{1}{2}\pi n + \frac{1}{\pi^2 n^2} \sin \tfrac{1}{2}\pi n - \frac{1}{\pi^2 n^2} \sin \pi n \quad .$$

Thus $\quad I_1 + I_2 = \dfrac{2}{\pi^2 n^2} \sin \tfrac{1}{2}\pi n - \dfrac{1}{\pi^2 n^2} \sin \pi n$

$$= \frac{2}{\pi^2 n^2} \sin \tfrac{1}{2}\pi n \quad ,$$

since $\sin \pi n$ is zero for all n.

Equation (10.E2) finally becomes

$$C_n = 4h(I_1 + I_2)$$

$$= \frac{8h}{\pi^2 n^2} \sin \tfrac{1}{2}\pi n \quad .$$

Thus $\quad C_1 = \dfrac{8h}{\pi^2} , \qquad C_2 = 0 ,$

$$C_3 = -\frac{8h}{9\pi^2} , \quad C_4 = 0 ,$$

$$C_5 = \frac{8h}{25\pi^2} , \quad C_6 = 0 ,$$

and so on.

The motion of the string with the initial conditions specified by (10.E1) can now be obtained by substituting for the C_n in (10.19), which gives

$$y(x,t) = \frac{8h}{\pi^2} \left(\sin \frac{\pi x}{L} \cos 2\pi f_1 t - \frac{1}{9} \sin \frac{3\pi x}{L} \cos 2\pi 3 f_1 t \right.$$

$$\left. + \frac{1}{25} \sin \frac{5\pi x}{L} \cos 2\pi 5 f_1 t + \ldots \right), \qquad (10.E4)$$

where the fundamental frequency f_1 is given by Mersenne's law as

$$f_1 = \frac{1}{2L} \sqrt{\left(\frac{T}{\mu}\right)} . \qquad (10.15)$$

Since the only frequencies present in (10.E4) are harmonics of the fundamental frequency f_1, the motion of the string is periodic; that is to say, the profile of the string will assume, momentarily, its initial shape at the instants of time $1/f_1$, $2/f_1$, $3/f_1$ and so on. In practice this never happens, because the energy originally put into the string when it was drawn aside becomes dissipated due to the viscosity of the air, and to friction effects and non-rigidity at the supports. In the case of stringed musical instruments, it is the movement of the supports, driven by that of the string, which transmits the vibration to the belly or sound-board of the instrument which, in turn, vibrates to cause the sound waves in the air.

Finally, we did not take into account the fact that all strings, to a certain extent, have rod-like charactersitics (i.e. they are not perfectly flexible); the frequencies of the normal modes are only approximately given by (10.14) and they are not quite harmonically related to each other. However, despite the lack of the inclusion of all these factors in our analysis (which would have made it extremely complicated), (10.E4) does provide an understanding of the principles of the vibrations of a stretched string.

10.4 FORMANTS

In the last section we analysed the transverse motion of an ideal stretched string and found that many of the properties of musical instruments could be accounted for. In this section we shall delve a little further into this topic and consider, in outline, the way in which the resonator (which may be the belly of a violin, or the soundboard of a pianoforte) modifies the vibrations originating at the string. Our reason for persisting with this subject are manifold — musical sounds are in many respects the simplest kinds of all, and the physics of musical instruments, a subject worthy of study in its own right, employs principles which are applicable in many other branches of science.

The sound which we hear from a stringed musical instrument comes mainly from the cavity resonator to which the string is mechanically coupled, rather than from the string itself. This can be demonstrated quite simply by holding one end of a string of, say, one metre length and tying a weight to the lower end. When the string is plucked, very little sound emerges (although the string is under tension) because there is no suitable resonator attached to the string to cause enough of a disturbance in the air to produce an audible sound.

It is primarily the large vibrating surface area of the resonator which is responsible for the sound. Here we have a mechanical 'amplifier' which, in company with any other sort of amplifier, has different gains at different frequencies. For example, the gain of an audio amplifier (i.e. the ratio of the output voltage to the input voltage) varies with frequency, but a good amplifier will have a constant gain for most of the audio range.

Now let us consider the violin. The primary vibrators in the instrument are the strings, which generate a waveform whose spectrum (for a single note held

for a long time) consists of delta functions at all the harmonics of the fundamental frequency. The various magnitudes of the delta functions are determined
(within the limitations of our analysis in the last section) by the coefficients C_n
in (10.19). But these are not the 'strengths' of the harmonics of the note as we
hear it, because, as we have seen, it is not the string which directly generates the
sound wave, but the resonator activated by the string. The 'gain' of the resonator,
because it varies with frequency, will modify the relative magnitudes of the delta
functions, and the spectrum of the sound eventually emitted is this modified
version. The resonator is said to exert a *formant* effect upon the 'signal' it
receives from the string.

To illustrate further the meaning of the formant, let us suppose that, by
some means or other, we have been able to excite vibrations in the string such

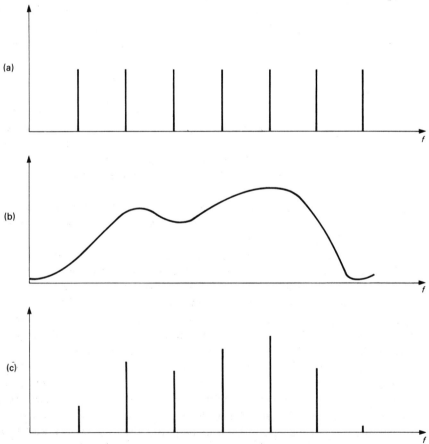

Fig. 10.3 – The effect of formants. (a) Amplitude spectrum of signal provided
by vibrations of the string. (b) Amplitude formant characteristic of
resonator. (c) Amplitude spectrum of sound wave emitted.

that all the harmonics are of equal 'strength' — that is that all the delta functions in the spectrum of the signal provided by the string are of equal magnitude. The amplitude spectrum (we will not concern ourselves with the phases of these delta functions) is sketched schematically in Fig. 10.3. Now by exciting the resonator with a pure tone of variable frequency but constant amplitude, and observing, with a microphone connected to a voltmeter, the magnitude of the sound wave emitted into the air at different frequencies, we can plot a 'gain' versus frequency curve for the resonator. (Again, we are not concerning ourselves with the phase of the output compared with that of the input, but just with the amplitudes.) This curve is called the *formant characteristic* of the particular resonator. An example of a formant characteristic is shown in Fig. 10.3b.

We are now in a position to determine the spectrum of the sound emitted. Since a pure tone of variable frequency produces output amplitudes as illustrated in Fig. 10.3b, then the signal illustrated in Fig. 10.3a will, by the principle of superposition, produce an output whose spectrum is the product of the original spectrum and the formant characteristic. This is illustrated in Fig. 10.3c. Thus, in this example, although the fifth harmonic had originally the same amplitude as all the others, it will be amplified more than the others because the formant characteristic has its maximum at this frequency. So whatever the spectrum provided by the primary vibrator may be, the resonator will exert its formant effect upon it.

The extreme importance of the formant becomes very apparent when we consider the effect of playing different notes on the instrument. Suppose we continue our (admittedly rather unreal) hypothesis that the string is somehow being excited to provide a spectrum where the harmonics are of equal strength, and that we consider two different notes played by the instrument. The first note is that illustrated in Fig. 10.3, which we have already dealt with. The second, which we will assume to be higher in fundamental frequency, is illustrated in Fig. 10.4. Here, in Fig. 10.4a, we see that the harmonics are further apart from each other than in Fig. 10.3. The formant characteristic, however, is identical to that in Fig. 10.3 because it is a property of the *violin,* and has nothing to do with the note being played. As a result of the variation in position of the spectral lines but constancy of the formant characteristic, we see that the fifth harmonic is no longer the strongest; it is the *second* harmonic now that is at a frequency corresponding to the peak in the formant curve, and it is this harmonic which is therefore strongest in the emitted sound.

It is thus the formant of the belly of a violin which impresses itself upon the harmonic content of whatever the performer is playing; although the spectra of different notes are different, they all have in common that they have been multiplied by the same formant characteristic. The frequency of the fundamental tells the brain of the listener what the pitch of the note is, and the formant characteristic, which 'colours' the spectrum of any note played, tells the listener that he is listening all the time to a violin. Indeed, since the formant is slightly

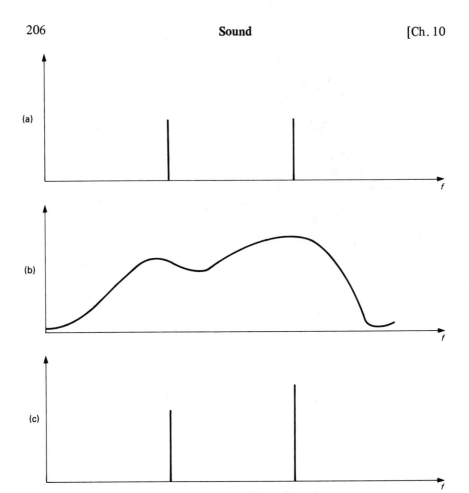

Fig. 10.4 – The effect of the formant of Figure 10.2b on a tone of higher fundamental frequency. (a) Amplitude spectrum of signal provided by the vibrations of
the string. (b) Amplitude formant characteristic of resonator. (c) Amplitude
spectrum of sound wave emitted.

different for different violins, enough 'format information' is presented to
a sensitive musically-trained listener to enable him to distinguish one violin
from another. It is interesting to speculate to what extent the 'Kreisler' tone
differs from the 'Menuhin' tone by virtue of the formant characteristics of
their respective violins as opposed to their different methods of playing.

Formants are clearly very important in musical and psychological acoustics.
We have dealt so far with the 'fixed' formant – i.e. an unchangeable property of
a particular instrument. But formants need not necessarily be of this type. For
instance, the cavities in the human head provide a formant which modifies the
spectrum of sounds made by the larynx. The characteristics of this formant can

be changed at will by altering the shape of the mouth cavity. By doing so we alter the spectrum of the sound emitted when we speak or sing and in this case the listener interprets the formant for a particular shape of the mouth as a *vowel*. It is evident, therefore, that the auditory system contains a very well-developed formant-recognizing mechanism; exactly how this works is not yet clearly understood, but it is certain that this is one of the fundamental properties of the ear-brain combination in its capacity as an information receiver and interpreter.

10.5 THE PERCEPTION OF SOUND

We have touched several times in this chapter upon the subject of perception of sound. Although the discussion has been mainly on the purely physical aspects of sound, it is impossible to isolate these entirely from the psychological aspects, because so many of the physical systems we have chosen to analyse owe their very existence to their use in musical contexts which involve sound perception. In this section we shall make a few general remarks about perception which will serve to augment what has already been said.

One of the most important facts about perception generally, and that of sound in particular, is summed up in the *Weber-Fechner Law*. We can best illustrate the ideas behind this law by a simple non-acoustical example. Suppose we blindfold a suitable volunteer, and put a ten-gram weight in his hand. Then if we add another ten-gram weight on top of the first he will immediately become aware that the total weight in his hand has increased. However, if we had started by putting a kilogram weight in his hand and then added a further ten-gram weight the increase in weight would be so slight that he would be unable to notice it. So the psychological effect of adding a given stimulus (namely the ten-gram weight) is profoundly affected by the magnitude of the stimulus which was already there.

The Weber-Fechner Law is a quantitative assertion which was originally based on research into the effects of placing additional weights on the hand. It states that the increase in stimulus necessary to produce a given increase in sensation is proportional to the pre-existing stimulus. In the context of our example it means that the increase in weight that would cause our volunteer to notice that it had been increased is proportional to the weight on his hand to start with.

To put this in more mathematical form, let us suppose that the original weight was W and that the just noticeable difference in stimulus, dS, is caused by the addition of a small weight dW. Then the assertion of the Weber-Fechner Law is that the dW which produces this must be proportional to W. If we let the constant of proportionality connecting these quantities be k, we have

$$dS = k \, \frac{dW}{W} \quad .$$

An integrated form of this equation is

$$S = k \log_e W \ .$$

$$(10.22)$$

Equation (10.22) is the mathematical description of the Weber-Fechner Law as usually stated.

Now how does this apply to the perception of sound? The first and easiest example is that of the pitch of a pure tone of given frequency. The *objective* quality in the tone is the *frequency* f which corresponds to the W in (10.22); the *subjective* quality to be correlated with f is the *pitch* of the note, p, which corresponds to S in that equation. For pitch perception, therefore, (10.22) becomes

$$p = k \log f \ .$$

It is usual in this connection to define the constant k as 1200/log 2. Thus

$$p = \frac{1200}{\log 2} \ \log f \ .$$

The reason for this becomes apparent in the following way. An octave rise in pitch corresponds to a doubling of the frequency. Thus, corresponding to a frequency f_0 we have a pitch p_0 given by

$$p_0 = \frac{1200}{\log 2} \ \log f_0 \ ,$$

while the pitch p_1, corresponding to a note one octave higher than f_0, is

$$p_1 = \frac{1200}{\log 2} \ \log 2f_0 \quad .$$

Subtracting the two equations,

$$p_1 - p_0 = \frac{1200}{\log 2} \ \log \frac{2f_0}{f_0}$$

$$= 1200 \ ,$$

giving us the rise in pitch (on the scale we have defined) corresponding to one octave. Now on the equal-tempered scale, the octave is divided into twelve equal pitch increments of semitones (i.e. equal frequency ratios) namely from A to A#, A# to B, B to C, and so on up to the A above; thus one semitone becomes equivalent to a pitch increase of 1200/12 = 100 units. The original definition of the constant k as 1200/log 2 therefore produces the effect of dividing each semitone into a hundred parts; the unit of pitch resulting from this definition, which is widely used when discussing pitch, is called the *cent* (although other units have been devised for special purposes).

We see that the Weber-Fechner Law is particularly applicable when describing musical pitch. It is not in fact true for very high and very low frequencies in the audible range, but is a very good approximation over a range of several octaves.

Let us now consider the loudness of a pure tone. Just as pitch was the subjective correlate of frequency, so is loudness the subjective correlate of intensity. Experiments have been performed to find the just noticeable increase in loudness upon increase in intensity and it has been found that the Weber-Fechner Law holds reasonably well, the loudness L corresponding to the subjective quality S on the left-hand side of (10.22), and intensity I to W on the right-hand side. The equation therefore becomes

$$L = k \log I . \qquad (10.23)$$

Departures from the above relationship, however, occur at very high and very low intensities. We have already mentioned the case of low intensities; below a certain *threshold* of intensity no sound can be heard at all — it therefore follows that there can be no psychological correlate of *increase* of intensity below the threshold. The threshold is a function of frequency and is at its lowest for frequencies in the range 1–2 kHz (i.e. the ear is at its most sensitive in this frequency range). At high intensities the sensation becomes that of pain, and the relationship (10.23) breaks down.

It is usual to define a scale of L such that k is unity and the logarithms are taken to the base ten. Experiment has shown that the usual root mean square pressure threshold at a frequency of 1 kHz is about 2×10^{-5} N m^{-2}. Let us designate the intensity corresponding to this pressure by I_0 and the loudness zero. We should therefore modify (10.23) to read

$$L = \log_{10} I - \log_{10} I_0 = \log_{10}(I/I_0) \qquad (10.24)$$

On this scale of L, the difference in loudness between sounds 1 and 2 is $\log_{10} (I_1/I_2)$ bels, after A. G. Bell who did so much of the pioneer work in this field. This turns out to be a rather cumbersome unit as we quickly find out by means of a simple example. Suppose the intensity is initially I_1, with a corresponding loudness L_1, and is then doubled, giving a loudness L_2. Initially, therefore, (10.24) becomes

$$L_1 = \log_{10} \frac{I_1}{I_0} ,$$

and after doubling I_1, it becomes

$$L_2 = \log_{10} \frac{2I_1}{I_0} .$$

Subtraction of the first of these equations from the second yields

$$L_2 - L_1 = \log_{10} \frac{2I_1}{I_0} - \log_{10} \frac{I_1}{I_0}$$

$$= \log_{10} 2$$

$$\cong 0.3 \text{ bels}$$

— a rather small number for a twofold increase in intensity. In practice we therefore use a unit one tenth the size of the bel, called the *decibel*, abbreviated in most scientific literature to dB, and in most engineering literature to db. A doubling of intensity therefore produces an increase in loudness of $10 \times 0.3 = 3$ dB. As a rule of thumb, an increase of intensity of 1 dB is just perceptible.

As we have seen, 0 dB is defined as corresponding to a root mean square pressure p_0 of 2×10^{-5} N m^{-2} at 1000 Hz. Since the intensity is proportional to the square of the acoustic pressure, (10.24) becomes

$$L = \log_{10} \frac{p^2}{p_0^2} \text{ bels}$$

$$= 10 \log_{10} \frac{p^2}{p_0^2} \text{ dB}$$

$$= 20 \log_{10} \frac{p}{p_0} \text{ dB} .$$

The right-hand side of this equation defines the *sound pressure level* (abbreviated to SPL) corresponding to the root mean square acoustic pressure p. Thus

$$\text{SPL} = 20 \log_{10} \frac{p}{p_0} \text{ dB} .$$

Although the SPL is useful in psychological work in acoustics, it must be emphasized that it is itself not a subjective quantity at all, as the last equation shows. It is a function merely of the prevailing root mean square sound pressure and the standard p_0.

The SPL is used not only to designate the sound pressure of a pure tone in a form which has relevance to its perception, but can be extended to define the level of *any* sound whose root mean square pressure p can be determined. It is still, however, defined with reference to a pure tone of 1000 Hz and of root mean square pressure p_0 of 2×10^{-5} N m^{-2}. To give some qualitative idea of the loudness corresponding to various SPLs the following list may be useful. An

SPL of 15 dB corresponds roughly to the ambient noise inside a broadcasting studio, 60 dB to that in the average living room during a conversation, 100 dB to that inside an underground train, and 130 dB to the noise made by a pneumatic drill situated a few metres away. Beyond about 140 dB one feels a sensation of pain, and this value is the so-called *threshold of pain*.

Example 10.2
Addition of two sound intensities
Suppose we have two sound sources, which are individually 90 dB and 100 dB. What is the loudness when they are both sounded together?

From the foregoing paragraph, the reader will appreciate that the answer is certainly not 190 dB! To obtain the correct answer, we use (10.24),

$$L = \log_{10} \frac{I}{I_0} \, ,$$

where I_0 is the intensity of the agreed origin of the decibel scale (corresponding to a root mean square pressure of $2 \times 10^{-5} \text{ N m}^{-2}$).

For the first sound source then,

$$I_1 = I_0 \, 10^{9.0} \, ,$$

and for the second source,

$$I_2 = I_0 \, 10^{10.0} \, .$$

We now must assume that the sources are *incoherent*, i.e. they produce no interference effects. This would not be the case if, for example, they were two sinusoidal tones of the same frequency; they would interfere, and the perceived intensity would depend on exactly where the observer was situated. On the other hand, if the sound sources were not correlated (for instance, a street band and a passing aeroplane), the total intensity I is the sum of the individual intensities,

$$\text{thus } I = I_1 + I_2 = I_0(1 + 0.1) \times 10^{10}$$

whence the loudness is

$$\log_{10}(I/I_0) = \log_{10}(1.1 \times 10^{10})$$
$$= 10.04 \text{ bels} = 100.4 \text{ dB}.$$

PROBLEMS

(10.1) The normal modes for vibrations of the air in a pipe closed at one end were shown to have frequencies $(2n + 1)c/4L$. What is the smallest value of n for which the frequencies corresponding to n and $n + 1$ are less than a semitone apart? What is this interval in cents?

(10.2) Deduce the frequencies of the normal modes for a pipe of length L open at both ends.

(10.3) Use a calculator to deduce $(3/2)^n$ for $n = 2, 3, 4, \ldots$ At what value of n is this very close to an integral power of 2? Of what musical significance is this?
  Show that $(3/2)^4$ is very close to $2^2 \times 5/4$. Of what musical significance is this?

(10.4) By considering the pressure wave in a closed organ pipe, deduce whether the end correction would cause the pipe to sound at a higher or a lower pitch than that which would apply in the absence of an end correction.

(10.5) A string of mass 0.01 kg is stretched between two points 0.5 m apart. The tension in the string 200 N. What is the frequency of (a) the fundamental (b) the third harmonic?

(10.6) A string is stretched between two points, and has a certain fundamental frequency. If these two points are moved slightly further apart, then T, μ, and L all change; show that the fundamental frequency must necessarily increase.

(10.7) A uniformly stretched string of linear density μ and length L under a tension T is initially displaced so that the points one quarter of the way from each end are oppositely displaced through a distance h, leaving the centre point unmoved. The string is released from this position at time $t = 0$.
  Assuming that $h \ll L$, deduce the nature of the subsequent motion of the string. What harmonics are missing?

(10.8) Deduce the energy in each of the harmonics for the vibrating string considered in Example 10.1.

(10.9) The sound level at a distance 100 m from an aeroplane is 100 dB. Assuming that the intensity is inversely proportional to the square of the distance away, deduce the distance at which the sound would be just audible.
  Explain why this answer is absurd.

(10.10) Deduce an expression for the pressure variations representing a pure tone of peak acoustic pressure p_1, of duration 5 s, the pitch rising at a constant rate from an initial value of 200 Hz to a final value of 3200 Hz. (Hint: refer to section 9.3.2).

(10.11) Two pure tones, 0.1 Hz apart in frequency, sound simultaneously in an acoustically dead room. A sound-level meter in the room records 60 dB as its maximum reading, and 20 dB as minimum. If 0 dB corresponds to an r.m.s. acoustic pressure of 2×10^{-5} N m^{-2}, calculate the acoustic pressure amplitudes of each of the two pure tones.

(10.12) Two independent sources of sound have loudnesses 50 dB and 55 dB when sounded separately. What is the loudness when they are sounded together?

(10.13) A sinusoidal voltage source is connected to the input of an amplifier, and a loudspeaker to its output. If the input voltage is doubled, by how many dB is the output increased?

(10.14) In many receivers and amplifiers, the volume control is 'logarithmic', i.e. the resistance between B and C is not proportional to the angle through which the control is rotated (as with a 'linear' control), but rather as shown below. Why is this a good arrangement?

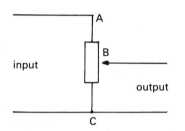
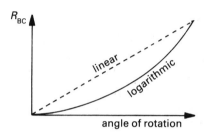

CHAPTER 11

Light

_____

11.1 THE ELECTROMAGNETIC THEORY OF LIGHT

11.1.1 Introduction

Although the wave nature of light had been established in the early part of the nineteenth century, when Thomas Young performed his classic interference experiment, it took a further half century before a satisfactory theory for light waves emerged. The great theoretical difficulty which had to be overcome was the explanation of how waves could be propagated in the absence of a medium, for all waves known at that time were mechanical in type and could not exist in the absence of a material medium.

The electromagnetic theory of light was formulated by James Clerk Maxwell in 1860. Maxwell had developed a set of equations, now referred to universally as Maxwell's electromagnetic equations, which related electric and magnetic quantities, and, in fact, summarized all the then known properties of electric and magnetic fields. Maxwell showed that these equations could be processed in such a way as to yield a wave equation. He went on to show from this that electromagnetic waves could be propagated in free space, with a wave velocity which could be deduced from electrical measurements unconnected with wave phenomena, which turned out to be very closely the same as the velocity of light. The latter velocity had been approximately determined, over a hundred years earlier, by the astronomers Römer and Bradley, and later (more precisely) by Fizeau and Foucault.

11.1.2 Electromagnetic waves in free space

We will now give in outline the arguments which led to the electromagnetic theory of light. We start with Maxwell's equations for the electromagnetic field in free space, which may be written as follows

$$\text{div } \mathbf{E} = 0 \qquad\qquad\qquad (11.1)$$

$$\text{div } \mathbf{B} = 0 \qquad\qquad\qquad (11.2)$$

$$\text{curl } \mathbf{E} = -\frac{\partial \mathbf{B}}{\partial t} \tag{11.3}$$

$$\text{curl } \mathbf{B} = \mu_0 \epsilon_0 \frac{\partial \mathbf{E}}{\partial t} \ . \tag{11.4}$$

In these equations the vectors **E** and **B** are, respectively, the *electric field strength* and the *magnetic flux density* at a point; the scalar constants ϵ_0 and μ_0 are, respectively, the *permittivity* and the *permeability* of free space. On the left of (11.1) to (11.4) are div and curl; these are *vector operators* which enable the equations to be written in concise form. They are defined as follows. If **F** is a field vector having cartesian components F_x, F_y, and F_z,

$$\text{div } \mathbf{F} = \frac{\partial F_x}{\partial x} + \frac{\partial F_y}{\partial y} + \frac{\partial F_z}{\partial z} \ ; \tag{11.5}$$

div **F** is a scalar quantity known as the *divergence* of the vector **F**.

If **G** = curl **F**, where **G** is a second field vector having components G_x, G_y and G_z, then

$$\left.\begin{aligned} G_x &= \frac{\partial F_z}{\partial y} - \frac{\partial F_y}{\partial z} \ , \\[2mm] G_y &= \frac{\partial F_x}{\partial z} - \frac{\partial F_z}{\partial x} \ , \\[2mm] G_z &= \frac{\partial F_y}{\partial x} - \frac{\partial F_x}{\partial y} \ . \end{aligned}\right\} \tag{11.6}$$

There is also a third vector operator which we shall refer to; this is the gradient operator 'grad'. If **F** = grad ψ, where **F** is a field vector and ψ a scalar which varies with position, then

$$F_x = \frac{\partial \psi}{\partial x}, F_y = \frac{\partial \psi}{\partial y}, F_z = \frac{\partial \psi}{\partial z} \ . \tag{11.7}$$

Equations (11.1) to (11.4) describe how the derivatives of the electromagnetic field vectors **E** and **B** with respect to both position and time are related at any point in free space. They will not be derived here as their proper derivation would occupy about half the present book; the reader is referred particularly to *Electricity and Magnetism* by W. J. Duffin (3rd ed.), McGraw-Hill (1980), for a full and lucid account. But a brief comment on the underlying physics might be helpful.

Equation (11.1) states, in mathematical terms, that there are no *sources* of electric field in free space. The sources of **E** are electrostatic charges; charges require the presence of matter, so free space can have none. Equation (11.1), in its most general form, is derived from the Coulomb (inverse square) law of force between electrostatic charges.

Equation (11.2) states that there are no sources of **B** in free space. In fact (11.2) is generally true: there are no sources of **B** whether the space is empty or not. The equation states, in effect, that magnetic monopoles, which would be the magnetic counterpart of electrostatic charges, do not exist.

Equation (11.3) is the Faraday-Henry law of electromagnetic induction (induced e.m.f. is proportional to rate of change of flux) expressed at a point. The left-hand side is a quantity which is derived from the e.m.f., and the right-hand side is clearly the rate of change of magnetic flux density.

Equation (11.4) is the only one of the four which cannot be explained in elementary terms. Maxwell himself proposed the so-called displacement current density ($\epsilon_0 \partial E/\partial t$) which appears on the right of this equation, and without which it would not be possible to predict the existence of electromagnetic waves, as we shall shortly see.

Clearly (11.1) to (11.4), when written in full component form with the aid of (11.5) and (11.6), have all the ingredients necessary to produce the differential equation for a wave. That is, they involve the *derivatives* of *disturbances* (**E** or **B**) with respect to both *position* and *time*. The actual derivation of the wave equation now follows.

Now it can be shown by expressing a vector **A** in terms of its components and carrying out the operation described by (11.5), (11.6) and (11.7), that the following identity holds

$$\text{curl curl } \mathbf{A} = \text{grad(div } \mathbf{A}) - \nabla^2 \mathbf{A},$$

where ∇^2 is the operator

$$\left(\frac{\partial^2}{\partial x^2} + \frac{\partial^2}{\partial y^2} + \frac{\partial^2}{\partial z^2} \right) \ .$$

If we operate upon both sides of (11.3) with curl we obtain

$$\text{curl curl } \mathbf{E} = \text{grad(div } \mathbf{E}) - \nabla^2 \mathbf{E} = \text{curl} \left(-\frac{\partial \mathbf{B}}{\partial t} \right).$$

But since div **E** = 0 (from (11.1)) this becomes

$$-\nabla^2 \mathbf{E} = \text{curl} \left(-\frac{\partial \mathbf{B}}{\partial t} \right).$$

We can take curl within the differential coefficient with respect to t to obtain

$$-\nabla^2 \mathbf{E} = -\frac{\partial}{\partial t} (\text{curl } \mathbf{B}) \ .$$

When we substitute for curl $\mathbf{B}$ from (11.4) we have

$$\nabla^2 \mathbf{E} = \mu_0 \epsilon_0 \frac{\partial}{\partial t} \left(\frac{\partial \mathbf{E}}{\partial t}\right) = \mu_0 \epsilon_0 \frac{\partial^2 \mathbf{E}}{\partial t^2} \ .$$

This final equation,

$$\boxed{\nabla^2 \mathbf{E} = \mu_0 \epsilon_0 \frac{\partial^2 \mathbf{E}}{\partial t^2}} \ , \tag{11.8}$$

will be seen to have the form of the partial differential equation governing wave propagation in three dimensions. By comparison with the examples of Chapter 5, we note that the wave velocity $c = 1/\sqrt{(\mu_0 \epsilon_0)}$, and that the quantity which fluctuates (the disturbance) is the vector $\mathbf{E}$. The constant μ_0 is fixed arbitrarily by the definition of the ampere as unit of current and has the value $4\pi \times 10^{-7}$ H m^{-1} exactly; ϵ_0 is determined by experiment and is found to be $\epsilon_0 = 8.85 \times 10^{-12}$ F m^{-1} (to two places). These give $c = 3.00 \times 10^8$ m s^{-1}, which is the velocity of light in vacuum.

If we repeat the same process, but taking the curl of (11.4) as the starting poing, we arrive at

$$\boxed{\nabla^2 \mathbf{B} = \mu_0 \epsilon_0 \frac{\partial^2 \mathbf{B}}{\partial t^2}} \ . \tag{11.9}$$

11.1.3 Plane electromagnetic waves

From (11.8) and (11.9) we see that both the electric field strength $\mathbf{E}$ and the magnetic flux density $\mathbf{B}$ vary in a wave manner in free space; variations of $\mathbf{E}$ and $\mathbf{B}$ exist simultaneously — we cannot have variations of $\mathbf{E}$ or $\mathbf{B}$ only. We shall now investigate what kinds of waves these are — whether they are longitudinal or transverse, or both.

Let us assume plane waves with direction of propagation parallel to the z-axis of coordinates. Let us also assume that there are no steady electric or magnetic fields. The wave fronts will therefore be parallel to the xy plane, and it follows from the definition of a wavefront that, at any given time, $\mathbf{E}$ and $\mathbf{B}$ must be constant over planes parallel to the xy plane, i.e.

$$\frac{\partial \mathbf{B}}{\partial x} = \frac{\partial \mathbf{B}}{\partial y} = \frac{\partial \mathbf{E}}{\partial x} = \frac{\partial \mathbf{E}}{\partial y} = 0 \ . \tag{11.10}$$

If **E** and **B** are resolved into their components E_x, E_y, E_z, and B_x, B_y, B_z along the coordinate axes, then, obviously, the derivatives of all the components of (11.10) will vanish also.

When we express (11.4) in component form, using the definition of curl given in (11.6), we obtain

$$\left.\begin{aligned}
\frac{\partial B_z}{\partial y} - \frac{\partial B_y}{\partial z} &= \epsilon_0 \mu_0 \frac{\partial E_x}{\partial t} , \\
\frac{\partial B_x}{\partial z} - \frac{\partial B_z}{\partial x} &= \epsilon_0 \mu_0 \frac{\partial E_y}{\partial t} , \\
\frac{\partial B_y}{\partial x} - \frac{\partial B_x}{\partial y} &= \epsilon_0 \mu_0 \frac{\partial E_z}{\partial t} .
\end{aligned}\right\} \tag{11.11}$$

On removing the terms which are zero from (11.10), (11.11) reduces to

$$\left.\begin{aligned}
-\frac{\partial B_y}{\partial z} &= \epsilon_0 \mu_0 \frac{\partial E_x}{\partial t} , \\
\frac{\partial B_x}{\partial z} &= \epsilon_0 \mu_0 \frac{\partial E_y}{\partial t} , \\
0 &= \epsilon_0 \mu_0 \frac{\partial E_z}{\partial t} .
\end{aligned}\right\} \tag{11.12}$$

A precisely similar analysis, but starting with (11.3) yields

$$\left.\begin{aligned}
-\frac{\partial E_y}{\partial z} &= -\frac{\partial B_x}{\partial t} , \\
\frac{\partial E_x}{\partial z} &= -\frac{\partial B_y}{\partial t} , \\
0 &= -\frac{\partial B_z}{\partial t} .
\end{aligned}\right\} \tag{11.13}$$

If we write (11.1) and (11.2) in terms of the components of **E** and **B** we obtain

$$\frac{\partial E_x}{\partial x} + \frac{\partial E_y}{\partial y} + \frac{\partial E_z}{\partial z} = 0 ,$$

and
$$\frac{\partial B_x}{\partial x} + \frac{\partial B_y}{\partial y} + \frac{\partial B_z}{\partial z} = 0 ,$$

which, on omitting terms which are zero from (11.10), become

$$\frac{\partial E_z}{\partial z} = 0 \ ,$$

$$\frac{\partial B_z}{\partial z} = 0 \ .$$

(11.14)

Thus $B_z = E_z = 0$ (assuming no superimposed steady fields). In other words, plane electromagnetic waves have no longitudinal component. But from the first two lines of (11.12) and (11.13) we see that neither the time derivative nor the z-derivative of B_x and B_y vanish, from which we conclude that *electromagnetic waves are transverse waves*.

Finally, we see from (11.12) and (11.13) that the x-component of **B** is related only to the y-component of **E**, and the y-component of **B** to the x-component of **E**. It follows from this that if **E** is entirely along the Ox axis (so that E_y and E_z vanish), then **B** must be entirely along the Oy axis. If we assume E_x has the form of a harmonic wave expressed in exponential terms as in (4.36), then

$$E_x = (E_x)_0 \exp i \, (kz - \omega t)$$

(11.14a)

and

$$\frac{\partial E_x}{\partial z} = ik \, (E_x)_0 \exp i \, (kz - \omega t) \ .$$

But

$$\frac{\partial E_x}{\partial z} = -\frac{\partial B_y}{\partial t} \quad \text{from (11.13)}$$

therefore $\quad -\dfrac{\partial B_y}{\partial t} = ik \, (E_x)_0 \exp i \, (kz - \omega t)$

and, integrating but disregarding constant fields,

$$B_y = \frac{k(E_x)_0}{\omega} \exp i \, (kz - \omega t)$$

or $\quad B_y = (B_y)_0 \exp i \, (kz - \omega t)$

(11.14b)

where $\quad (B_y)_0 = \dfrac{k}{\omega} (E_x)_0 = \dfrac{1}{c} (E_x)_0 \ .$

(11.14c)

So we see that the **E** and **B** waves are in phase with one another, and the ratio of their amplitudes, E_0/B_0, is equal to the speed of light. The waves of (11.14a) and (11.14b) are shown in Fig. 11.1. A wave of the kind shown having **E** in one direction only, is said to be *plane polarised*.

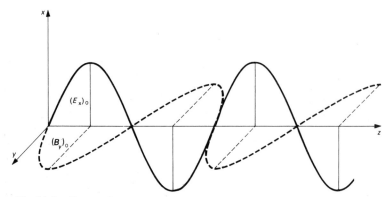

Fig. 11.1 – Perspective representation of a plane harmonic electromagnetic wave.

11.1.4 The electromagnetic spectrum

We have shown, starting from Maxwell's equations, that plane electromagnetic waves can be propagated in free space at the speed of light, and that the waves are transverse in character. Shortly after the appearance of Maxwell's theory of electromagnetic waves, Hertz provided experimental corroboration in which electromagnetic disturbances produced by an oscillating circuit were received by an isolated detector. Following the establishment of Maxwell's theory, a wide range of different types of radiation became recognized as electromagnetic waves of different frequencies (and therefore wavelengths). Radio waves, micro-waves, infrared radiation, visible light, ultraviolet rays, X-rays and γ-rays are all examples of electromagnetic waves, differing from one another only in wave-length. They form the *electromagnetic spectrum,* which is illustrated in Fig. 11.2. The wavelength range covered by the spectrum is enormous – from

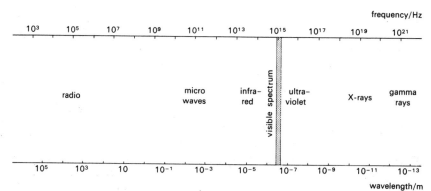

Fig. 11.2 – The electromagnetic spectrum.
(Frequency and wavelength plotted on a logarithmic scale)

hundreds of miles for radio waves originating from distant nebulae down to one ten-thousand-millionth part of a millimetre for γ-rays. We see from Fig. 11.2 that light waves − the only electromagnetic waves which stimulate the eye − cover only a tiny part of this spectrum.

11.1.5 Electromagnetic waves in media

So far we have only considered electromagnetic waves in free space. Maxwell's equations − as given in (11.1) to (11.4) − can be extended to cover a perfectly insulating, homogeneous, isotropic medium, containing no formal charges, merely by replacing ϵ_0 and μ_0 by $\epsilon_r\epsilon_0$ and $\mu_r\mu_0$, where ϵ_r and μ_r are numerical (dimensionless) constants, known respectively as the *relative permittivity* and the *relative permeability* of the medium. Such a medium is referred to as a *dielectric*; we are particularly interested here in dielectrics in which light waves may be propagated. If we repeat the analysis of section 11.1.2, but with ϵ_0 and μ_0 replaced, respectively, with $\epsilon_r\epsilon_0$ and $\mu_r\mu_0$, we arrive at the following partial differential equations in place of (11.8) and (11.9)

$$\nabla^2 \mathbf{E} = \epsilon_r\epsilon_0 \mu_r\mu_0 \frac{\partial^2 \mathbf{E}}{\partial t^2} \,, \tag{11.15}$$

$$\nabla^2 \mathbf{B} = \epsilon_r\epsilon_0 \mu_r\mu_0 \frac{\partial^2 \mathbf{B}}{\partial t^2} \,. \tag{11.16}$$

We conclude from (11.15) and (11.16) that electromagnetic waves can be propagated in a dielectric with wave velocity

$$v = \frac{1}{\sqrt{(\epsilon_r\epsilon_0\mu_r\mu_0)}} \,. \tag{11.17}$$

It turns out that ϵ_r cannot be less than unity; and in the case of a dielectric, μ_r is approximately unity. Thus the velocities of electromagnetic waves in media are less than the velocity in free space.

If we reserve the symbol c for the wave velocity in free space, we see from (11.17) that

$$\boxed{v = \frac{c}{\sqrt{(\epsilon_r\mu_r)}} \,.} \tag{11.18}$$

The *refractive index* n of a dielectric medium is defined as the ratio of the wave velocity in free space to that in the medium, i.e.

$$n = \frac{c}{v} \,; \tag{11.19}$$

we see therefore from (11.18) that $n = \sqrt{(\epsilon_r \mu_r)}$. Since $\mu_r \cong 1$,

$$n \cong \sqrt{\epsilon_r} \, .$$ (11.20)

Equation (11.20) would seem to indicate that the refractive index of a dielectric is constant. The quantity ϵ_r, however, turns out to be frequency dependent. If the value of ϵ_r measured by a statical method is used, then (11.20) holds reasonably well at low frequencies but breaks down completely at high frequencies.

11.2 POLARIZATION

It was deduced in section 11.1.3 that plane light waves (indeed plane electromagnetic waves in general) are transverse. The experimental evidence for the transverse nature of light waves is the fact that light waves can be *polarized*. Light beams obtained from most common sources (e.g. the hot gas in a discharge tube) are made up of a very large number of waves. The E-vectors of these waves (we are still assuming plane waves) are arranged in all directions in space normal to the propagation direction, and such light beams are said to be *unpolarized*. If the light is filtered in some way such that the E-vectors are suppressed in all directions save one, we are left with a unique direction of vibration and the light is said to be *plane polarized*.

Light may be rendered plane polarized in one of a number of ways. One method is by passing the light through a Nicol prism, that is, a pair of calcite crystals cut in a special way and cemented together. Another way is by passing light through a dichroic crystal — one for which the absorption of light is much greater for a given direction of vibration of **E** than for the direction perpendicular to it, so that if the light passes through a sufficient length of such a crystal, effectively all the amplitude in one direction is attenuated. This is the basis of the Polaroid method. A third method is by reflection; when a beam of light is directed on to a plane glass surface at an angle of incidence of about 57° (Brewster's angle), none of the light with electric vector vibrating parallel to the plane of reflection is reflected, so the reflected light is plane polarized, with vibration direction perpendicular to the reflection plane.

If a beam of light is plane polarized by, say, passing it through a Nicol prism, and then passed through a second Nicol prism which can be rotated about the direction of propagation of the light, it is found that for certain angular positions of the second prism no light emerges from it. This is incontrovertible experimental evidence that light waves are transverse. The first prism is referred to as the *polarizer* and the second as the *analyser*. If the polarizer and analyser are rotatable and are equipped with angular scales, this simple system can be used to investigate the state of linear polarization of any light beam. An application of this is in crystal physics, for many crystals polarize light, and analysis of the state of the light emerging from such crystals can yield important information.

11.3 INTERFERENCE AND DIFFRACTION

11.3.1 Introduction – Huygens' principle and the scalar approximation

These are subjects of very great importance and interest which really require a book to themselves. It is impossible here to do more than merely introduce them in a rather general way, and to show their significance within the wider subject of wave motion.

Interference takes place when light waves are superposed. Diffraction results when light waves are impeded or restricted in some way, for example, by placing an opaque obstacle in their path. It is enormously difficult to determine the effect of an obstacle on light waves from first principles. We should have first to find the electric and magnetic boundary conditions placed upon (11.8) and (11.9) by the presence of the obstacle, and then to solve the equations according to these conditions. Fortunately, results, correct to a very good approximation, can be obtained in a very much simpler way be means of the *scalar approximation* and *Huygens' principle*.

According to the scalar approximation, the disturbance caused by a light wave may be represented by a single scalar variable when interference and diffraction effects are being considered (but not, obviously, for polarization). So with this approximation we can represent a plane harmonic light wave by

$$\phi = a \sin (\omega t - kx) \ ,$$

where ϕ is the scalar disturbance.

Huygens' principle states that each point on a wavefront may be regarded as a new source of waves. It is relatively easy to show that Huygens' principle is consistent with the laws of rectilinear propagation, reflection and refraction. This we will now do, starting with rectilinear propagation. A plane wavefront AB (Fig. 11.3) is moving in the direction of the arrow with velocity v; at any instant we may regard each point on AB as a source of secondary wavelets which give rise to spherical wavefronts. After a time t these wavefronts will all have radius vt and their common tangent A'B' will clearly occupy the same position as that the original wavefront will have reached after time t. Thus Huygens' principle is consistent with rectilinear propagation, as long as we choose to ignore the wave moving in the reverse direction which Huygens' principle predicts.

We will examine next the law of reflection. In Fig. 11.4 a plane wavefront AB is shown incident at an angle of incidence i upon a plane reflecting surface XY at the instant when the point A has just reached the surface. We can regard A as a Huygens point source. In the further time it takes for B to reach the reflecting surface at D, the radius of the spherical wavefront emanating from A will grow to the value AC; since the incident and reflected waves are in the same medium, they will have the same velocity, so that AC and BD are equal. The reflected wavefront is obtained by drawing the tangent from D to the surface of the spherical wavefront at C, so that the normal to CD gives the direction of travel of the reflected wave. We see at once the triangles ACD and ABD are congruent;

the angles BAD and CDA are therefore equal and the angle of incidence is equal to the angle of reflection.

A similar construction (Fig. 11.5) leads to the law of refraction. Here PQ represents the plane boundary between two media of refractive indices n_1 and n_2 respectively $(n_2 > n_1)$. Again we have a plane wavefront AB incident

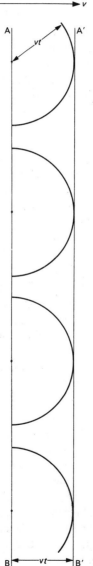

Fig. 11.3 – Rectilinear propagation of a plane wavefront.

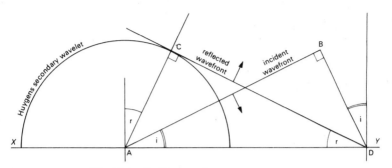

Fig. 11.4 – Reflection of a plane wavefront.

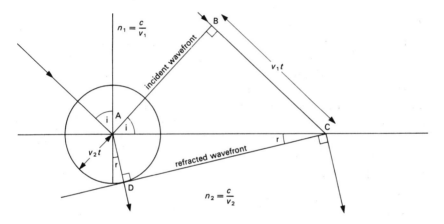

Fig. 11.5 – Refraction of a plane wavefront.

at angle of incidence i on to the boundary and shown at the instant when the point A has just reached the boundary. Suppose the point B takes a further time t to reach the boundary at C, so that $BC = v_1 t$ (where v_1 is the velocity of light in the first medium). To find where the disturbance due to A has reached in this time, we regard A as a Huygens secondary source and draw a sphere of radius $v_2 t$ with centre A (v_2 is the velocity in the second medium). The wavefront in the second medium is represented by CD, the tangent from C to the section through the sphere in the plane of the drawing. The angle between the normal to CD and the normal to the boundary is the angle of refraction r. We note from the definition of refractive index (11.19) that, since $n_2 > n_1$, the velocity must be less in the second medium than the first. From the geometry of Fig. 11.5 we see that

$$\sin i = \frac{BC}{AC} = \frac{v_1 t}{AC}$$

and $\qquad \sin r = \dfrac{AD}{AC} = \dfrac{v_2 t}{AC}$,

therefore $\qquad \dfrac{\sin i}{\sin r} = \dfrac{v_1 t}{v_2 t} = \dfrac{c/n_1}{c/n_2}$, $\qquad$ from (11.19) ,

so that $\qquad \dfrac{\sin i}{\sin r} = \dfrac{n_2}{n_1}$.

Thus the sines of the angles of refraction and incidence are in the same ratio as the refractive indices of the media on either side of the boundary and this ratio is constant for a given wavelength; this is the law of refraction or *Snell's law*.

11.3.2 Interference

We have established that Huygens' principle is reasonable by showing that the three fundamental laws of geometrical optics can be deduced from it; we now go on to apply the principle to try to account for the phenomena of interference and diffraction. Let us first investigate what happens when an observer receives light waves *simultaneously* from two point sources. Let the point sources S_1 and S_2 (Fig. 11.6) be a distance a apart, and let the observer be at a point P at distances x_1 and x_2 from S_1 and S_2 respectively. Let us represent the disturbances at P due to the two light waves as

$$\phi_1 = a_1 \sin(\omega t - kx_1) , \tag{11.21}$$

$$\phi_2 = a_2 \sin(\omega t - kx_2 - \epsilon) . \tag{11.22}$$

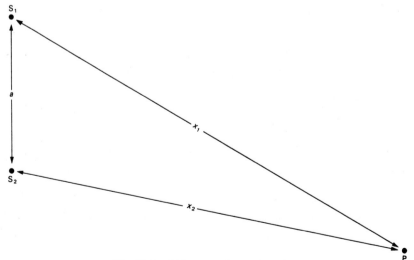

Fig. 11.6 – Light waves from two point sources.

Here, we are assuming that we have pure sine waves, both sources emitting with the same frequency and wavelength but different amplitudes. The phase constant ϵ in (11.22) takes care of any difference in phase between the sources themselves. By the principle of superposition, the net disturbance ϕ at P is the sum of the individual disturbances ϕ_1 and ϕ_2. So we have

$$\phi = \phi_1 + \phi_2 = a_1 \sin (\omega t - kx_1) + a_2 \sin (\omega t - kx_2 - \epsilon) \ . \quad (11.23)$$

For a fixed position P, the only quantity on the right-hand side which varies is t, so for convenience we will write

$$kx_1 = \alpha_1 \ ,$$

$$kx_2 + \epsilon = \alpha_2 \ . \quad (11.24)$$

When we substitute these into (11.23) we get

$$\phi = a_1 \sin (\omega t - \alpha_1) + a_2 \sin(\omega t - \alpha_2) \ .$$

When we expand the sine terms and factorize, this becomes

$$\phi = (a_1 \cos \alpha_1 + a_2 \cos \alpha_2) \sin \omega t - (a_1 \sin \alpha_1 + a_2 \sin \alpha_2) \cos \omega t \ .$$

If we now define two further quantities R and θ such that

$$R \cos \theta = a_1 \cos \alpha_1 + a_2 \cos \alpha_2 \ ,$$

$$R \sin \theta = a_1 \sin \alpha_1 + a_2 \sin \alpha_2 \ ,$$

and then substitute these into the previous equation, we obtain

$$\phi = R \sin(\omega t - \theta) \ .$$

We see, therefore, that the net disturbance at P is simple harmonic in character, with the same frequency as that of the original waves, and of a phase angle relative to them defined by θ. It will be seen from squaring and adding $R \cos \theta$ and $R \sin \theta$ that

$$R^2 = a_1^2 + a_2^2 + 2a_1 a_2 \cos(\alpha_1 - \alpha_2) \quad (11.25)$$

and also that

$$\tan \theta = \frac{a_1 \sin \alpha_1 + a_2 \sin \alpha_2}{a_1 \cos \alpha_1 + a_2 \cos \alpha_2} \ .$$

It is worth noting, in passing, that (11.25) has the familiar appearance of the cosine formula for the solution of triangles. This suggests a useful graphical method for 'adding' two sine waves of the same frequency. If we represent the waves by two vectors whose lengths are proportional to the respective amplitudes of the waves, and the angle between the vectors is the difference between the phases of the waves, as shown in Fig. 11.7, then the amplitude of the resultant is obtained (on the same scale) by completing the

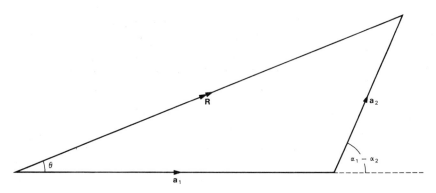

Fig. 11.7 – Vector addition of sine waves.

triangle, and the phase of the resultant with respect to the first wave is given by the angle between the respective vectors.

In the case of light waves, it is the intensity, not the amplitude, which is the important quantity. Detectors of light waves, such as the eye and photographic film, all respond to intensity. Indeed, there is no known method of measuring light amplitude directly. We saw at the end of Chapter 6 that intensity is proportional to the square of the amplitude, for waves in strings. This is also true for light waves, so we may take R^2 (11.25) as a measure of the way in which the intensity due to the superposition of our two light waves varies from place to place as we move P around. (Strictly, as P moves, a_1 and a_2 will vary, since we are dealing with spherical waves; we will, however, ignore this variation). For simplicity we will put $a_1 = a_2 = a$, and assume that the two sources S_1 and S_2 are exactly in phase with each other, so that $\epsilon = 0$. When we make these simplifications (11.25) becomes

$$R^2 = 2a^2[1 + \cos(\alpha_1 - \alpha_2)] \ .$$

Thus R^2 is maximum when

$$\cos(\alpha_1 - \alpha_2) = + 1 \ ,$$

i.e. when $\alpha_1 - \alpha_2 = 2n\pi$;   (11.26)

and minimum (zero) when

$$\cos(\alpha_1 - \alpha_2) = - 1,$$

i.e. when $\alpha_1 - \alpha_2 = (2n + 1)\pi$.   (11.27)

In (11.26) and (11.27), n is zero or any positive or negative integer. But we see from (11.24) that

$$\alpha_1 - \alpha_2 = k(x_1 - x_2) \ ,$$ (11.28)

since we have set ϵ to be zero. So the conditions (11.26) and (11.27) become, on replacing k by $2\pi/\lambda$

$$x_1 - x_2 = n\lambda \qquad \text{for maxima}$$

and $\qquad x_1 - x_2 = (n + \tfrac{1}{2})\lambda \qquad \text{for minima} \; .$

Thus, if P moves from place to place, we shall have maximum intensity $(R^2 = 4a^2)$ when

$$S_1P - S_2P = n\lambda \; ,$$

and minimum intensity $(R^2 = 0)$ when

$$S_1P - S_2P = (n + \tfrac{1}{2})\lambda \; .$$

If S_1, S_2 and P are always in the same plane, then the curves of maximum and minimum intensity form a family of hyperbolas, as shown in Fig. 11.8.

One might suppose, on the basis of the above reasoning, that two point sources of light would produce a pattern of bright and dark lines of the kind shown in Fig. 11.8. However, if completely separate sources are used, we do *not* get such a pattern. The reason for this is that — apart from lasers which are mentioned later — independent light sources do not fulfil one of the conditions that we have assumed, but without really saying so, namely that α_1 and α_2 do not vary with time.

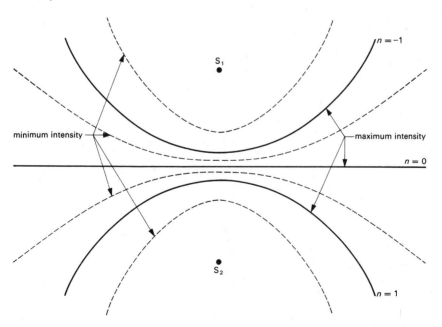

Fig. 11.8 – Hyperbolas of maximum and minimum intensity.

To understand why we do not obtain such a pattern, we must pause for a moment to describe how light originates in common light sources. In a sodium-vapour lamp, for example, we have an assemblage of sodium atoms all moving about with random velocities. When collisions take place, the energy acquired in the collision process by one of the atoms may cause an electron in it to be excited into a higher energy state. Subsequently, the electron in the atom returns to its original state and in doing so releases a burst of light energy. This light energy is in the form of a light wave of very limited duration − of the order 10^{-8} s (i.e. a complete wave resulting from this process would take only 10^{-8} s to pass a point). It follows from the velocity of light in free space ($\sim 3 \times 10^8 \,\text{m s}^{-1}$) that the light waves would extend over about 3 m in space. The frequency f of such a light wave is related to the difference in energy ΔE between the two energy states of the atom by

$$\Delta E = hf \,, \tag{11.29}$$

where h is the Planck constant. But we have seen in Chapter 7 that the only wave which has a single frequency is a sinusoidal wave of infinite duration, so the present short-duration wave will have a spread of frequencies whose mean will be the f of (11.29). The wavelength spread of spectral lines resulting from this effect, though measurable, is extremely small. Actually, a considerable contribution to the broadening of spectral lines is due to the Doppler effect, since the atomic sources are moving randomly; this broadening can be reduced by streaming the vapour in a direction perpendicular to that in which the light is being examined.

An extremely important feature of these waves of atomic origin is that when a given atom emits two successive waves, the phase of the second is randomly related to that of the first. It follows therefore that two separate light sources, each consisting of many millions of individual atomic sources, cannot possibly have a constant phase relationship for times which are more than a fraction of 10^{-8} s. We say that sources of this kind are *incoherent*, whilst sources for which there is a constant phase difference are said to be coherent with respect to one another. If we have two such incoherent sources, the resultant intensity is still given by (11.25) − except that the term $\cos(\alpha_1 - \alpha_2)$ is not constant, as it would be for coherent sources, but various very rapidly with time. The average of this quantity over a long time is zero, so the resultant is

$$R^2 = a_1^2 + a_2^2 \,.$$

That is, for incoherent sources, the resultant is everywhere just the sum of the individual intensities, and consequently there is no pattern of maximum and minimum intensity of the kind shown in Fig. 11.8.

The simplest way to overcome this problem of incoherence is to derive both sources from a common original source. One way of doing this is shown in Fig. 11.9, in which the light waves emanating from a point source S fall on to two pinholes S_1 and S_2 in an otherwise opaque screen. By Huygens' principle,

S_1 and S_2 act as sources of secondary spherical wavelets. In the region to the right of the screen, where these secondary wavelets superpose, we have the necessary condition to observe intensity variation, for a constant phase relationship between S_1 and S_2 is maintained. The pattern of intensity we see is known as an interference pattern, and the process which produces this is known as optical interference. At any point in the region where the interference pattern is clearly seen, we deduce that a disturbance arrives via S_1 at the same instant as another disturbance arrived via S_2, but that these two disturbances started off from S at times which differed from one another by only a small amount compared with 10^{-8} s.

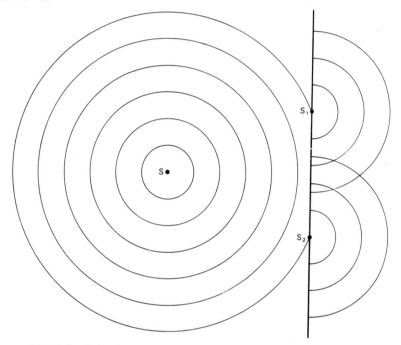

Fig. 11.9 – Coherent sources derived from a single common source S.

In practice, it is much more convenient to use slits rather than pinholes for S, S_1 and S_2 in Fig. 11.9. This arrangement is known as Young's slits after Thomas Young who first performed the experiment in 1807. If monochromatic light emerging from S_1 and S_2 is viewed at a distance D from the screen, which is very many times greater than the separation a of S_1 and S_2, then a series of alternate bright and dark fringes (Young's fringes) may be seen. It is relatively easy to show, though we will not do so here, that the fringes are equispaced and that the centres of adjacent bright fringes are a distance $\lambda D/a$ apart. Thus, if we wish to obtain distinct fringes of separation, say, half a millimetre with light of wavelength 5×10^{-7} m, we must arrange for the ratio of D/a to be 1000:1.

Young's fringes are an example of interference by *division of wavefront,* since the slits S_1 and S_2 select different portions of a wavefront in order to provide Huygens' secondary sources. Other common examples of interference by division of wavefront are Lloyd's mirror and Fresnel's biprism.

Another way of providing coherent sources is by making use of the fact that when light waves are incident upon a glass surface, part of the amplitude is transmitted through the glass and part is reflected. This is schematically shown in Fig. 11.10. The physical situation at the interface is exactly analogous to that at the junction of strings of different densities discussed in Chapter 6. The two waves b and c emerging from the glass surface fulfil the conditions necessary for interference provided the time taken for c to traverse the extra path is small compared with 10^{-8} s. If these waves are brought into superposition, by means of a lens, we shall have brightness if the respective disturbances are in phase, but darkness if they are in antiphase. This is the basis of interference by *division of amplitude,* of which Newton's rings are the best-known example.

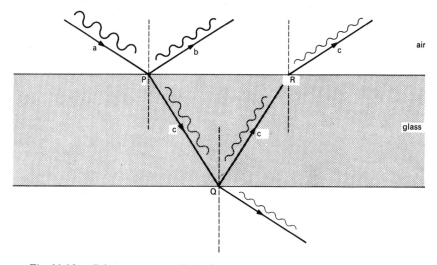

Fig. 11.10 – Coherent sources obtained by partial reflection of light waves at an air-glass interface. A light wave a is incident at point P. A part b of the wave is reflected, and a part c transmitted. After internal reflection at Q, c eventually emerges at R; c is coherent with b but will, in general, have a different phase since it has traversed an extra path.

The above discussion applies to light waves derived from the sources which were available before the invention of the *laser* in 1960. The laser produces coherent light and consequently it is far superior to other light sources for interference and diffraction experiments.

11.3.3 Diffraction

As we mentioned at the beginning of section 11.3, diffraction occurs when waves are limited or obstructed in some way. We shall consider the case of plane, monochromatic light waves incident normally upon a parallel-sided opening in an otherwise opaque screen. The experimental arrangement for this is shown in Fig. 11.11. The plane wavefronts are derived from a lamp L with the aid of two converging lenses L_1 and L_2 and a restricting slit S_1. After passing through the diffracting slit in the screen S_2, the light waves are collected by a converging lens L_3. A screen arranged in the focal plane of L_3 will be seen to be illuminated by a series of bright and dark fringes; the central fringe which is situated on the optical axis of the system will be brightest, with successive fringes above and below becoming rapidly fainter as we move away from the centre. This arrangement of fringes is known as a diffraction pattern. It is entirely due to the restriction placed on the light waves by the slit in S_2, for if S_2 is removed, it will be seen that the diffraction pattern vanishes, being replaced by a single bright line which is the optical image of the illuminated slit S_1.

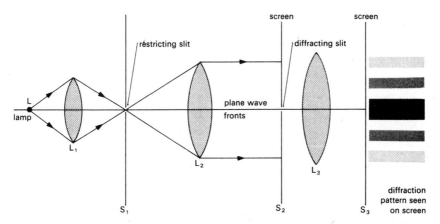

Fig. 11.11 – Experimental arrangement for obtaining single-slit diffraction pattern.

We will now see how this pattern can be accounted for. Figure 11.12(a) shows a given plane wavefront proceeding away from the slit of width a in the screen S_2. Suppose the direction of motion of this particular wavefront makes an angle θ with the optical axis of the system. The action of the lens L_3 is to collect together all the light along this wavefront and bring it to focus along a line on the screen S_3, indicated by P_θ in the section shown in Fig. 11.12(b). The wavefronts for which θ is zero are focused at P_0 on the optical axis of the system. The total effect at the point P_θ is obtained by dividing the wavefront shown in Fig. 11.12(a) into thin strips of equal width, the lengths of the strips being parallel to the length of the slit (i.e. perpendicular to the plane of the paper).

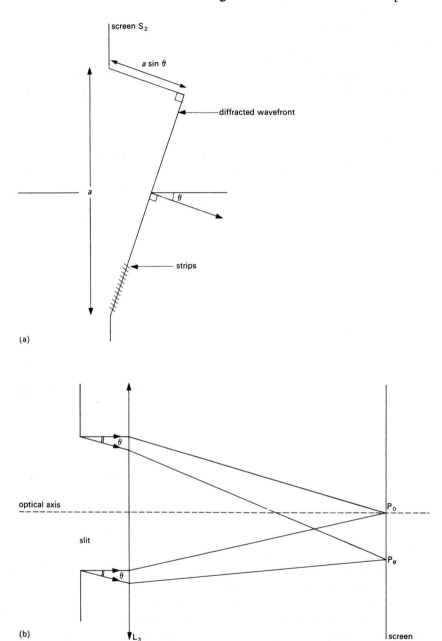

Fig. 11.12 – (a) Wavefront diffracted through angle θ. (b) Action of a lens in focusing wavefronts with different directions on to different positions on screen.

Each strip will give rise to the same disturbance at P_θ, so we have to superpose the disturbances due to all the strips by the principle of superposition, taking account of any difference in phase between the individual disturbances. Now we note from equation (11.28) that

$$\text{phase difference} = \frac{2\pi}{\lambda} \, (\text{path difference}) \, .$$

It is apparent from Fig. 11.12(a) that the difference between the paths travelled by the strips at the two extreme ends of the wavefront shown is just $a \sin \theta$. Thus the extreme phase difference ϕ is given by

$$\phi = \frac{2\pi}{\lambda} \, a \sin \theta \, . \tag{11.30}$$

Therefore the extreme phase difference across the wavefront is proportional to the distance apart of the strips concerned. It follows that the phase difference between disturbances due to any two strips is proportional to their distance apart, so that since the strips are all of equal width, the difference in phase between any two adjacent strips will have a constant value which we shall designate by δ. Let there be N strips and let the amplitude at P_θ due to each be b. We can find the net disturbance at P_θ by an extension of the vector method for superposing waves illustrated in Fig. 11.7. Since we have a number N of disturbances to superpose, we have a polygon in place of a triangle, and the resultant is obtained by completing the polygon as shown in Fig. 11.13(a). The vectors all have the same length b, and each is inclined to its neighbour by the phase angle δ. We now let the strips become infinitely thin, and the number of them, N, infinitely large in such a way that the product Nb remains finite. As we go to this limit the vector polygon of Fig. 11.13(a) becomes an arc of a circle, and the resultant R is the chord to this arc as shown in Fig. 11.13(b). Let the arc have centre O and radius r. Clearly the extreme phase difference ϕ (see (11.30)) is represented by the angle between the tangents to the two ends of the arc as shown.

We see from the geometry of Fig. 11.13(b) that

$$R = \text{PQ} = 2r \sin \tfrac{1}{2}\phi$$

and that $\text{arc PQ} = r\phi = Nb$.

Thus $$R = \frac{2Nb}{\phi} \sin \tfrac{1}{2}\phi \, .$$

But, since $\tfrac{1}{2}\phi = \dfrac{\pi}{\lambda} \, a \sin \theta$

(from (11.30)), we have, putting $Nb = A$,

$$R = \frac{A \sin[(\pi a \sin \theta)/\lambda]}{(\pi a \sin \theta)/\lambda}.$$ (11.31)

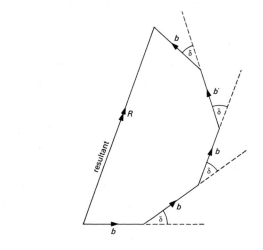

(a)

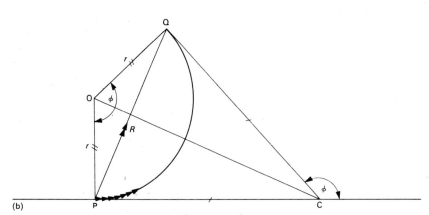

(b)

Fig. 11.13 – (a) Vector polygon for finding the resultant of a number of disturbances. (b) Vector diagram when individual disturbances become infinitely small.

It turns out that the diffraction pattern is only visible over a region of the screen corresponding to small values of θ, for which $\sin \theta \cong \theta$, so we may rewrite (11.31) as

$$R = \frac{A \sin(\pi a \theta/\lambda)}{\pi a \theta/\lambda}$$ (11.32)

or $\quad R = \dfrac{A \sin\alpha}{\alpha}$ $\qquad\qquad\qquad\qquad$ (11.33)

if we substitute α for $\pi a\theta/\lambda$.

Equation (11.33) tells us how the amplitude varies from place to place across the screen. The function has the form shown in Fig. 11.14(a), but since we are able to see only the *intensity* distribution, the curve shown in Fig. 11.14(b) of the square of (11.33), i.e.

$$R^2 = \frac{A^2 \sin^2\alpha}{\alpha^2} \quad,$$

is of more interest. Both curves are symmetrical about $\alpha = 0$, where the zero-order maximum occurs. In the lower curve the successive maxima fall quickly away in agreement with the experiment fact mentioned earlier. In fact the zero, first, second and third maxima in Fig. 11.14(b) can be shown to be in the ratio $1 : \frac{1}{21} : \frac{1}{61} : \frac{1}{120}$.

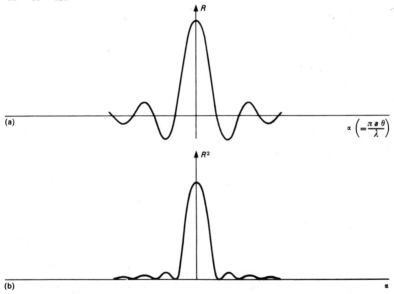

(a)

(b)

Fig. 11.14 — (a) Amplitude and (b) intensity distributions in single-silt diffraction pattern.

It is also of interest to see the effect upon the pattern of altering the width of the diffracting slit. Now the nth maximum from the centre, at angular position θ_n, is defined by a particular value of α which we will call α_n. Since

$$\alpha = \frac{\pi a\theta}{\lambda}$$

by definition, then for the nth maximum, the value of $\pi a \theta_n / \lambda$ is constant. Thus $\theta_n \propto 1/a$, so that if we increase a, θ_n decreases, which means that the whole pattern closes in towards the centre. Similarly, if we decrease a, θ_n increases and the whole pattern expands outwards. This reciprocal relationship between size of slit and size of pattern is of considerable importance and interest in diffraction theory.

Example 11.1

Diffraction of sound by an open window

Consider the following question: light and sound are both waves, so why is it that light always travels in straight lines, but sound can go round a corner?

An appreciation of diffraction enables us to answer this. We have seen that it *is* possible for a ray of light to deviate from a straight line if it passes through an aperture, but this effect will not be noticeable if the aperture is large compared with the wavelength of light ($\sim 5 \times 10^{-7}$ m). If for instance a beam of light from a torch passes through a hole of radius 1 cm in a black card, it travels in a straight line and diffraction effects are negligible. But if for instance a sodium street lamp is viewed through an umbrella, an unexpected pattern is observed. This occurs because the umbrella material contains very many tiny holes of dimensions which are not large compared with the wavelength of light.

In the case of sound, the wavelengths are much greater (Problem 4.5), and sounds, especially of low frequency (long wavelength), will readily travel round corners.

Consider a room with an open window of dimensions 1 m x 1 m. Suppose that inside the room, well away from the window, is a sound source. We have then an acoustic analogue of the single slit already analysed. There will be significant diffraction of the sound so long as $(a \sin \theta)/\lambda \lesssim 1$ (equation (11.31), whence $\lambda > 0.25$ m for an angle of $30°$. Since $c = 340$ m s^{-1} for sound, the corresponding frequency for significant diffraction of sound is $\lesssim 1.3$ kHz. A householder wishing to summon his dog from the garden should therefore shout towards the window — but would be ill advised to blow an ultrasonic dog whistle (unless there is an uninterrupted straight line between man and dog).

11.3.4 Fraunhofer diffraction and the Fourier transform

In the analysis of the last section the diffraction pattern was viewed at the back focal plane of a converging lens. Such a pattern is known as a *Fraunhofer diffraction pattern*. The general case of diffraction is much more difficult to analyse mathematically, and we will not consider it further. However, Fraunhofer diffraction presents some points of interest, and we will go into it rather more deeply than in the last section. Let us consider the Fraunhofer diffraction pattern obtained when the single-slit screen S_2 of Fig. 11.11 is replaced by a screen which is opaque in parts and transparent in parts. For simplicity we will treat it as if it had only one dimension and was of effectively infinite length; the reader is reassured that an analysis of a two-dimensional screen gives similar results (but only after rather greater algebraic manipulation). Let distance along the screen be x, as shown in Fig. 11.15, and let the screen's transparency be $g(x)$. That is, those parts of the screen which are transparent have $g(x) = 1$, and those which are opaque have $g(x) = 0$. The screen S_2 is irradiated from the left by monochromatic light of wavelength λ. We consider plane wavefronts whose normals make an angle θ with the optical axis of the system. These wavefronts will eventually be collected by the converging lens L_3 (Fig. 11.11) and focused at a point on the final screen S_3 corresponding to the angle θ. The amplitude of the net disturbance at this point will be the sum of the amplitudes (added together with due regard to phase) from each elemental length dx, such as the one shown at point Q. For the case $\theta = 0$, all the elemental disturbances, $g(x)\,dx$, from the whole screen S_2 travel the same optical path length to screen S_3 and therefore add up in phase to give the total disturbance at P_0 as

$$\int_{-\infty}^{\infty} g(x)\,dx \quad .$$

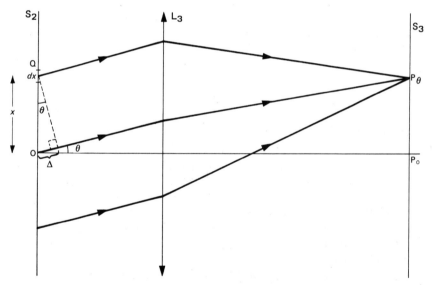

Fig. 11.15 — Normals to the wavefronts producing a Fraunhofer diffraction pattern on screen S_2.

However, at non-zero angles θ we must account in our integral for the fact that all the elemental disturbances travel different optical distances in passing from the screen S_2 to P_θ, and therefore will no longer be in phase with each other. Taking the phase at the point O as zero, we immediately see from Fig. 11.15 that the light being diffracted from Q at an angle θ and that diffracted from

O through the same angle travel paths to P_θ which differ in length by Δ. This corresponds to a phase difference

$$\phi = 2\pi\Delta/\lambda \ .$$

Now from the geometry of Fig. 11.15 we see that

$$\Delta = x \sin\theta \ .$$

Thus $\quad \phi = \dfrac{2\pi x \sin\theta}{\lambda} \ ,$

making the elemental amplitudes (in the complex exponential notation)

$$g(x)\exp(-i\phi)\,\mathrm{d}x$$

or $\quad g(x)\exp\left[\dfrac{-2\pi ix \sin\theta}{\lambda}\right]\mathrm{d}x \hfill (11.34)$

instead of the rather simpler

$$g(x)\,\mathrm{d}x$$

that we had for $\theta = 0$. In fact, we see that (11.34) reduces to $g(x)\,\mathrm{d}x$ for $\theta = 0$, as indeed it should. So the disturbance at the point P_θ on the final screen is

$$\int_{-\infty}^{\infty} g(x)\exp\left[-2\pi ix\,\frac{\sin\theta}{\lambda}\right]\mathrm{d}x \ .$$

We now replace $\sin\theta/\lambda$ by S, so the disturbance, say $G(S)$ at P_θ is

$$G(S) = \int_{-\infty}^{\infty} g(x)\exp(-2\pi ixS)\,\mathrm{d}x \ . \hfill (11.35)$$

Examination of (11.35) shows that $g(x)$ and $G(S)$ are Fourier-transform pairs; we have thus demonstrated the remarkable fact (which more rigorous analysis confirms except for minor details) that the amplitude distribution in a Fraunhofer diffraction pattern is related to the transparency distribution in the original screen by Fourier transformation. Since the amplitude (or intensity) of the Fourier transform of any real function is even, it therefore follows that all Fraunhofer diffraction patterns of partially opaque screens are symmetrical about the optical axis.

Let us now treat the example of the single slit of the last section by means of Fourier transforms. The screen S_2 is characterized by the function

$$g(x) = \begin{cases} 1 & |x| \leqslant a/2 \ , \\ 0 & |x| > a/2 \ , \end{cases}$$

where a is the width of the slit. Thus, by (11.35),

$$G(S) = \int_{-a/2}^{+a/2} \exp(-2\pi i x S)\, dx$$

$$= -\frac{1}{2\pi i S} \left[\exp(-2\pi i x S)\right]_{-a/2}^{+a/2}$$

$$= -\frac{1}{2\pi i S} \left[\exp(-2\pi i \tfrac{1}{2} a S) - \exp 2\pi i \tfrac{1}{2} a S\right]$$

$$= \frac{1}{\pi S} \left(\frac{\exp 2\pi i \tfrac{1}{2} a S - \exp(-2\pi i \tfrac{1}{2} a S)}{2i}\right)$$

$$= \frac{\sin \pi a S}{\pi S}$$

$$= \frac{a \sin \pi a S}{\pi a S}$$

$$= a \operatorname{sinc} a S \ ,$$

a result identical in form to (11.32).

We have in Fraunhofer diffraction, then, an important direct application of the Fourier transform. Diffraction patterns generally are related to the diffracting objects by an integral transform, but only in the case of Fraunhofer diffraction is the character of the transform normally simple enough to be interpreted with any ease. Fraunhofer diffraction is, moreover, very important in its own right. The diffraction of X-rays by crystals turns out to be of the Fraunhofer type; the amplitude distribution of the diffracted radiation is therefore related to the structure of the crystal (actually its electron density) by Fourier transformation, thus enabling us, in suitable circumstances, to deduce the atomic arrangement in the crystal from its X-ray diffraction pattern.

11.4　AN INSTANCE OF LIGHT NOT BEHAVING AS A WAVE

The wave theory of light, as developed from Maxwell's equations, has been completely successful in explaining all the observed optical phenomena relating to polarization, interference, and diffraction. However, for some phenomena arising from the interaction of light with electrons in atoms the wave theory is quite inadequate.

An example is the photoelectric effect. When light is directed on to the surface of a freshly cut alkali metal, it is found that the surface becomes electrically charged. The effect may be demonstrated by a cell of the kind shown in Fig. 11.16 in which a piece of alkali metal C is housed in an evacuated glass envelope. If electrode A is arranged at the opposite end of the tube, and C and A are connected in the circuit as shown, it is found that when the potential of A is made positive with respect to C, and visible light is directed on to C, a current flows in the circuit. A tube of this kind is known as a photoelectric tube and has many important applications, but our concern here is with the mechanism by which it works and, particularly, with the role of the incident light in this mechanism.

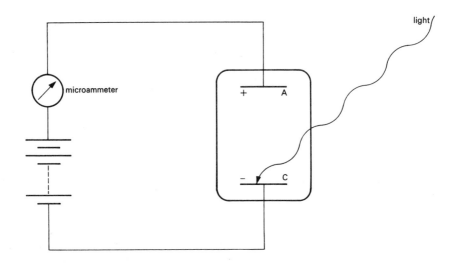

Fig. 11.16 – The photoelectric tube.

The polarity of A and C tells us at once that the current carriers within the tube are negatively charged and can therefore be immediately identified as electrons, since these are the only negatively charged entities in an alkali metal. If the light incident upon C is cut off, the current stops flowing, so we deduce that the light is somehow causing electrons to come out of the metal. Now it has been accepted for a very long time that metals contain electrons which are free to move about; this is why metals are good conductors of electricity. The electrons are kept within the confines of the boundary of the metal by means of a potential barrier at the surface, so that in order to escape from the metal an electron must acquire sufficient energy to surmount the barrier. In the above experiment, this energy must clearly be obtained from the incident light.

So far we have encountered nothing that cannot be explained in terms of the wave theory of light. But if we investigate the effect of varying the *frequency* of the incident light we are immediately confronted by a very strange result, for below a certain frequency, say f_0, it is found to be impossible to cause a current to flow in a given cell, no matter how intense the incident light is made. More sophisticated experiments show that, when the incident light is of sufficiently high frequency to cause a current to flow, the number of electrons emitted per unit time increases as the intensity of the light is increased (for fixed frequency) but that the velocity of the electrons escaping from near the surface remains constant. It is found that the *velocity* of these electrons can only be increased by increasing the frequency of the incident light.

None of this can be explained in terms of wave theory of light, for on this theory a given electron would eventually acquire sufficient energy to surmount the potential barrier no matter how low the frequency of the incident light. An explanation was offered by Einstein in 1905. Einstein suggested that instead of being spread uniformly over the wavefronts, the light energy is concentrated in packets or *quanta*, and that each *quantum* contains a fixed amount of energy E, related to the frequency of the light f by

$$E = hf ,$$

where h is a universal constant (the Planck constant).

The quanta are to be regarded as discrete packets of energy which cannot be split up, so that if a light quantum strikes an electron within the metal, the electron acquires the whole of the energy hf of the quantum. If this extra amount of energy is sufficient to enable the electron to overcome the potential barrier, the electron escapes and contributes to the photoelectric current. On the other hand, if hf is less than that required to surmount the barrier, the electron remains within the metal. Only in the extremely rare case of two quanta striking an electron simultaneously will the electron be able to obtain sufficient energy to escape.

We see that Einstein's theory explains why a more intense beam releases more electrons, but does not increase their velocity, for a more intense beam will have more quanta per second crossing unit area, but the energy of each quantum will be unaffected so long as the frequency does not change.

We see therefore that radiation has a dual character, acting in some circumstances as a wave phenomenon and in others as a particle phenomenon. However, it is not only light that is quantized in this way. Acoustical waves also behave in a quantum manner in certain circumstances. Electromagnetic quanta are known as *photons*, and acoustical quanta as *phonons*.

PROBLEMS

(11.1) In the S.I. system of units, μ_0 is *defined* as exactly $4\pi \times 10^{-7}$ H m^{-1}, and ϵ_0 is a measured quantity, which has a value 8.85×10^{-12} F m^{-1}. Show that the speed of electromagnetic waves in free space is 3.00×10^8 m s^{-1}. The reader familiar with electromagnetism is challenged to show that the dimensions of $(\text{H m}^{-1}\,\text{F m}^{-1})^{-\frac{1}{2}}$ is indeed $[\text{m s}^{-1}]$.

(11.2) Show for a plane wave as illustrated in Fig. 11.1, that $E_x/H_y = \sqrt{(\mu_0/\epsilon_0)}$ where $\mathbf{H}$ is the *magnetic field strength* and is given by $\mathbf{B}/\mu_0$ in vacuum. Show that this is 377Ω, using the data in Problem 11.1. The reader familiar with electromagnetism may wish to show that the units are indeed ohms.
(N.B. $\sqrt{(\mu_0/\epsilon_0)}$ is known as the impedance of free space).

(11.3) A coil is connected to a sinusoidal voltage source of frequency 50 Hz. Hence a magnetic field is produced, which propagates through free space as an electromagnetic wave. This must be so, since if a second coil is placed in the field, a voltage is induced in this coil. Suppose the magnetic field strength $\mathbf{H}$ (see problem 11.2) at this second coil has amplitude 100 A m^{-1}, which is fairly small; then the result of Problem 11.2 appears to indicate that the electric field has the enormous amplitude 37.7 kV m^{-1}.
   This is clearly wrong, but where is the fallacy?

(11.4) The refractive index of water, measured by various optical methods, is approximately 1.3. The relative permittivity, measured by electrical methods, is approximately 80. Explain why where is an apparent violation of equation (11.20).

(11.5) This problem is recommended to a reader wishing to obtain insight into 'circular polarization' which is important in optics.
   A string is stretched along the z-axis of coordinates, and a sinusoidal transverse wave $x = a \sin(\omega t - kz)$ is propagated along it. A second sinusoidal wave $y = a \sin(\omega t - kz)$ is now superimposed, its plane being perpendicular to that of the first. By making sketches of the disturbance in the x–y plane at $z = 0$, show that the resulting wave is of amplitude $\sqrt{2}\, a$, polarized in a plane at $45°$ to the x-axis.
   Suppose now that the second wave is instead $a \cos(\omega t - kz)$. Show that an instantaneous photograph of the string would reveal it to have the shape of a helix. Would it be a right-handed or a left-handed helix? (Compare it with a conventional screw thread). Consider an observer at a fixed position z_0. Show that in this z_0 plane, he would observe a disturbance rotating in a circle. If he is *facing* the incoming waves, would the disturbance rotate clockwise or anticlockwise?

(11.6) A sound source at ground level is detected by a distant observer also at ground level. There is a wind in the direction from the source to the observer. Remembering that the wind speed will increase with height (why?), construct Huygens wave fronts from the source. Hence explain why 'sound travels better with the wind'.

(11.7) Prove the result stated in section 11.3.2 for Young's slits, namely that the bright fringes produced on a screen are $\lambda D/a$ apart. If a thin piece of glass were placed over one of the slits on the side nearer the screen, what would be the effect on the fringe pattern?

(11.8) Use a calculator to plot the functions $(\sin \alpha)/\alpha$, and $(\sin^2\alpha)/\alpha^2$. Hence find the first value of α (other than zero) for which $(\sin^2\alpha)/\alpha^2$ is a maximum, and the value of that maximum.

(11.9) A diffraction grating is made in such a way that its transparency $g(x)$ varies sinusoidally along its length. What would be the appearance of the Fraunhofer diffraction pattern? If $g(x)$ were instead a Gaussian function $g_0\exp(-x^2/a^2)$, what would now be the appearance of the pattern?

Appendix A
Microcomputer program for the visual demonstration of waves

A.1 INTRODUCTION

Prompted by the advent of the microcomputer age, together with the appeal of the visual demonstration, we detail in this appendix a program which can be used to show a variety of wave phenomena. This is intended to facilitate the study of such facets of the subject as beats, stationary waves, group velocity, and Fourier summation, either for private contemplation or for class demonstration.

One obvious problem lies in the diversity and ephemeral nature of microcomputers. We therefore give a program appropriate to the 6502 microprocessor, which at the time of writing is used in a wide variety of commercial microcomputers. Detailed programs are given for the Commodore PET, Acorn Atom, and BBC machines, but these should be easily adaptable for any microcomputer which has a visual display unit in which the screen locations are memory-mapped in a sequential manner (for example the OSI and UK101). No program is given for machines using the Z80 microprocessor (for example the Sinclair ZX81), which is at present the principal 'rival' of the 6502. The patient reader may, however, develop such a program using the flow diagram given.

The reason why the program is appropriate only for a specific microprocessor is that part of it has been written in machine code to achieve the speed necessary for visual display of a wave which may be rapidly moving. The parts of the program not involving the wave display are in BASIC.

A.2 OUTLINE OF THE PROGRAM

The program provides a visual display of the function

$$y = a_1\sin(\omega_1 t + k_1 x + \phi_1) + a_2\sin(\omega_2 t + k_2 x + \phi_2) + \ldots +$$
$$+ a_n\sin(\omega_n t + k_n x + \phi_n) + \ldots \tag{A.1}$$

which is, in general, the sum of several travelling waves of arbitrary amplitudes a_i circular frequencies ω_i, circular wavenumbers k_i and phase constants ϕ_i. The operator types in from the keyboard the values of amplitude a_1, phase constant ϕ_1, circular wavenumber k_1, and wave speed c_1 of the first component wave. The computer stores a_1, ϕ_1, k_1 and the circular frequency $\omega_1(= k_1 c_1)$.

The procedure is repeated for all the component waves. The operator is free to choose as many or as few terms as desired. A single term will suffice to show a travelling wave. With two terms, stationary waves, beats and group velocity can be studied. Static sinusoidal waves can also be displayed, simply by inserting a value zero for the wave speed. This facility allows, for example, the display of the sum of several terms of a Fourier series.

A.3 THE PROGRAM

The part of the program where speed of execution is of no importance has been written in BASIC.

The listing below is given with particular reference to the Commodore PET microcomputer (models 3032 and 4032). Where possible, indications are made on how to adapt for other machines. Before proceeding to enter the program on such a machine, the reader is advised to ascertain that it uses a 6502 microprocessor, and not for example a Z80.

The program makes use of memory locations $0C00 - $0EFF (see Fig. A.1), which are free for use in the Commodore PET. For other computers, the user should check that the memory block $0C00 - $0EFF is free for use, and is not used by the computer for some other purpose. If this block cannot be used, a more suitable location must be chosen, which involves modifying lines 50, 80, 90, 110, 120, 130, 140, 320, 410, 420, 430, 480 and 500. It is also necessary to modify OC, OD and OE in the machine code routines (section A.5 and Fig. A.4). This is achieved by altering 12, 13 and 14 in lines 600 − 880 wherever they occur (except for the 14 in line 690).

Line		Notes
5	REM.WAVE DEMONSTRATION PROGRAM	See note 1
6	REM.GOUGH,RICHARDS and WILLIAMS	See note 1
7	REM.COPYRIGHT ELLIS HORWOOD LTD.	See note 1
8	REM.LISTING FOR COMMODORE PET	See note 1
10	PRINT"COLD START(C) OR WARM START(W)?"	
20	INPUT A$:IF A$="W"GOTO 100	
30	PRINT"THINKING"	
40	RESTORE	
50	FOR I=0 TO 229:READ Z:	Loads machine code
	POKE3072+I,Z:NEXT I	See note 2

```
60   X=3.1416/128                              See note 3
70   FOR I=0 TO 64
80   POKE3584+I,INT(.5+120*SIN(I*X)):         Fills a quarter of the
     NEXT I                                   sine table
90   SYS(3072)                                See note 4
100  C=40:R=24:W=40:S=32768                   See note 5
110  POKE3452,INT((LOG(500/R))/LOG(2))        Vertical scaling factor
120  POKE3453,W:POKE3454,C
130  S=S+2*C:S1=INT(S/256):POKE3455,S1        See note 6
140  POKE3223,S-256*S1                        See note 7
300  PRINT:PRINT
310  PRINT"HOW MANY SINE WAVES TO BE ADDED?"
320  INPUT N:POKE 3451,4*N
330  A1=0:FOR I=1 TO N:PRINT
340  PRINT"ENTER AMPLITUDE, PHASE CONST
     (IN DEGREES),"
350  PRINT"CIRCULAR WAVENO. AND WAVE SPEED"
360  INPUT A(I),P,K,C                         See note 8
370  IF C>=0 GOTO390
380  PRINT:PRINT"WAVE SPEED MUST NOT BE
     NEGATIVE":GOTO 300
390  U=0:IF K<0 THEN U=1                      See note 9
400  P=P-360*INT(P/360)                       See note 10
410  POKE3453+4*I,P*256/360
420  POKE3454+4*I,INT(K*128/3.14/W)+256*U     See notes 3 and 9
430  POKE3455+4*I,ABS(C*K)
440  A1=A1+ABS(A(I)):NEXT I
450  IF A1=0 THEN A1=1                        See note 11
460  FOR I=1 TO N                             Scales and stores
                                              amplitudes
470  R=0:IF A(I)<0 THEN R=1                   See note 9
480  POKE3452+4*I,INT(.5+120*ABS
     (A(I))/A1)+128*R                         See note 9
490  NEXT I
500  SYS(3096):GOTO 500                       Display routine.
                                              See note 4
600  DATA162,0,160,64,189,0,14,153            See note 2
610  DATA64,14,9,128,157,128,14,153
620  DATA192,14,232,136,16,238,96,0
630  DATA160,64,169,128,153,191,13,136
640  DATA208,250,162,0,185,129,13,141
650  DATA53,12,185,128,13,141,119,13
660  DATA10,141,120,13,173,0,14,72
```

```
670  DATA41,127,141,121,13,104,41,128
680  DATA141,122,13,152,72,169,0,160
690  DATA7,14,120,13,144,4,24,109
700  DATA121,13,78,121,13,136,208,241
710  DATA74,72,173,119,13,77,122,13
720  DATA42,104,176,4,73,255,105,1
730  DATA24,125,192,13,157,192,13,104
740  DATA168,173,53,12,24,121,130,13
750  DATA141,53,12,232,236,125,13,208
760  DATA169,200,200,200,200,204,123,13
770  DATA208,152,162,4,160,0,173,127
780  DATA13,141,152,12,169,32,153,0
790  DATA0,200,208,250,238,152,12,202
800  DATA208,244,172,124,13,189,192,13
810  DATA74,136,208,252,168,173,127,13
820  DATA141,201,12,173,151,12,24,109
830  DATA126,13,144,3,238,201,12,136
840  DATA16,244,141,200,12,169,42,157
850  DATA0,0,232,236,125,13,208,210
860  DATA172,123,13,185,125,13,24,121
870  DATA127,13,153,125,13,136,136,136
880  DATA136,208,240,96,0,0
900  END
```

Notes

1. These REMARK statements do not form part of the program, and may be omitted.
2. In line 50 the machine code is loaded into $0C00–$0CE5 from the data given in lines 600–880. On some computers there may be a more satisfactory procedure for loading machine code. For instance it may be possible to load it directly from a tape cassette, in which case there is no necessity to incorporate it in the BASIC program. Alternatively, if the computer has an assembler, the machine code can be written in assembler language; the reader is referred to section A.6.
3. PI may be used instead of 3.14_{16} if this is recognized by the microcomputer.
4. This calls a machine code routine. Other microcomputers may have different instructions, e.g. CALL3072, or a LINK instruction. On the UK101, the USR function can be used, with the low and high byte of the hex machine code address inserted in memory locations 11 and 12 respectively. The modified lines are in this case

```
90   POKE11,0:POKE12,12:X=USR(X)
500  POKE11,24:POKE12,12:X=USR(X):GOTO 500
```

5. These values of C, R, W, and S are those appropriate to the Commodore PET. For other machines, the information must be obtained from the manufacturer's data. For the UK101 (based on the OSI), the appropriate values are 64,16,48 and 53260 respectively.

6. The height of the top of the display can be altered by changing the "2" to some other integer.

7. The less significant byte of S (expressed as a two byte word) is stored at location $0C97, and is part of the machine code routine.

8. The amplitudes are stored in an array A(I). The array dimensions may need to be defined on some machines, for example if more than ten waves are to be compounded. The user may therefore need a statement such as

    325 DIM A(16) or, if acceptable, 325 DIM A(N)

9. If the microcomputer recognises Boolean expressions, lines 390 and 470 can be omitted; lines 420 and 480 are modified to read

    420   POKE3454+4*I,INT(K*128/3.14/W)-256*(K<0)

    480   POKE3452+4*I,INT(.5+120*ABS(A(I))/A1)-128*(A(I)<0)

    These new lines are correct if, as for the UK101 for instance, a Boolean expression is given a value 0 if the argument is false, and -1 if it is true.

10. An alternative listing is

    400   IF P<0 THEN P=P+360:GOTO400

    405   IF P>=360 THEN P=P-360:GOTO405

11. This line avoids an error message if the user has inadvertently given zero amplitude to the wave(s). It is not essential and may be omitted.

A.4 EXPLANATION OF THE BASIC PART OF THE PROGRAM

(a) Initial routine.

This routine is executed if the program is being run for the first time after loading (a 'cold start'), otherwise it is bypassed.

Line 50 in conjunction with lines 600–880 loads the machine code into memory locations $0C00–$0CE3 in preparation for the display of the wave.

Then a table of sine values over one complete cycle is compiled. This is stored in locations $0E00–$0EFF, to be used later in calculating the wave forms. Lines 60–80 produce the first quarter of the table (a sine value $0 \to 1$), the rest of the table being produced rapidly from these values by a short machine code routine.

$0C00–$0CE3 (3072–3299) Machine code program

$0C00–$0C16	Completion of sine table
$0C18–$0CE3	Display routine
$0C35	Sine table pointer
$0C96–7	Address of left edge of the third screen line
$0CC8–9	Screen pointer

$0D77–$0D7F (3447–3455) Stored data

$0D77	Wave amplitude including sign bit
$0D78	Wave amplitude without sign bit
$0D79	Sine value, without sign bit
$0D7A	Sign flag of the sine value
$0D7B	4 × (number of waves N)
$0D7C	Logarithmic vertical scaling factor
$0D7D	Screen width W
$0D7E	Number of columns C
$0D7F	More significant byte of left edge of the third line of the screen

$0D80–$0DBF (3456–3519) Wave data

$0D80	Scaled amplitude of the first wave component
$0D81	Scaled phase of the first wave component
$0D82	Scaled circular wavenumber of the first wave component
$0D83	Speed of the first wave component
$0D84	Scaled amplitude of the second wave component
$0D85	Scaled phase of the second wave component
$0D86	Scaled circular wavenumber of the second wave component
$0D87	Speed of the second wave component

. . . .

$0DC0–$0DFF (3520–3583) Ordinate memory block

$0DC0	Ordinate of the first point (X = 0)
$0DC1	Ordinate of the second point (X = 1)

. . . .

$0E00–$0EFF (3584–3839) Table of sine values
See Table A.1.

Fig. A.1 – Memory map.

Now each memory location contains one byte (an 8 bit word) which can range from 0 to 255 ($00 to $FF hexadecimal). To allow for negative sine values, the following procedure has been adopted. The most significant bit is reserved as a sign bit, 0 meaning positive and 1 negative; the other 7 bits give the magnitude, which must therefore lie between 0 and 127. The numbers stored in the table are 120 sin $2\pi I/256$ (rounded to the nearest integer), where I ranges from 0 to 255 (see table A.1).

Table A.1.
Table of sine values

Location	I	120 sin $2\pi I/256$	decimal	binary	hex
				Value stored	
$0E00	0	0	0	0000 0000	$00
$0E01	1	2.94	3	0000 0011	$03
$0E02	2	5.89	6	0000 0110	$06
. . . .					
$0E40	64	120	120	0111 1000	$78
. . . .					
$0E7F	127	2.94	3	0000 0011	$03
$0E80	128	0	0	0000 0000	$00
$0E81	129	−2.94	131	1000 0011	$83
$0E82	130	−5.89	134	1000 0110	$86
. . . .					
$0EC0	192	−120	248	1111 1000	$F8
. . . .					
$0EFF	255	−2.94	131	1000 0011	$83

(b) Screen display

The screen display is divided up into a matrix of small squares or rectangles as shown in Fig. A.2, with C (normally 32−64) columns and R (normally 16−32) rows. The screen width W may be equal to C, but this is not necessarily true, since there may be a few columns not displayed. The complete display is assumed to be 'mapped' sequentially on to a part of the memory of the microcomputer. For instance, in the Commodore PET, for which C=40 and R=24, the top left location S is linked to locaton 32768 (=$8000 hexadecimal), and the rest of the row to 32769 ($8001) − 32807 ($8027). The second row is mapped to 32808 ($8028) − 32847 ($804F), and so on, down to the bottom right hand corner 33727 ($83BF).

For microcomputers other than the PET, the appropriate values of C, R, W, and S should be inserted in line 100.

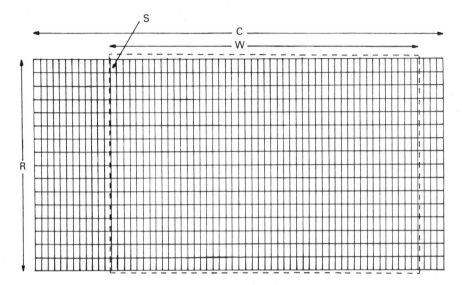

Fig. A.2 – The memory-mapped screen display.

W and C are stored in locations $0D7D and $0D7E respectively. In line 110, a logarithmic vertical scaling factor is calculated and stored in $0D7C. This will be used to ensure that whatever the value of R, the displayed wave will occupy a convenient size on the screen. Next, the hexadecimal address of the left-hand edge of the third line of the screen is calculated. The more significant byte is stored in $0D7F and the less significant in $0C97 (which is part of the machine code routine).

(c) Input of wave parameters

The program now invites the operator to insert the relevant information concerning the waves to be displayed. Firstly, the number of waves N to be compounded is typed in, and 4 times this number is stored in $0D7B.

Then for each wave in turn, the amplitude a, phase ϕ in degrees, circular wavenumber k and wave speed c are successively typed. Negative values of ϕ and k can be used, but c should always be positive (see section A.8).

To each phase ϕ is added or subtracted an integral multiple of 360 such that the result lies between 0 and 360; the result is then scaled down and rounded to an integer between 0 and 255.

From the circular wavenumber k is calculated $128\,k/\pi W$, which is the phase difference between successive screen abscissae (where 256 units = 360°). A little thought will reveal that *one screen width represents unit length*. For instance if $k = 2\pi$ (i.e. $\lambda = 1$), the phase difference between adjacent abscissae is $(360°/W)$, and exactly one complete cycle of the sine wave is displayed.

The wave speed is now multiplied by k, and the modulus of the product, which is the circular frequency ω is deduced. This will not be the circular frequency of the wave displayed on the screen, since this latter depends on the speed of operation of the machine code and may vary from one microcomputer to another.

Finally, the sum of the moduli of the amplitudes of all the component waves is computed to obtain a scaling factor A1. The individual amplitudes are then divided by this factor. This procedure ensures that whatever the amplitudes entered, the display will occupy a convenient size on the screen. The scaled amplitudes are multiplied by 120 and rounded to the nearest integer, and 128 is added if the sign is negative (cf. the procedure for encoding the sine values given in (a) above).

These modified values of the amplitude, phase, circular wavenumber and circular frequency of the component waves are stored in a block of memory locations commencing at $0D80, the first wave going into $0D80–3, the second into $0D84–7, and so on. There is space in this block for 16 waves, which is well in excess of even the most elaborate synthesis likely to be required.

A.5 EXPLANATION OF THE MACHINE CODE PART OF THE PROGRAM

(a) Completion of the sine table.

This short routine has already been discussed in section A.4(a). The listing is given below (see section A.6 for assembler language).

```
3072 dec.
0C00  A2 00      LDX#$00        0C0F  99 C0 0E   STA $0EC0,Y
0C02  A0 40      LDY#$40        0C12  E8         INX
0C04  BD 00 0E   LDA $0E00,X    0C13  88         DEY
0C07  99 40 0E   STA $0E40,Y    0C14  10 EE      BPL $0C04
0C0A  09 80      ORA#$80        0C16  60         RTS
0C0C  9D 80 0E   STA $0E80,X    0C17  unused
```

(b) Display routine

A flow diagram for this routine is given in Fig. A.3 and a complete listing in Fig. A.4. Again the program in assembler language can be followed in section A.6.

The Y register of the 6502 microprocessor has been used to designate which of the component waves is involved at any moment. $Y = 0, 4, 8, \ldots 4\,(N-1)$ refers to the first, second, third, . . . Nth wave. The X register designates the horizontal (x) component on the screen, and ranges from 0 to W. The corresponding vertical (y) coordinates are stored in memory locations $0DC0 to $0DFF. Initially these are all set, by instructions $0C18–$0C21, to a value 128 (=$80), which is interpreted as the 'zero level'. A value greater than 128 corresponds to negative y, one less than 128 to positive y.

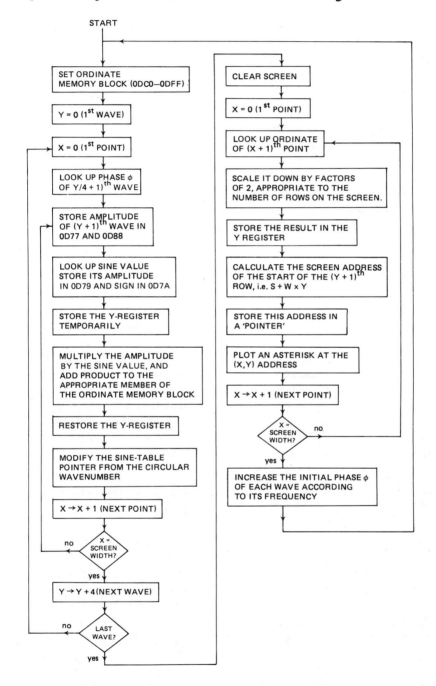

Fig. A.3 – Flow diagram for the display routine.

0C18 A0 40	LDY#$40
0C1A A9 80	LDA#$80
0C1C 99 BF 0D	STA $0DBF,Y
0C1F 88	DEY
0C20 D0 FA	BNE $0C1C
0C22 A2 00	LDX#$00
0C24 B9 81 0D	LDA $0D81,Y
0C27 8D 35 0C	STA $0C35
0C2A B9 80 0D	LDA $0D80,Y
0C2D 8D 77 0D	STA $0D77
0C30 0A	ASL
0C31 8D 78 0D	STA $0D78
0C34 AD(-) 0E	LDA $0E--
0C37 48	PHA
0C38 29 7F	AND#$7F
0C3A 8D 79 0D	STA $0D79
0C3D 68	PLA
0C3E 29 80	AND#$80
0C40 8D 7A 0D	STA $0D7A
0C43 98	TYA
0C44 48	PHA
0C45 A9 00	LDA#$00
0C47 A0 07	LDY#$07
0C49 0E 78 0D	ASL $0D78
0C4C 90 04	BCC $0C52
0C4E 18	CLC
0C4F 6D 79 0D	ADC $0D79
0C52 4E 79 0D	LSR $0D79
0C55 88	DEY
0C56 D0 F1	BNE $0C49
0C58 4A	LSR
0C59 48	PHA
0C5A AD 77 0D	LDA $0D77
0C5D 4D 7A 0D	EOR $0D7A
0C60 2A	ROL
0C61 68	PLA
0C62 B0 04	BCS $0C68
0C64 49 FF	EOR#$FF
0C66 69 01	ADC#$01
0C68 18	CLC
0C69 7D C0 0D	ADC $0DC0,X

0C6C 9D C0 0D	STA $0DC0,X
0C6F 68	PLA
0C70 A8	TAY
0C71 AD 35 0C	LDA $0C35
0C74 18	CLC
0C75 79 82 0D	ADC $0D82,Y
0C78 8D 35 0C	STA $0C35
0C7B E8	INX
0C7C EC 7D 0D	CPX $0D7D
0C7F D0 A9	BNE $0C2A
0C81 C8	INY
0C82 C8	INY
0C83 C8	INY
0C84 C8	INY
0C85 CC 7B 0D	CPY $0D7B
0C88 D0 98	BNE $0C22
0C8A A2 04	LDX#$04
0C8C A0 00	LDY#$00
0C8E AD 7F 0D	LDA $0D7F
0C91 8D 98 0C	STA $0C98
0C94 A9 20	LDA#$20
0C96 99(-) (-)	STA $----
0C99 C8	INY
0C9A D0 FA	BNE $0C96
0C9C EE 98 0C	INC $0C98
0C9F CA	DEX
0CA0 D0 F4	BNE $0C96
0CA2 AC 7C 0D	LDY $0D7C
0CA5 BD C0 0D	LDA $0DC0,X
0CA8 4A	LSR
0CA9 88	DEY
0CAA D0 FC	BNE $0CA8
0CAC A8	TAY
0CAD AD 7F 0D	LDA $0D7F
0CB0 8D C9 0C	STA $0CC9
0CB3 AD 97 0C	LDA $0C97
0CB6 18	CLC
0CB7 6D 7E 0D	ADC $0D7E
0CBA 90 03	BCC $0CBF
0CBC EE C9 0C	INC $0CC9
0CBF 88	DEY

0CC0 10 F4	BPL $0CB6		0CD6 18	CLC
0CC2 8D C8 0C	STA $0CC8		0CD7 79 7F 0D	ADC $0D7F,Y
			0CDA 99 7D 0D	STA $0D7D,Y
0CC5 A9 2A	LDA#$2A		0CDD 88	DEY
0CC7 9D(-)(-)	STA $----,X		0CDE 88	DEY
0CCA E8	INX		0CDF 88	DEY
0CCB EC 7D 0D	CPX $0D7D		0CE0 88	DEY
0CCE D0 D2	BNE $0CA2		0CE1 D0 F0	BNE $0CD3
			0CE3 60	RTS
0CD0 AC 7B 0D	LDY $0D7B			
0CD3 B9 7D 0D	LDA $0D7D,Y		0CE4–0CFF	unused

Fig. A.4 – Machine code listing, display routine.

At first, X and Y are both zero, which means that the first point on the first wave is being treated. The amplitude of this wave is temporaily stored in $0D77, and its modulus (i.e. the amplitude with the sign bit removed) in $0D78. The (scaled) phase ϕ is placed in $0C35, which is actually part of the machine code routine, and acts as a 'pointer' to the look-up table of sine values. The appropriate sine value is found, its magnitude (bits 0–6) is stored in $0D79, and its sign bit (bit 7) in $0D7A.

There now follows ($0C45–$0C59) a routine for multiplying the amplitude (in $0D78) by the sine value (in $0D79), and establishing the sign of the product ($0C5A–$0C60). If this sign is positive, the product is replaced by its two's complement. This product is then added to location $0DC0, which will ultimately give the ordinate of the first point on the display.

The next step ($0C71–$0C7A) involves increasing the value of the sine table pointer in $0C35 by the (scaled) circular wavenumber (i.e. the phase difference between successive x-values).

The X register is increased, and the procedure repeated until X has reached its maximum value of W. The first component wave has now been calculated. The whole procedure is repeated for the other waves, if any, these ordinates being added to those already stored in $0DC0 et seq. The pattern is now ready for display.

The screen is now completely erased ($0C8A–$0CA1). The first y value is recovered from $0DC0, and scaled down by the vertical scaling factor discussed in A.4(b) ($0CA2–$0CAC). The resulting number is the row, measured from the top, at which the point must be displayed. It is therefore multiplied by C, and the result is added to the address of the top left corner of the display. The sum, which is the address of the start of the appropriate row, is stored in the machine code itself at $0CC8–9. An asterisk is displayed at a point X places to the right from here. Should the reader wish to use a different symbol, he should modify $0CC6 by altering the '42' in line 840. X is now increased, and the procedure repeated until X reaches W, when the whole wave will be displayed.

The pattern will remain on the screen for some milliseconds, the time taken for the microcomputer to calculate the ordinates of the next pattern.

To each phase value (in $0D81, $0D85 ...) is added the appropriate circular frequency value (from $0D83, $0D87 ...), the results being the new initial phase values ϕ_1, ϕ_2 for the next display ($0CD0–$0CE3). The whole procedure is repeated from the beginning, by returning to line 500 of the BASIC program.

The result is a moving display on the screen, which will continue until the user stops or resets the program.

A.6 PROGRAM LISTING FOR THE ACORN ATOM MICROCOMPUTER, INCLUDING ASSEMBLER LANGUAGE

The Acorn Atom is at present a widely used machine, but its BASIC language is significantly different from that of the PET. In order that the user should avoid the tedium of 'translating' from the latter, we give a full listing here.

The machine code is written in assembler language, which may be valuable for the programming of other microcomputers possessing an assembler.

The memory block used for the sine look-up table etc. is $3A00–$3BFF.

```
5     REM. WAVE DEMONSTRATION PROGRAM
6     REM. GOUGH,RICHARDS and WILLIAMS
7     REM.COPYRIGHT ELLIS HORWOOD LTD.
8     REM.LISTING FOR ACORN ATOM
10    DIM LL(14)
20    P."COLD START(C) OR WARM START(W)" '
30    INPUT $A;IF $A="W" GOTO 100
40    GOSUB600;GOSUB600
50    P."THINKING" '
60    %X=PI/128
70    FOR I=0 TO 64
80    ?(#3B00+I)=%(.5+120*SIN(I*%X))
90    NEXT I;LINK LL0
100   C=32;R=16;W=32;S=#8000
110   ?#3A7C=%(LOG R/LOG2)
120   ?#3A7D=W;?#3A7E=C
130   ?#3A7F=S/256
300   P."HOW MANY SINE WAVES TO BE ADDED"
310   INPUT N;?#3A7B=4*N
320   FDIM%AA(N)
330   %Z=0;FOR I=1 TO N
340   P."ENTER AMPL.,PHASE CONST(IN DEGREES)" '
350   P."CIRCULAR WAVENO. AND WAVE SPEED" '
360   P."PRESS'RETURN'AFTER EACH ENTRY" '
```

```
370   FINPUT%A,%P,%K,%C
380   %AA(I)=%A
390   ?(#3A7D+4*I)=%P*256/360
400   ?(#3A7E+4*I)=%(128*(%K/PI/W+1−SGN(%K)))
410   ?(#3A7F+4*I)=%ABS(%C*%K)
420   %Z=%Z+%ABS(%AA(I));NEXT I
430   IF%Z=0 THEN%Z=1
440   FOR I=1 TO N
450   ?(#3A7C+4*I)=%(120*%ABS(%AA(I))/%Z)+64*(1−SGN(%AA(I)))
460   NEXT I
470   LINK LL2
480   END
600   DIM P(−1)
610   [
620   :LL0 LDX@0;LDY@#40
630   :LL1 LDA#3B00,X;STA#3B40,Y
640   ORA@#80;STA#3B80,X;STA#3BC0,Y
650   INX;DEY;BPL LL1;RTS
660   :LL2 LDY@#40;LDA@#80
670   :LL3 STA#3ABF,Y;DEY;BNE LL3
680   :LL4 LDX@0;LDA#3A81,Y;STA LL5+11
690   :LL5 LDA#3A80,Y;STA#3A77
700   ASLA;STA#3A78;LDA#3B00;PHA
710   AND@#7F;STA#3A79;PLA;AND@#80
720   STA#3A7A;TYA;PHA;LDA@0;LDY@7
730   :LL6 ASL#3A78;BCC LL7;CLC;ADC#3A79
740   :LL7 LSR#3A79;DEY;BNE LL6;LSRA
750   PHA;LDA#3A77;EOR#3A7A;ROLA
760   PLA;BCS LL8;EOR@#FF;ADC@1
770   :LL8 CLC;ADC#3AC0,X
780   STA#3AC0,X;PLA;TAY;LDA LL5+11
790   CLC;ADC#3A82,Y;STA LL5+11
800   INX;CPX#3A7D;BNE LL5;INY;INY
810   INY;INY;CPY#3A7B;BNE LL4
820   LDX@4;LDY@0;LDA#3A7F
830   STA LL9+2;LDA#20
840   :LL9 STA#8000,Y;INY;BNE LL9
850   INC LL9+2;DEX;BNE LL9
860   :LL10 LDY#3A7C;LDA#3AC0,X
870   :LL11 LSRA;DEY;BNE LL11;TAY
880   LDA#3A7F;STA LL13+10;LDA LL9+1
890   :LL12 CLC;ADC#3A7E;BCC LL13;INC LL13+10
900   :LL13 DEY;BPL LL12;STA LL13+9
```

```
910  LDA@#2A;STA#1111,X;INX
920  CPX#3A7D;BNE LL10;LDY#3A7B
930  :LL14 LDA#3A7D,Y;CLC
940  ADC#3A7F,Y;STA#3A7D,Y;DEY
950  DEY;DEY;DEY;BNE LL14;JMP LL2
960  ]
970  RETURN
```

(N.B. To stop the display, press BREAK and type in OLD)

A.7 PROGRAM LISTING FOR THE BBC AND APPLE II MICROCOMPUTERS

In view of the current popularity of the BBC and Apple II microcomputers (and their availability to the authors!), we devote this section to giving the program for these machines. Although satisfactory execution has been tested only for the BBC model B, it is believed that the program will also work on the model A without further modification.

The machine code routine and sine table have been re-located to $2C00– $2EFF. The complete program for the BBC then as given in section A.3, with the following changes.

Line or or part of line	Listing in section A.3	Modification for BBC
9	None	HIMEM=&2BFF
50	POKE3072+I,Z	?(11264+I)=Z
80	POKE3584+I,INT(. . .)	?(11776+I)=INT(. . .)
90	SYS(3072)	CALL11264
100	S=32768	S=31744
110	POKE3452,INT(. . .)	?(11644)=4
120	POKE3453,W:POKE3454,C	?(11645)=W:?(11646)=C
130	POKE3455,S1	?(11647)=S1
140	POKE3223,S−256*S1	?(11415)=0
320	POKE3451,4*N	?(11643)=4*N
325	None	DIM A(N)
410	POKE3453+4*I,P*256/360	?(11645+4*I)=P*256/360
420	POKE3454+4*I,INT(. . .)	?(11646+4*I)=INT(. . .)
430	POKE3455+4*I,ABS(C*K)	?(11647+4*I)=ABS(C*K)
480	POKE3452+4*I,INT(. . .)	?(11644+4*I)=INT(. . .)
495	None	CLS
500	SYS(3096):GOTO500	CALL11288:GOTO500

Also, in lines 600–880, the data 12, 13 and 14 should be replaced by 44, 45 and 46 respectively (except for the 14 in line 690, which is not to be changed).

To exit from the display, ESCAPE is pressed.

The Apple II microcomputer does not have a sequentially-mapped screen display, and the machine code routine would need to be modified to give the best possible display. However, reasonable results can be obtained by the program listed in section A.3 with the following minor modifications.

In lines 50,80,90,110,120(twide),130,140,320,410,420,430,480, and 500: 8192 should be added to the number between 3000 and 4000. In lines 600–880, the same changes as mentioned for the BBC above should be implemented. Finally, line 100 should read

100   C = 128: R = 8: W = 40: S = 936

A.8 USE OF THE PROGRAM

When the program is in the microcomputer, typing RUN will initiate execution. On the first RUN after the program has been loaded, C must be pressed in response to the question 'Cold start(C) or warm start(W)?', and W may be typed for subsequent runs.

We now give a number of demonstrations as examples of what can be achieved. In all cases, the values given are not definitive, and the user should be encouraged to experiment with other values.

It should be realised that the vertical resolution is limited by the number of lines in the display. Consequently there may be some distortion, particularly near sharp peaks.

For convenience, we repeat equation A.1 here

$$y = a_1\sin(\omega_1 t + k_1 x + \phi_1) + a_2\sin(\omega_2 t + k_2 x + \phi_2) + \ldots +$$
$$a_n\sin(\omega_n t + k_n x + \phi_n) + \ldots \qquad [A.1]$$

Now when waves are described mathematically, it is conventional to regard ω, k, and the wave speed c as being positive quantities. A sinusoidal wave travelling in the positive/negative direction of x is usually written $y = a \sin(\omega t \mp kx + \phi)$. In order that the computed function (A.1) could describe a wave travelling in either direction, we take the ω's and c's as always positive, but allow the k's to be positive or negative. A positive/negative k corresponds to a motion of that wave component in the negative/positive direction of x.

(a) Sinusoidal curves
Number of waves 1

Amplitude	Phase constant	Circular wavenumber	Wave speed
Any positive number	90	12	0

Since the circular wavenumber $k = 2\pi/\lambda$, the wavelength $\lambda \approx \frac{1}{2}$ (the unit of length being one screen width). Approximately two complete cycles of a cosine curve should therefore appear.

(b) Superposition of two sinusoidal curves
Number of waves 2

Amplitude	Phase constant	Circular wavenumber	Wave speed
1	0	12	0
1	0	24	0

(c) Fourier synthesis of a square wave

Although Fourier analysis was developed in Chapter 7 with time t as the variable, we can obviously show Fourier synthesis with x in place of t, and k in place of ω. A suitable wave is then given (following Example 7.1 with $\alpha = \frac{1}{2}$, and a shift in the origin) by

$$f(x) = \sin kx + \tfrac{1}{3} \sin 3kx + \tfrac{1}{5} \sin 5kx + \ldots$$

The sum of the first 3 terms is displayed as follows

Number of waves 3

Amplitude	Phase constant	Circular wavenumber	Wave speed
1	0	10	0
0.33	0	30	0
0.2	0	50	0

It is instructive to show increasing numbers of terms in this sum, and to note the ensuing closer approximation to the desired function.

(d) Travelling wave
Number of waves 1

Amplitude	Phase constant	Circular wavenumber	Wave speed
Any non-zero	any	−15	1

Since $y = a \sin(\omega t + kx + \phi)$ is displayed, a negative (positive) value of k will produce a wave travelling in the positive (negative) direction of x. (It should be remebered that ω is always positive or zero).

(e) Standing wave
Number of waves 2

Amplitude	Phase constant	Circular wavenumber	Wave speed
1	0	−20	0.2
1	0	20	0.2

(f) Beats
Number of waves 2

Amplitude	Phase constant	Circular wavenumber	Wave speed
1	0	−30	2
1	0	−31	2

(g) Group velocity

This is probably the most interesting and most instructive of all these demonstrations, but the values of k and c must be chosen carefully to make it convincing. Those given below produce the best results that this author has been able to achieve, but the reader may be able to improve on this.

Number of waves 2

Amplitude	Phase constant	Circular wavenumber	Wave speed
1	0	−30	0.38
1	0	−40	0.3

The individual waves appear to be destroyed at the front of the profile, and created at the rear. The result is that the profile appears to move more slowly than the individual waves. The reader may attempt to measure both speeds, and verify the equation $c_g = d\omega/dk$, bearing in mind that the wave speed is ω/k.

(h) Amplitude modulation

Number of waves 3

Amplitude	Phase constant	Circular wavenumber	Wave speed
1	0	38	0
3	0	45	0
1	0	52	0

Appendix B

Solution of the differential equations for free, damped and forced vibrations

---

B.1 UNDAMPED VIBRATIONS

The differential equation of motion of a particle moving in one dimension under the influence of a restoring force proportional to the displacement was introduced in Chapter 2 (equation (2.1)), namely

$$\frac{d^2x}{dt^2} + \omega^2 x = 0 \ . \tag{B.1}$$

Here ω is a real and positive constant, and $\omega^2 x$ is the acceleration towards the origin.

To solve B.1, we first multiply throughout by $2\dfrac{dx}{dt}$,

$$2\frac{dx}{dt}\frac{d^2x}{dt^2} + 2\omega^2 x\frac{dx}{dt} = 0 \ .$$

Integration with respect to t gives

$$\left(\frac{dx}{dt}\right)^2 + \omega^2 x^2 = \text{constant} \ .$$

As will become evident, the most convenient way of expressing this constant is $\omega^2 a^2$, where a is another constant. We are anticipating the result that a will be shown to be the amplitude of the motion. Hence,

$$\frac{dx}{dt} = \omega(a^2 - x^2)^{\frac{1}{2}} \ . \tag{B.2}$$

This expression gives the velocity of the particle as a function of x.

To obtain x as a function of t, we rearrange (B.2) and integrate again,

$$\int \frac{dx}{(a^2 - x^2)^{1/2}} = \omega \int dt$$

whence $\sin^{-1} \dfrac{x}{a} = \omega t + \epsilon$

where ϵ is another constant of integration.

Thus, $x = a \sin(\omega t + \epsilon)$.   (B.3)

B.2 DAMPED VIBRATIONS

We now solve the equation (3.8) introduced in Chapter 3,

$$\frac{d^2 x}{dt^2} + 2b \frac{dx}{dt} + \omega_0^2 x = 0 .$$ (B.4)

This equation is appropriate, for instance, to a single particle of mass m subject to a damping force $m(2b \, dx/dt)$ and a restoring force $m\omega_0^2 x$. Here ω_0 must not be interpreted as the circular frequency of any ensuing damped oscillations, but rather as the circular frequency of the oscillations which would have occurred had there been no damping.

(B.4) is an example of a *second-order* differential equation, which means that the highest derivative involved in the equation is the second, $d^2 x/dt^2$. Now it can be shown that the general solution of such an equation will have *two* arbitrary constants. For instance, the solution of (B.1) has been shown to be (B.3), where a and ϵ are the two arbitrary constants. To take another simple example, the solution of the equation $d^2 y/dx^2 = 1$ is readily shown to be $y = \frac{1}{2} x^2 + Ax + B$, where A and B are the two arbitrary constants.

The converse is also true. Any solution of a second-order differential equation with two arbitrary constants is a general solution. Therefore, to solve (B.4) it is merely necessary to find any solution involving two arbitrary constants. It would therefore have been quite in order to have written down the solution (B.11) below, and verified that it satisfies (B.4). However, for the sake of elegance, we proceed forwards from (B.4) to the solution.

(B.4) can be written

$$\left(\frac{d}{dt} + \alpha_1 \right)\left(\frac{dx}{dt} + \alpha_2 x \right) = 0$$ (B.5)

where $\alpha_1 + \alpha_2 = 2\,b$, and $\alpha_1\alpha_2 = \omega_0^2$. From these two latter equations,

$$\alpha_1^2 - 2b\,\alpha_1 + \omega_0^2 = 0$$

Hence $\alpha_1 = b \pm \sqrt{(b^2 - \omega_0^2)}$

and $\alpha_2 = b \mp \sqrt{(b^2 - \omega_0^2)}$ (B.6)

With the substitution $u = \dfrac{dx}{dt} + \alpha_2 x$ (B.7)

(B.5) becomes $\dfrac{du}{dt} + \alpha_1 u = 0$.

Rearranging, $\dfrac{du}{u} = -\alpha_1\,dt$,

whence on integration, $\log_e u = -\alpha_1 t + \text{constant}$

Therefore, $u = K \exp(-\alpha_1 t)$,

where K is an arbitrary constant.

From (B.7), $\dfrac{dx}{dt} + \alpha_2 x = K \exp(-\alpha_1 t)$.   (B.8)

We have reduced the problem to that of solving a first order differential equation. The reader familiar with the solution of such equations will recognise that the procedure is to multiply throughout by the *integrating factor,* which in this case is $\exp(\alpha_2 t)$, giving

$$\frac{dx}{dt} \exp(\alpha_2 t) + \alpha_2 \exp(\alpha_2 t)\, x = K \exp(\alpha_2 - \alpha_1)t .$$

The L.H.S. is the derivative of $x \exp(\alpha_2 t)$, and so

$$x \exp(\alpha_2 t) = K \int \exp(\alpha_2 - \alpha_1)t\, dt \qquad\qquad (B.9)$$

$$= \frac{K}{\alpha_2 - \alpha_1} \exp(\alpha_2 - \alpha_1)t + B ,$$

where B is a constant. We have assumed that $\alpha_1 \neq \alpha_2$ here.
Writing A for $K/(\alpha_2 - \alpha_1)$, we have

$$x = A \exp(-\alpha_1 t) + B \exp(-\alpha_2 t) .\qquad\qquad (B.10)$$

Finally, substitution from (B.6) gives the final solution

$$x = A \exp\{-b + \sqrt{(b^2 - \omega_0^2)}\}\, t + B \exp\{-b - \sqrt{(b^2 - \omega_0^2)}\}t . \quad (B.11)$$

(The lower signs of $\pm$ and $\mp$ in (B.6) have been used. Clearly it makes no difference which choice is adopted.)

B.3 EXAMINATION OF THE SOLUTION FOR DAMPED VIBRATIONS

The behaviour of x as a function of t depends on the size of the damping constant b, and it is necessary to examine separately three different cases.

Case 1, $b > \omega_0$ (heavy damping)
In this case, α_1 and α_2 are real quantities, and x is interpreted from (B.10) and (B.11) in a straightforward manner. It is simply the sum of two functions, exponentially decreasing at different rates.

Case 2, $b = \omega_0$ (critical damping)
Here $\alpha_1 = \alpha_2 = b$. It will be recalled, however, that in the derivation of (B.11), it was assumed that α_1 and α_2 were different. We therefore return to (B.9), which becomes on substituting b for α_2, and writing A instead of K,

$$x\, e^{bt} = A \int dt = At + B$$

where B is a constant of integration. The solution is therefore

$$x = (At + B)\, e^{-bt} \ . \tag{B.12}$$

Case 3, $b < \omega_0$ (light damping)
The solution (B.11) is valid in this case, but the exponents are complex quantities. We therefore rewrite (B.11) in the form

$$x = e^{-bt} \ \{A \exp i\sqrt{(\omega_0^2 - b^2)}t + B \exp -i\sqrt{(\omega_0^2 - b^2)}t \}$$

$$= e^{-bt} \ \{(A + B) \cos \sqrt{(\omega_0^2 - b^2)}t + i(A - B) \sin \sqrt{(\omega_0^2 - b^2)}t \} \ .$$

For generality, A and B must be complex quantities, but clearly $(A + B)$ and $i(A - B)$ must both be real. Putting these respectively as D and C, we have

$$x = e^{-bt} \ \{C \sin \sqrt{(\omega_0^2 - b^2)}t + D \cos \sqrt{(\omega_0^2 - b^2)}t \} \ . \tag{B.13}$$

An alternative solution is obtained by introducing the phase constant ϵ,

$$x = a\, e^{-bt} \sin\{\sqrt{(\omega_0^2 - b^2)}t + \epsilon\} \tag{B.14}$$

where a is interpreted as the amplitude of the motion at time $t = 0$.
This solution is conveniently expressed

$$x = a\, e^{-bt} \sin(\omega t + \epsilon) \tag{B.15}$$

where $\omega = \sqrt{(\omega_0^2 - b^2)} \ . \tag{B.16}$

B.4 FORCED VIBRATIONS

This section is concerned with the problem of a damped oscillator subjected to a sinusoidally varying force. The equation of motion is (compare with (B.4))

$$\frac{d^2x}{dt^2} + 2b\,\frac{dx}{dt} + \omega_0^2 x = P \sin pt \ . \tag{B.17}$$

This equation would appear to be rather formidable, but there is a simple way of proceeding. Suppose we were in our investigations to come across *some particular solution* x_P (i.e. one in which there were no arbitrary constants). Then

$$\frac{d^2x_P}{dt^2} + 2b\,\frac{dx_P}{dt} + \omega_0^2 x_P = P \sin pt$$

Subtracting this from (B.17), and writing x_C for $x - x_P$,

$$\frac{d^2x_C}{dt^2} + 2b\,\frac{dx_C}{dt} + \omega_0^2 x_C = 0 \ .$$

This will be recognised as an equation which has been solved in its generality in section B.2.

The solution x of (B.17) is therefore the sum of two parts (a) *any* particular solution (or particular integral) x_P of this equation, (b) the solution (or complementary function) x_C of the equation obtained by replacing the R.H.S. of (B.17) by zero. This complete solution is a general solution, because the complementary function x_C contains two arbitrary constants, and (B.17) is a second-order equation.

The complementary function is readily found by the analysis given in section B.2, and it merely remains to seek a particular solution to (B.17).

Now it will be recalled that the complementary function is one which dies away as time progresses, therefore the steady state oscillations will be described in the particular integral. These will have the same frequency as the driving force. It is therefore clear that we should try a solution of the form

$$x = F \sin (pt - \delta) \tag{B.18}$$

where F is the steady-state amplitude, and δ is the phase lag of the oscillator behind the driving force. (The use of a negative sign in (B.18) ensures that δ is always a quantity lying between 0 and π.)

Substitution of (B.18) in (B.17) gives

$$(\omega_0^2 - p^2)\, F \sin(pt - \delta) + 2bp\, F \cos(pt - \delta) = P \sin pt \ .$$

The only way in which this equation can be satisfied at *all* times t is for the coefficients of sin pt *and* cos pt to be equal on both sides of the equation, whence

$$(\omega_0^2 - p^2) F \cos \delta + 2 bp F \sin \delta = P \tag{B.19a}$$

and $$- (\omega_0^2 - p^2) F \sin \delta + 2 bp F \cos \delta = 0 . \tag{B.19b}$$

The second of these equations gives the phase constant,

$$\tan \delta = \frac{2 bp}{\omega_0^2 - p^2} . \tag{B.20}$$

F is now obtained from (B.19a) as follows

$$(\omega_0^2 - p^2) F + 2 bp F \tan \delta = P \sec \delta = P(1 + \tan^2 \delta)^{\frac{1}{2}} .$$

Hence, from (B.20),

$$\left\{ (\omega_0^2 - p^2) + \frac{4 b^2 p^2}{\omega_0^2 - p^2} \right\} F = P \left\{ \frac{(\omega_0^2 - p^2)^2 + 4 b^2 p^2}{(\omega_0^2 - p^2)^2} \right\}^{\frac{1}{2}} .$$

Rearrangement gives finally

$$F = \frac{P}{\{(\omega_0^2 - p^2)^2 + 4 b^2 p^2\}^{\frac{1}{2}}} .$$

The particular integral is therefore given by

$$x = \frac{P \sin(pt - \delta)}{\{(\omega_0^2 - p^2)^2 + 4 b^2 p^2\}^{\frac{1}{2}}} \tag{B.21}$$

where the phase constant δ is given by (B.20).

The complete solution of the original equation (B.17) is therefore the sum of the R.H.S. of (B.21), and that of (B.11), (B.12) or (B.14) as appropriate.

Solutions to Problems

CHAPTER 2

2.1   (i) $\alpha = a \cos \epsilon$, $\beta = a \sin \epsilon$,
(ii) $a = (\alpha^2 + \beta^2)^{\frac{1}{2}}$, $\epsilon = \tan^{-1}\beta/\alpha$.
5. a is the hypotenuse of a right-angled triangle where the other two sides are 3 and 4.

2.2   (i) 10^{-4} J, (ii) 1.0001 N.

2.3 $2\pi(l/2g)^{\frac{1}{2}}$.

2.5   (i) 2, (ii)3. 25 and 26 cycles of x and y respectively.

2.8 $2\pi \sqrt{\dfrac{Mm}{k(M+m)}}$.

2.9 $\dfrac{1}{2\pi}\sqrt{\dfrac{k}{2m}}$, in phase, the lower having double the amplitude of the upper.

$\dfrac{1}{2\pi}\sqrt{\dfrac{2k}{m}}$, in antiphase, with the same amplitudes.

$\dfrac{u}{3}\sqrt{\dfrac{2m}{k}}\left(\sin\sqrt{\dfrac{k}{2m}}\,t + \sin\sqrt{\dfrac{2k}{m}}\,t\right)$

2.10 $\dfrac{3}{2\pi}\sqrt{\dfrac{T}{ml}}$, the particles all in phase, the outer ones having the same amplitude, and the middle one double this amplitude.

$\dfrac{3}{2\pi}\sqrt{\dfrac{3T}{ml}}$, the middle particle stationary, the outer two being in antiphase and having the same amplitude.

$\dfrac{3}{\pi}\sqrt{\dfrac{T}{ml}}$, the amplitudes all being the same, with the two outer ones in

phase, and the middle one in antiphase with them.

CHAPTER 3

3.1   Less. 0.34 mm.

3.4   (a) $(\log_e 2)/300$ s^{-1}, (b) $300/\log_e 2$ s, (c) 4.6×10^{-3}, (d) 684,
(e) 1.15×10^{-5} J.
Of the order of 10^{-3} Hz.

3.7 $R \geqslant 2000\ \Omega$. (a) 1.59 kHz, (b) 2ms, (c) 10, (d) $10^{-6}\pi$ J.

3.8   (a) $\sqrt{99}/2\pi$ MHz, (b) $\sqrt{98}/2\pi$ MHz, $5/\pi$ MHz, (c) 5.

CHAPTER 4

4.1   (i) 4/3 in the positive direction of x.
(iv) ω/k in the negative direction of x.
(v) $\frac{1}{2}$ in the positive direction of x.
(viii) 2 in the negative direction of x.

4.2 $25, 5, 5, 2\pi/5$.

4.4 $2\pi f/c$ dx. Q lags behind P.

4.5   11.3 m, 22.7 mm.

4.6   (i) 3 m, (ii) 6×10^6 m, (iii) 6×10^{14} Hz, (iv) 3×10^{18} Hz.

4.9 k_1 and k_2 are the components of $\mathbf{k}$ considered as a vector. $\omega(k_1^2 + k_2^2)^{-\frac{1}{2}}$.

CHAPTER 5

5.1   774 m s^{-1}.

5.2   5.06 km s^{-1}.

5.3   34.3 m s^{-1}, 81.

5.4 $2(l/g)^{\frac{1}{2}}$.

5.5   2.19 N m^{-2}.

5.6   (a) 2.40×10^9 N m^{-2}, (b) about 3% greater than its surface value.

5.7   (a) 0.5 m, (b) 0.264 m.

5.8   108 Ω.

5.9 $Kf/(c^2 \rho\, C_v) = 2.3 \times 10^{-7}$.

CHAPTER 6

6.3 $T = 4k_i k_t/(k_i + k_t)^2$, $R = (k_i - k_t)^2/(k_i + k_t)^2$.

6.4   (i) $2A/3$, (ii) $-A/3$. There is a phase change. $8/9$ transmitted, $1/9$ reflected.

6.5   Acoustic impedance matching.

6.6 $0.533\ \mu H\ m^{-1}$, $83.3\ pF\ m^{-1}$.

6.7 $5/9$ absorbed, $4/9$ reflected. 5.

6.8 $A_t = \dfrac{2\rho_1 c_1}{\rho_1 c_1 + \rho_2 c_2}\, A_i$, $A_r = \dfrac{\rho_1 c_1 - \rho_2 c_2}{\rho_1 c_1 + \rho_2 c_2}\, A_i$.

CHAPTER 7

7.3 $G_m = \dfrac{2A}{m\pi}\sin\dfrac{m\pi}{2}\ (m \neq 0)$, $G_0 = 0$.

$G_m = \dfrac{-iA}{m\pi}\,(1 - \cos m\pi)$.

Amplitudes are the same, but the phases are altered. Complex amplitude is multiplied by $\exp -2\pi i m f_0 t_0$; if $t_0 = T$, this is unity.

7.4 $S_m = -(2a/m\pi)\cos m\pi$.

7.6 $C_0 = a/2$, $C_m = -(2a/m^2\pi^2)(1 - \cos m\pi)$.

7.8   F.T. of a Gaussian function is another Gaussian.

7.10 $\pi \exp -|t|$.

7.11   The amplifier should cover the band from perhaps about 4 kHz to 6 kHz.

CHAPTER 8

8.2 $\exp -(2\pi i f t_0 + 2\pi^2 f^2 T^2)$, $(\exp -2\pi i f t_0)/4\pi^2 f^2 T^2$.

8.5   At least $10 f_1$ to $10 f_2$.

8.6 $-if(\pi/\alpha)^{3/2}\exp -\pi^2 f^2/\alpha$, $\frac{1}{2}\left(\dfrac{\pi}{\alpha^3}\right)^{\!\frac{1}{2}}\!\left(1 - \dfrac{2\pi^2 f^2}{\alpha}\right)\exp -\pi^2 f^2/\alpha$.

8.7 $\dfrac{v_0}{\left\{R^2 + (2\pi f_0 L - \dfrac{1}{2\pi f_0 C})^2\right\}^{\frac{1}{2}}}\ \cos(2\pi f_0 t - \phi)$

$$2\pi f_0 L - \dfrac{1}{2\pi f_0 C}$$

where $\tan \phi = \dfrac{2\pi f_0 L - \dfrac{1}{2\pi f_0 C}}{R}$

8.11 The only component present is at zero frequency.

CHAPTER 9

9.1 The car is moving at 37.8 m s^{-1}, therefore the driver is exceeding the speed limit.

9.3 $f_{O+S} = f(c + v_W - v_O)/(c + v_W - v_S)$.

9.5 Of the order of 6×10^{-12} m.

9.7 3.95 m s^{-1}.

9.8 No. Same as the wave velocity.

9.9 $\lambda \ll 1.7$ cm, 0.68 m s^{-1}.

9.10 $c = V + K\lambda$, where K is a constant. $K = 0$ for a physically acceptable solution.

CHAPTER 10

10.1 17; 96.2 cents.

10.2 $nc/2L$.

10.3 12. Twelve major fifths are very close to seven octaves. This is one reason for having 12 notes in the musical scale.

Four major fifths (minus two octaves) is very close to the simple ratio of 5/4 (a major third). Thus C and E produce a consonant sound.

10.4 Lower.

10.5 (a) 100 Hz, (b) 300 Hz.

10.7 $y(t) = \displaystyle\sum_n A_n \sin \dfrac{n\pi x}{L} \cos \dfrac{n\pi c t}{L}$

where $A_n = \dfrac{16h}{n^2\pi^2}\left\{\sin \dfrac{n\pi}{4} - \sin \dfrac{3n\pi}{4}\right\}$, and $c = \sqrt{(T/\mu)}$.

The missing harmonics are 1,3,4,5,7,8,9, . . .

10.8 $(16h^2 T/\pi^2 n^2 L) \sin^2 \tfrac{1}{2}\pi n$.

10.9 10^4 km! No account is taken of absorption by the air.

10.10 $p_1 \sin[2\pi \times 361 \exp(0.5545\ t)]$.

10.11 $1.43 \times 10^{-2}\,\mathrm{N\,m^{-2}}$, $1.40 \times 10^{-2}\,\mathrm{N\,m^{-2}}$.

10.12 56.2 dB.

CHAPTER 11

11.3 The wave at the second coil is not plane.

11.4 The measurements are made at very different frequencies.

11.5 Right-handed. Clockwise. (Remember that x,y,z must form a right-handed coordinate system).

11.7 The centre of the pattern moves.

11.8 4.49, 0.047.

11.9 There are 3 lines, one being at $\theta = 0$, the others being equally spaced either side of this.
The intensity of the pattern is $I = I_0 \exp -(2\pi^2 a^2 \sin^2\theta)/\lambda^2$, where I_0 is a constant.

Index